SO-AWB-471

A Handbook Series on
Electromagnetic Interference and
Compatibility

Volume 1

Fundamentals
Of
Electromagnetic
Compatibility

William G. Duff

Interference Control Technologies, Inc.
Gainesville, Virginia

Interference Control Technologies, Inc.
Route 625, Gainesville, VA 22065
TEL: (703) 347-0030   FAX: (703) 347-5813

© 1988 by Interference Control Technologies, Inc.
All rights reserved.
Published 1988
Printed in the United States of America
95 94 93 92   5 4 3 2

Library of Congress Catalog Card Number: 88-80527
ISBN: 0-944916-01-5

This book, or any part thereof, may not be reproduced
in any form without written permission from the publisher.

Dedication

This book is dedicated to a very special "lady" in my life—my wife Sandi. Her love and encouragement inspired and motivated me to start writing this book. Her patience and understanding helped me to complete the task.

No one knows better than an author's wife how much time and effort is required to complete a book such as this. Thank you, Sandi, for always being there when I needed encouragement and support.

Introduction

The 12 volumes of this *Handbook Series on Electromagnetic Interference and Compatibility* are the culmination of nearly four years of work. They update, build upon and replace the grey six-volume series which was published in 1980.

Obstacles to completing such a massive publishing project are many and varied: authors become ill, change professions or simply lack the stamina to complete their assumed tasks; government and private agencies overhaul EMC standards a week after a chapter on them is completed; manuscripts get lost in the mail, and so on. As we dealt with the normal range of major and minor catastrophes, as technology marched relentlessly on and as editorial deadlines came and went, it became apparent that the original vision of an ultimate, all-encompassing document on electromagnetic compatibility would prove elusive.

Even so, within these volumes some of today's most prominent EMC specialists share both theoretical and practical knowledge encompassing shielding, grounding, filtering and the other staple technologies of EMC. The series also provides data on major international and domestic standards and regulations, test methods and procedures and, in general, constitutes the world's most complete compendium of EMC-related information. The reader may be assured that whatever deficiencies exist in this work will be corrected in the next revision, at which time we will introduce an entirely new melange of imperfections.

It is appropriate to thank all who contributed their energy and expertise to the project, including contributing editors Christine

Miller, Roger Theise, Steve Roberts, Michael Violette and Walter Loope. The production chores were handled admirably by Gil Fitzpatrick, Shawn Noel, Elizabeth Parrish, Richard Irvin, Bill Will and Margaret Webb, and typesetters Sue McGuire and Judy Funkhouser worked with saintly patience. Last but not least, appreciation must go to Don White, who inspired and supported the project with all his usual vigor.

Jeffrey K. Eckert
Editor

Acknowledgement

Electromagnetic compatibility (EMC) is a difficult subject involving many areas of technology. Over the years that electromagnetic interference (EMI) has been a concern, many individuals have contributed to our knowledge on this subject. I would like to acknowledge that the material presented in this handbook represents the contributions of these many individuals, and I would especially like to express my appreciation to those individuals who have furnished some of the material presented in this handbook. In addition, I would like to thank all of those individuals who have worked in the field of EMC.

For the 29 years that I have been working in the field of EMC, I have been employed by Atlantic Research Corporation, and I am grateful to Atlantic Research for providing me with the opportunity to engage in many challenging assignments in the field of EMC. I would like to acknowledge that I am currently in the Professional Services Group of Atlantic Research and thank my employer for permitting me to participate in this endeavor.

Throughout the period of time that I have been involved in working on the various papers and reports that formed the basis for this handbook, I have been assisted by Janet Agee, and I am especially grateful to her for this assistance.

On a personal note, I would like to thank my wife Sandi for her love, encouragement and support during the period of time that I was preparing this handbook.

William G. Duff

Other Books in the 12-Volume Series

Contents

Chapter 3 EMC Design of Telecommunication Systems

Chapter 6 Shielding Theory, Materials and Protection Techniques

Chapter 11 The EMI/EMC Community

Preface

Almost every aspect of modern life is significantly influenced by and depends on the use of the electromagnetic spectrum. This permits production and transmission of electrical power, communications, navigation, radar and the like. Without the use of this valuable and essential natural resource, the basic nature of our society would be completely different.

Electromagnetic compatibility (EMC) is a necessary condition for effective communication-electronic (CE) system performance. EMC is the ability of equipments and systems to function as designed in their intended operational environment without adversely affecting, or being affected adversely by, other equipments or systems. Thus, the manner and efficiency in which modern life is conducted depends on the ability to achieve and maintain EMC.

Electromagnetic interference (EMI) is the culprit which does not allow radio, TV, radar, navigation and the myriad of electrical, electromechanical, electronic and communication devices, apparatus and systems to operate compatibly in a common frequency spectrum environment. EMI can result in a jammed radio, heart-pacer failures, navigation errors and many other nuisance or catastrophic events. Therefore, it follows that this spectrum pollution problem has reached international levels of concern and must be dealt with in proportion to the safety and economic impact involved.

The basic EMC requirement is to plan, specify and design circuits, equipments and systems that can be installed in their operational environments without creating or being susceptible to interference. To help satisfy this requirement, careful consideration must be given to a number of factors that influence EMC. It is particularly necessary to consider major sources of EMI, modes of coupling and points or conditions of susceptibility.

There is much written material on EMI which is generally available in trade journals, symposium records and the like. With certain exceptions, this material represents a collection of miscellaneous subjects and topics which do not interrelate very well. Certainly, to either a newcomer to the EMI or EMC disciplines, or to others already in these disciplines who are seeking tutorial or how-to-do-it knowledge, it is very frustrating.

The primary purpose of this volume is to provide the reader with a tutorial overview of the major factors that must be considered in designing circuits, equipments and systems for EMC. This handbook emphasizes fundamentals and provides information that will help the reader to understand the rationale that forms the basis for many of the standard EMC practices and procedures. In addition, wherever possible, this handbook illustrates "how to do it" so that much of the "black magic" associated with the EMC field is clarified.

William G. Duff

Common Terms
and Abbreviations
in EMC Literature

Prefixes for Decimal Multiples

10^{12}	tera	T
10^9	giga	G
10^6	mega	M
10^3	kilo	k
10^2	hecto	h
10	deka	da
10^{-1}	deci	d
10^{-2}	centi	c
10^{-3}	milli	m
10^{-6}	micro	μ
10^{-9}	nano	n
10^{-12}	pico	p

Technical Terms

absolute	abs
alternating current	ac
American wire gage	AWG
ampere	A
ampere per meter	A/m
ampere-hour	Ah
amplitude modulation	AM
amplitude probability distribution	APD
analog to digital	A/D
analog to-digital converter	ADC or A/D converter
anti-jamming	AJ
arithmetic logic unit	ALU
audio frequency	AF
automatic data processing	ADP
automatic frequency control	AFC
automatic gain control	AGC

average	avg
bandwidth	BW
binary coded decimal	BCD
bit	b
bit-error rate	BER
bits per second	bps
British thermal unit	Btu
broadband	BB
byte	B
bytes per second	Bps
centimeter-gram-second	cgs
central processing unit	CPU
characters per second	cps
common-mode coupling	CMC
common-mode rejection ratio	CMRR
complementary metal-oxide semiconductor	CMOS
continuous wave	CW
coulomb	C
cubic centimeter	cm^3
decibel	dB
decibel above 1 milliwatt	dBm
decibel above 1 volt	dBV
decibel above 1 watt	dBW
degree Celsius	°C
degree Fahrenheit	°F
degree Kelvin	°K
diameter	dia
differential-mode coupling	DMC
digital multimeter	DMM
digital to analog	D/A
digital voltmeter	DVM
digital-to-analog converter	DAC or D/A conv.

diode-transistor logic .... DTL
direct current .... dc
double pole double throw . DPDT
double sideband .... DSB
double sideband suppressed
   carrier........................... DSB-SC
dual in-line package.......... DIP
electric field..................... E-field
electromagnetic
   compatibility .... EMC
electromagnetic
   interference.................. EMI
electromagnetic pulse....... EMP
electromotive force........... EMF
electron volt..................... eV
electronic countermeasures ECM
electrostatic discharge ...... ESD
emitter-coupled logic .... ECL
extremely high frequency . EHF
extremely low frequency... ELF
farad............................... F
fast Fourier transform ...... FFT
field intensity .... FI
field intensity meter .... FIM
field-effect transistor......... FET
foot................................. ft or '
frequency .... freq
frequency division multiplex FDM
frequency modulation .... FM
frequency shift keying ...... FSK
gauss .... G
gram............................... g
ground .... gnd
ground loop coupling........ GLC
ground support equipment GSE
hazards of electromagnetic
   radiation to ordnance..... HERO
henry .... H
hertz (cycles per second)... Hz
high frequency .... HF
high-power transistor-
   to-transistor logic .... HTTL
high-speed complementary
   metal-oxide
   semiconductor .... HCMOS
high-threshold logic .... HTL
hour................................ hr
inch................................. in or "
inch per second .... ips
industrial, scientific and
   medical .... ISM
infrared........................... IR
input/output .... I/O
inside dimension.............. ID

instantaneous automatic
   gain control................... IAGC
insulated-gate field-effect
   transistor....................... IGFET
integrated circuit IC
interference-to-noise ratio . I/N
intermediate frequency ..... IF
joule .... J
junction field-effect
   transistor....................... JFET
kilogram .... kg
kilohertz........................... kH
kilovolt............................. kV
kilowatt............................ kW
kilowatt-hour .... kWh
lambert L
large-scale integration....... LSI
least significant bit........... LSB
length l
length (of cable) .... l_c
line impedance stabilization
   network......................... LISN
line of sight..................... LOS
liter................................. l
local oscillator .... LO
low frequency.................. LF
lower sideband .... LSB
lumen.............................. lm
lux lx
magnetic field .... H-field
master oscillator power
   amplifier....................... MOPA
maximum......................... max
maxwell .... Mx
mean time between failure MTBF
mean time to failure .... MTTF
mean time to repair.......... MTTR
medium frequency
   (300 kHz to 3 MHz)...... MF
metal-oxide semiconductor MOS
metal-oxide semiconductor
   field-effect transistor...... MOSFET
metal-oxide varistor.......... MOV
meter............................... m
microfarad........................ μF
microhenry....................... μH
micron (10^{-6} meter)........ μ
micro-ohm........................ $\mu\Omega$
microwave .... MW
mile .... mi
military specification .... MIL-SPEC
military standard.............. MIL-STD
milliamp........................... mA

million instructions per second	MIPS
millisecond	ms
millivolt	mV
milliwatt	mW
minimum	min
minimum discernable signal	MDS
minute	min
modulator-demodulator	modem
most significant bit	MSB
multilayer board	MLB
multiplex, multiplexer	mux
nanofarad	nF
nanohenry	nH
nanosecond	ns
narrowband	NB
negative	neg
negative-positive-negative (transistor)	npn
negative-to-positive (junction)	n-p
newton	N
noise equivalent power	NEP or P_n
non-return to zero	NRZ
N-type metal-oxide semiconductor	NMOS
nuclear electromagnetic pulse	NEMP
oersted	Oe
ohm	Ω
ohm-centimeter	Ωcm
ohms per square	Ω/sq
ounce	oz
outside dimension	OD
peak	pk
peak-to-peak	p-p
phase lock loop	PLL
phase modulation	PM
positive	pos
positive-negative-positive (transistor)	pnp
positive-to-negative (junction)	p-n
pound (sterling)	£
pound per square centimeter	p/cm^2
pound per square inch	psi
power factor	PF
printed circuit board	PCB
private branch exchange	PBX
P-type metal-oxide semiconductor	PMOS
pulse per second	pps

pulse position modulation	PPM
pulse repetition frequency	PRF
pulse-amplitude modulation	PAM
pulse-code modulation	PCM
pulse-duration modulation	PDM
pulse-width modulation	PWM
quasipeak	QP
radiation hazard	RADHAZ
radio frequency	RF
radio interference and field intensity	RI-FI
radio-frequency interference	RFI
random access memory	RAM
receiver	RX
reference	ref
relative humidity	RH
resistance-inductance-capacitance	RLC
return to zero	RTZ
revolutions per minute	rpm
roentgen	R
root-mean-square	rms
second	s
sensitivity time control	STC
shielding effectiveness	SE
sideband	SB
siemens	S
signal-to-interference (ratio)	S/I
signal-to-noise (ratio)	S/N
silicon controlled rectifier	SCR
single sideband	SSB
square meter	m^2
standing-wave ratio	SWR
super high frequency	SHF
super low frequency	SLF
surface acoustic wave	SAW
surface-mount technology	SMT
surface-mounted component	SMC
surface-mounted device	SMD
television	TV
temperature coefficient	TC
tesla	T
time division multiplex	TDM
transistor-to-transistor logic	TTL
ultra high frequency (360 MHz to 3 GHz)	UHF
ultraviolet	UV
very high frequency (30 MHz to 300 MHz)	VHF
very high-speed integrated circuit	VHSIC
very large-scale integration	VLSI
very low frequency (3 kHz to 30 kHz)	VLF

List of Abbreviations

volt	V
volt meter	VM
voltage standing wave ratio	VSWR
voltage-to-frequency converter	VFC
voltampere	VA
volt-ohm meter	VOM
watt	W
waveguide beyond cuttoff	WGBCO
weber	Wb
words per minute	wpm
yard	yd

length (coil turn, ground loop, etc.)	l
length in millimeters	l_{mm}
magnetic susceptibility	χ
magnetizing force	H
parasitic capacitance	C_p
permeability of free space	μ_0
permeability of medium relative to μ_0	μ_r
phase constant	β
radius	r
relative permittivity	ϵ_r
resistance (in ohms)	R
rise time	τ_r
shield thickness	d
time	t
time constant, transmission factor	τ
velocity, volume	V
wavelength	λ

Mathematical Functions and Operators

absolute value	abs
approximately equal	$\approx$
argument	arg
cosine	cos
cosine (hyperbolic)	cosh
cotangent	cot
cotangent (hyperbolic)	coth
determinant	det
dimension	dim
exponential	exp
imaginary	im
inferior	inf
limit	lim
logarithm, common (base$_{10}$)	log
logarithm, Napierian (base$_e$)	ln
sine	sin
tangent	tan
tangent (hyperbolic)	tanh

Common Variables in EMC Equations

attenuation constant, absorption factor	α
Boltzmann's constant	K
capacitance (in farads)	C
charge	Q
coefficient of self-inductance	L
conductance in mho	G
conductivity, propagation constant, leakage coefficient, deviation	σ
current	I
dielectric constant, permittivity	ϵ
frequency (in Hz)	f
impedance	Z
induced voltage	E
inductance (in henrys)	L
infinity	∞

Chapter 1

An Introduction To EMC and EMI

Electromagnetic compatibility (EMC) is the ability of equipments and systems to function as intended without degradation or malfunction in their intended operational electromagnetic environment. Further, the equipment or system should not adversely affect the operation of, or be adversely affected by, any other equipment or system.

Electromagnetic interference (EMI) is a specific kind of environmental pollution which produces associated damage. With the national emphasis today on the elimination or reduction of environmental pollution, the layman readily recognizes and understands water, air, noise and other forms of pollution. He probably has not heard of or doesn't know much about spectrum pollution (sometimes called electromagnetic or electrical noise pollution) because it is more esoteric, i.e., it cannot be directly seen, tested, smelled or felt. Therefore, he asks, "How can it be a problem?" However, it is just as damaging as the other forms of pollution, as explained below.

1.1 Examples of EMI

Some of the simple examples of EMI are familiar to almost everyone and are generally regarded as a nuisance or inconvenience. For example, it is readily known that certain types of electric shavers will jam a nearby radio. The resulting buzzing or crackling noise results in the inability to listen to the radio while the shaver is in use. Here the conducted or radiated electrical noise jams the radio picking up the broadcast stations. Another example is when an un-suppressed automobile idling outside of a house or an apartment causes interference on one's TV picture by blotching, developing intermittent dash lines or bars or even causing complete flipping (loss of sync) of the picture. Electrical noise from radiated automobile ignition is the culprit here. Sometimes either vehicular (or fixed) station radio operations inadvertently jam one's AM radio, TV or other FM receiver.

These situations are merely nuisances. More serious examples of spectrum pollution occur if a person having a heart pacemaker uses electrical appliances, shop equipment, automobiles or other RF energy emitting sources which cause his pacemaker to operate improperly or in a different mode. Here, results could manifest themselves in unconsciousness or even death. Another example in-cludes a sudden loss of telephone conversation by jamming due to high-power electrical signals or interfering background noise. If one were in the middle of giving his stockbroker an important sell or buy order, or if an important business deal were being negotiated, the EMI problem would no longer be a nuisance only. It can be economically damaging or catastrophic.

The spectrum pollution problem has been and can be far more damaging than the loss of a single life or of one's economic fortune. It can involve many people, industries and the like. For example, if two airplanes collide during inclement weather due to either EMI navigation errors or computer memory loss because of electrical transients in a storm, the loss of life and property become substan-tial. If police mobile radios are jammed during a riot at rush hour due to the composite effects of many automobile ignition noises, the consequences can be enormous. Similarly, if a field army in limited warfare or full combat finds that its communications, radar and other modes of combat effectiveness are jammed by its own spectrum pollution noise sources, a battle can be lost, along with many lives and much property.

Some major electrical power blackouts can result from a pyramiding effect of fault-sensing transient devices during an elec-trical storm. Here the impact can involve millions of lives and have enormous economic consequences.

And so it develops that the EMI or electrical noise problem giving rise to spectrum pollution is indeed of national concern even though its more esoteric manner is not readily perceived by the layman. Fortunately, the U.S. and foreign governments, and certain industrial elements, have issued specifications with which all electrical, electromechanical and electronic equipment must comply. Unfortunately, policing and enforcing these specifications is another matter, and so the problems persist. This is explained more fully in a subsequent section.

1.2 Basic Elements of All EMI Situations

Figure 1.1 illustrates the three basic elements required to produce EMI. They consist of electrical noise emitters, propagation media and receptors. These are the necessary (but not necessarily sufficient) conditions required to produce either degradation or malfunction responses in receptors. The method of coupling between emitters and receptors of electrical noise shown in the figure are divided between radiation (space separation with no hardline connection) and conduction such as through wires or cables.

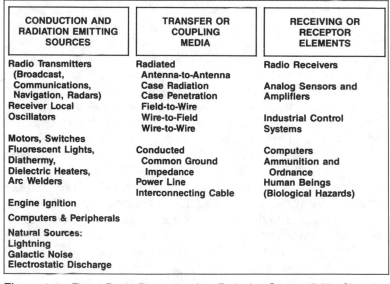

CONDUCTION AND RADIATION EMITTING SOURCES	TRANSFER OR COUPLING MEDIA	RECEIVING OR RECEPTOR ELEMENTS
Radio Transmitters (Broadcast, Communications, Navigation, Radars) Receiver Local Oscillators	Radiated Antenna-to-Antenna Case Radiation Case Penetration Field-to-Wire Wire-to-Field Wire-to-Wire	Radio Receivers Analog Sensors and Amplifiers Industrial Control Systems
Motors, Switches Fluorescent Lights, Diathermy, Dielectric Heaters, Arc Welders	Conducted Common Ground Impedance Power Line Interconnecting Cable	Computers Ammunition and Ordnance Human Beings (Biological Hazards)
Engine Ignition		
Computers & Peripherals		
Natural Sources: Lightning Galactic Noise Electrostatic Discharge		

Figure 1.1—Three Basic Elements of an Emission-Susceptibility Situation

1.3

Many equipments listed in Fig. 1.1 act as both emitters and receptors of EMI. This is quite obvious for transmitters and receivers which are part of the same equipment. However, it may not be as apparent for equipments such as computers. Here, computer peripherals (e.g., line or page printers) exhibit high broadband transient noise; at the same time, computer memory sense amplifiers are rather susceptible to higher-level emissions.

1.3 Intrasystem vs. Intersystem Interference

EMC is defined as the gainful operation of electric, electromechanical and electronic devices, equipments and systems in a common environment such that no degradation of performance exists due to internally or externally conducted or radiated electromagnetic emissions. EMC, then, covers the technological discipline of controlling the otherwise damaging effects of EMI. This is best accomplished in the planning stage, i.e., the conception and early design stages of devices, equipments and systems. The ability to implement this pragmatically is predicated in part on whether EMI develops within a system or equipment (intrasystem interference) or between two or more removed and discrete systems (intersystem interference).

Figure 1.2 shows a conceptual block diagram involving both forms of EMI. The transmitter on the left is attempting to communicate with the receiver in the center of the figure. The receiver, however, is also subject to a number of other electromagnetic emissions including those internally developed and those from both intentional and unintentional emitters shown on the right. Examining Fig. 1.2 in further detail reveals that the information to be conveyed starts at the information source associated with the transmitter shown in the lower left. For example, this may be voice, pictures, data or a radar pulse train. The information is then converted through a source transducer to the proper electronic format for direct electromagnetic transmission.

At this point EMI may first develop as shown by either (E) radiated energy from higher power levels of the transmitter or (G) conducted through ground-current loops or from a common power supply, or both. Since either of these source-coupling-receptor routes may be located within the system, they are called **intrasystem**

interference. A second example of intrasystem EMI is shown in the center of Fig. 1.2 by paths (E) and (G) within the receiver system. After modulation, frequency translation (if applicable) and amplification, the modified source information is transmitted from its antenna (or over a transmission line, if applicable) as shown in the upper left portion of Fig. 1.2.

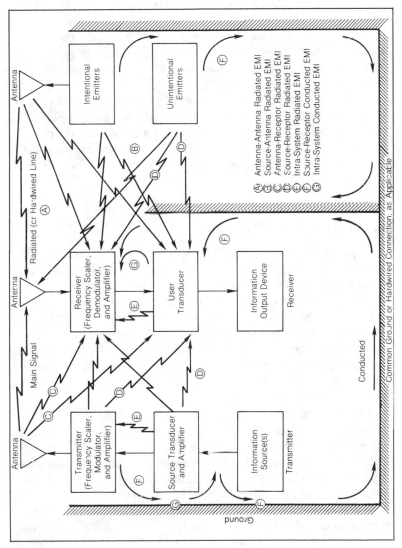

Figure 1.2—Examples of Both Intrasystem and Intersystem Interference

The receiver antenna, which picks up the desired transmitter radiations, may also intercept undesired antenna-radiated emissions from other intentional emitters (A) such as from communications, navigation and radar equipments. The receiver antenna may also intercept emissions from unintentional radiations (B) such as from incidental man-made devices. Interference resulting from (A), (B) or both is called **intersystem interference** because it results between two or more systems.

To complete the situation shown in Fig. 1.2, intercepted radiations are processed through the receiver, converted through the user transducer and presented in the form of output voice, teleprint, pictures, meters or other graphic displays or outputs required by the user. This is where the above latent form of EMI finally manifests itself by distortion, erroneous data or lost information. Figure 1.2 also shows other alternate intersystem paths of EMI coupling including radiated routes (C) and (D) and conducted routes (F) such as by a common co-site grounding, power supply or cable distribution system.

1.3.1 Intrasystem EMI

To gain a better understanding of the distinction between intrasystem and intersystem EMI, a closer look is appropriate. Intrasystem interference comes about as a result of self-jamming or undesirable emission coupling within a system as shown in Fig. 1.3. In this illustration, undesired interference is developing because electrical noise spikes appearing on nearby power cables and wiring harnesses are magnetically or electrically coupled into low-level, sensitive cables. Noise may also couple by a voltage drop across a common ground impedance or by direct radiation from box to box, box to cables or cables to box.

In addition to the examples shown in Fig. 1.3, intrasystem interference control practices almost always carry the attendant requirements for control of overall emissions from the equipment or system as well as hardening it to emissions of outside origin. These requirements exist in anticipation of the possible simultaneous intrasystem and intersystem interference once the specimen is installed in its real operational environment. Design methods and techniques to contain the intrasystem form of EMI, which are almost always within the control of the equipment or system designer, are introduced in this volume.

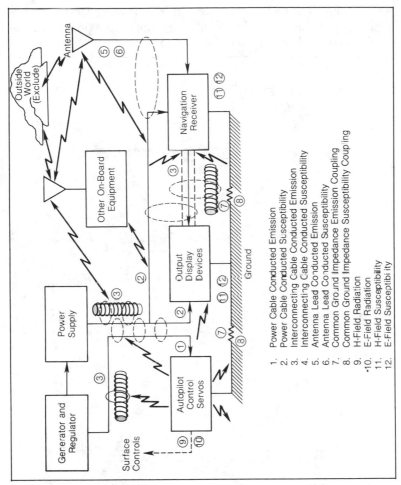

Figure 1.3—Examples of Intrasystem EMI

1.3.2 Intersystem EMI

Intersystem interference is illustrated in Fig. 1.4. Many different types of equipments, systems, and vehicles are shown. Most communication-electronic (CE) equipments both radiate and are receptive to electromagnetic emissions.

This form of interference is more difficult to contain because the totality of equipments and systems are not generally under the control of a single user, agency or company. The figure illustrates intentional emitters which can range from low power (e.g., 3 W from walkie talkies) to high power (e.g., 10 MW from radars). The frequency spectrum involved typically may range from power-line frequencies of 60 Hz to field radars at 35 GHz.

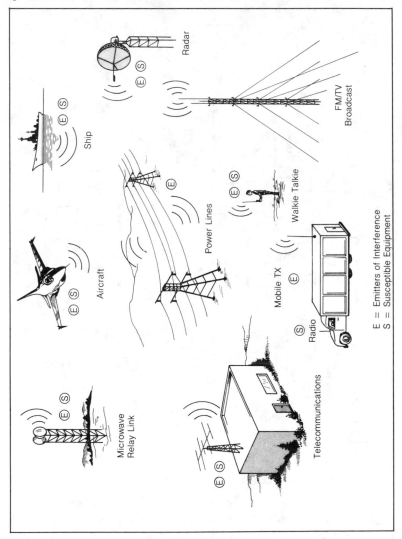

Figure 1.4—Examples of Intersystem EMI

To further illustrate the problem of having no single user control, consider a microwave relay link and a radar system as shown in Fig. 1.5. The systems are purchased, installed and operated by entirely different parties having totally different missions. The second harmonic radiation from the S-band radar may lie close to or directly in the reception channel of the C-band microwave relay link. In this case the radar system is the culprit.

Alternatively, the fundamental of the radar may lie within the image-frequency response of the microwave link, assuming the latter operates at S-band. In this case, either can be the culprit as shown in Fig. 1.5. Therefore, while EMC control is still best effected in the design stage; i.e., to reduce image frequency response and fundamental spectrum bandwidth and harmonic levels, the various applications and uses often render EMC difficult to put into practice for intersystem interference situations.

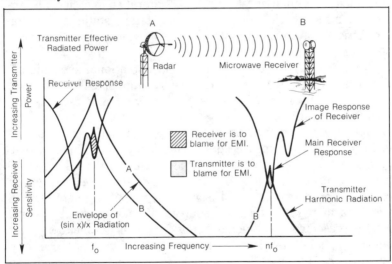

Figure 1.5—Electromagnetic Interference Between a Radar and Microwave Relay Link

The reduction of existing spectrum pollution or EMI control after the completion of design and installation becomes much more expensive and often is less effective due to the economics or logistics of a retrofit. Yet, EMC control is more frequently put into operation after a damaging interference problem has forced such a step.

This may be compared to the criteria involving the installation of a stop sign or traffic light after a serious accident has taken place at an intersection. It may be argued that traffic controls cannot economically or realistically be installed everywhere. Thus, intra-system EMC design and control methods and techniques are the subject of Chapter 4 of this volume.

1.4 Sources of EMI

This section surveys sources of EMI emissions, both natural and man-made, in the 10 Hz to 30 GHz frequency spectrum. These sources are summarized in Fig. 1.6. Natural sources include terrestrial atmospheric noise and precipitation static and extra-terrestrial emissions originating from the sun, cosmos and radio stars.

Man-made EMI sources include both intentional and unintentional radiations. The former emphasizes fundamental emissions from CE equipments such as radar, navigation and telecommunications.

Unintentional radiations include emissions at nonfundamental frequencies from the same CE equipments. They also include incidental emissions from automotive ignition systems; power lines; electric tools, machines, and appliances; industrial devices and certain consumer products. Table 1.1 is a further amplification of Fig. 1.6 and lists many specific EMI sources. Whenever practical, this volume presents typical radiated emissions in terms of either power density or field intensities, generally at stipulated distances from identified EMI sources. Most such data are presented in broadband radiated units of either $dBm/m^2/kHz$ or dB V/m/kHz (see Chapter 2). Some CE spectrum signatures, however, are reported in narrow-band terms of power (e.g., watts) power density (e.g., watts/cm^2) or power relative to the fundamental in the transmitter output.

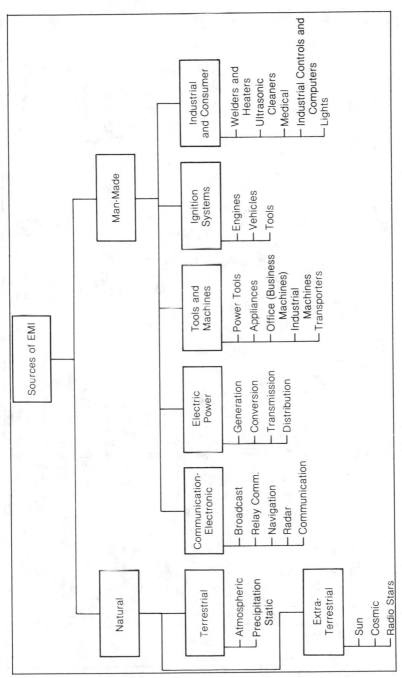

Figure 1.6—Sources of Electromagnetic Interference

Table 1.1—Examples of Sources of EMI

1. Natural Sources
1.1 Terrestrial Sources
  a. Atmospherics (thunder-storms around the world)
  b. Lightning discharges (local storms)
  c. Precipitation Static
  d. Whistlers
1.2 Extra-Terrestrial Sources
  a. Cosmic Noise
  b. Radio Stars
  c. Sun
    Disturbed
    Quiet
2. Man-Made Sources
2.1 Electric Power
  a. Conversion (Step-Up/Down)
    Faulty/Dirty Insulators
    Faulty Transformers
  b. Distribution
    Faulty/Dirty Insulators
    Faulty Transformers
    Faulty Wiring
    Pickup and Reradiation
    Poor Grounding
  c. Generators
  d. Transmission Lines
    Faulty/Dirty Insulators
    Pickup and Reradiation
2.2 Communication-Electronic (CE)
  a. Broadcast
    MF Amplitude Modulation
    VHF/FM
    VHF/FM
    VHF/UHF TV
  b. Communications (non-relay)
    Aeronautical Mobile
    Amateurs (Hams)
    Citizens radio
    Facsimile
    HF Telegraphy
    HF Telephony
    Land Mobile
    Maritime mobile
    Radio-Control Devices
    Telemetry
    Telephone Circuits
    Wireless Microphone
  c. Navigation (non-radar)
    Aircraft Beacons
    Instrument Landing Systems
    Loran
    Marker Beacons
    Omega
    VOR/TACAN/VORTAC
  d. Radar
    Air Search
    Air Surface Detection
    Air Traffic Control
    Harbor
    Mapping
    Police Speed Monitor
    Surface Serach
    Tracking/Fire Control
    Weather
  e. Relay Communications
    Ionospheric Scatter
    Microwave Relay Links
    Satellite Relay
    Tropospheric Scatter
2.3 Tools and Machines
  a. Appliances
    Air Conditioners
    Blenders
    Deep Freezers
    Fans
    Lawn Mowers, Electric
    Mixers
    Ovens, Electric
    Ovens, Microwave
    Refrigerators
    Sewing Machines
    Vacuum Cleaners
    Water Pumps
  b. Industrial Machines
    Electric Cranes
    Fork-Lift Trucks
    Lathes
    Milling Machines
    Printing Presses
    Punch Presses
    Rotary Punches
    Screw Machines
  c. Office/Business Machines
    Adding Machines
    Calculators
    Cash Registers
    Electric Typewriters
    Reproduction Equipment
  d. Power Tools
    Band Saws
    Drill Press
    Electric Drills
    Electric Hand Saws
    Electric Grinders
    Electric Sanders
    Hobby Tools
    Routers/Joiners
    Table Saws
  e. Transporters
    Conveyor Belts
    Elevators
    Escalators
    Moving Sidewalks
2.4 Ignition Systems
  a. Engines
  b. Tools
    Auxiliary Generators
    Lawn Mowers
    Portable Saws
  c. Vehicles
    Aircraft
    Automobiles
    Farm Machinery
    Inboard Motors
    Minibikes
    Motorcycles
    Outboard Motors
    Tanks
    Tractors
    Trucks
2.5 Industrial and Consumer (non-motor/engines)
  a. Heaters and Gluers
    Dialectric Heaters
    Plastic Preheaters
    Wood Gluers
  b. Industrial Controls and Computers
    Card Punches
    Card Readers
    Computers
    Machine Controllers
    Peripheral Equipment
    Process Controllers
    Silicon-Controlled Rectifiers
    Teletypewriters
  c. Lights
    Faulty Incadescent
    Fluorescent Lamps
    Fluorescent Lamps
    Light Dimmers
    Neon Lights
    RF Excited, Gas Display Signs
    RF Excited, Gas Laser
  d. Medica Equipment
    Defibrillators
    Diathermy
    X-Ray Machines
  e. Ultrasonic Cleaners
  f. Welders and Heaters
    Arc Welders
    Heliarc Welders
    Induction Heaters
    Plastic Welders
    RF Stabilized Welders

1.5 EMI Coupling Paths

The mode(s) of coupling between an emitter and a receptor can be very complicated. In general, the coupling paths are more extensive than those for intersystem EMI and are not as well defined since considerably less effort has been spent in the development of coupling path models. Coupling can also result from a combination of paths, such as conducted from an emitter to a point of radiation, then picked up by induction, and reconducted to the victim.

A general idea of EMI coupling paths is suggested in Fig. 1.7, where both radiation and conducted paths are illustrated. While not all-inclusive, these paths account for perhaps 98 percent of all intrasystem EMI situations. The object is to classify each potential EMI situation into one or more of the coupling paths illustrated.

The radiation paths are:
1. Antenna to antenna
2. Box to wire
3. Antenna to box
4. Wire to antenna
5. Antenna to wire
6. Wire to box
7. Box to antenna
8. Wire to wire
9. Box to Box

The conduction paths are:
1. Wire to wire
2. Common ground impedance
3. Filters
4. Common source impedance

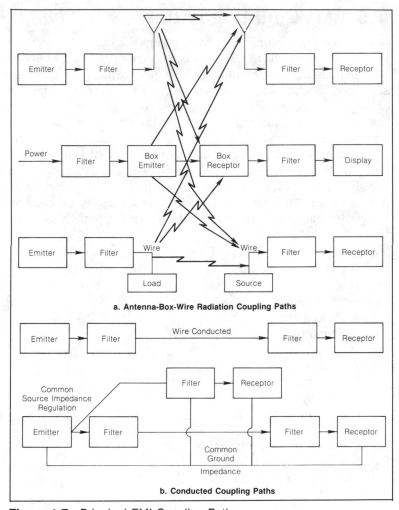

Figure 1.7—Principal EMI Coupling Paths

1.6 EMI Susceptibility

The previous section surveyed potential EMI sources. However, it takes both an emission source and a susceptible receptor to create EMI. The term **receptor** refers to the generic class of devices, equipments, and systems which, when exposed to conducted or radiated electromagnetic energy from emitting sources, will either degrade in performance or malfunction. Thus, receptors include those summarized in Fig. 1.8. It is noteworthy that many devices, equipments and systems can serve as both emission sources and susceptible receptors. Examples include most CE equipments (they contain both transmitters and receivers) and computers (including peripherals).

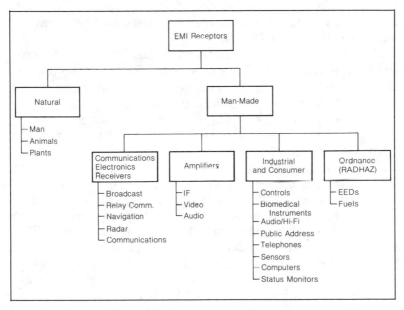

Figure 1.8—Electromagnetic Interference Receptors

This volume surveys EMI receptors such as CE receivers, low-level sensors, IF amplifiers, video and audio amplifiers, computers, and status monitors and indicators. Associated susceptibility criteria of these receptors are also summarized. Among others, these criteria include voice intelligibility, digital error acceptance, radar and visual displays and other outputs. The EMI characteristics of many types of receptors will be discussed in Chapters 3 and 4 of this volume. The hazards of electromagnetic radiation to ordnance devices or to personnel are summarized briefly in the following sections.

1.6.1 Hazards of Electromagnetic Radiation to Ordnance (HERO)

A special case exists when the receptor of Fig. 1.1 is an ordnance device. Here the problem manifests itself not by inadvertently jamming or causing disturbance to a receiver's information output but, rather, by producing sufficiently high ambient electromagnetic energies to ignite ordnance devices. In the parlance of the trade, the problem is known as **hazards of electromagnetic radiation to ordnance (HERO)**.

Electrically triggered ordnance devices are known as **electro-explosive devices (EEDs)** or **squibs**. They may be used to actuate switches, to separate fastenings between structures, to set off blasting explosives or to ignite explosive rocket motors. Because of the violent consequences either of failure to operate or premature operation, the susceptibility of such devices to electromagnetic influences is of serious concern.

Heating of the explosive material to a less-than-sufficient temperature for ignition can also make it unresponsive to a succeeding firing signal. This is called **dudding** and is a reliability threat. Consequently, either failure to respond or premature response may result from spurious input radiation energy. This energy, which may cause damage or inadvertent firing, may take the form of any electrical input from static discharges to microwave radiations.

The intended firing signal of an EED is normally a direct current applied to a fine wire which acts as a fuse to ignite the explosive material by temperature rise. Another approach is the **exploding bridge wire**, in which the disintegration of the wire creates a shock which ignites an explosive. It is possible in the presence of a strong electromagnetic field to couple energy into the firing circuit if portions of the wire leads act as an effective antenna, even though shielding and wire twisting are used.

Energy may be coupled into the explosive material which acts as a dielectric between wire leads and ground. Cavity resonance effects can also develop in the squib at microwave frequencies. Because of the high energy levels required to overcome attenuation in the normal installation of such devices, the primary precaution employed is to avoid exposure to near-field energy from powerful transmitters, especially radars. Certain other precautions are used in handling EEDs which are important but are not guarantees against accidental exposure to spurious energy. These precautions include short circuiting the firing wires until the device is to be armed for action, twisting the firing wire leads to avoid energy pickup in a circuit loop, isolating firing circuitry from other wiring and requiring a high-level firing signal for actuation.

1.6.2 Radiation Hazards to Humans

Another special case of interference exists when the receptor of Fig. 1.1 is a human being. If humans are exposed to high ambient electromagnetic energies such as from radars or possibly microwave ovens over periods of time, damaging biological results may develop. Although there is considerable controversy about the levels of electromagnetic radiation that are hazardous to humans, there are several widely accepted standards which provide radiation hazard limits. One is provided by the American National Standards Institute (ANSI). The radiation hazard limits provided by the ANSI Standard are presented in Figure 1.9 and are used in the U.S.A. and many other countries. Figure 1.9 also presents radiation hazard limits that have been proposed or are in use by other organizations or countries. For radiation exposure levels above those stated, damage may result in reproductive organs, producing sterility, or in eyeballs, producing cataracts. Relatively little is known, however, about the possible cumulative biological effects of lower-level, RF-field exposures over an extended period of time or if the peak power density levels, rather than average thermal levels, may also play a role in adversely affecting human behavior.

In recent years, the Russians have indicated that thermal biological effects of exposure of humans to average RF fields are not of major concern. They report that a much more significant impact exists to the human central nervous system on an extended time basis even when exposed to RF density levels from two to three orders of magnitude below the level used in the U.S.A. (i.e., 1 to 100 μW/cm^2). This in part results from the peak pulse power densities involved, the much shorter time constants associated with the human nervous system as contrasted with the heating effects of organs and the cumulative effects of extended time of exposure. Reaction, according to the Russians, is evident in headaches, attitude, listlessness, changed sexual behavior and other responses.

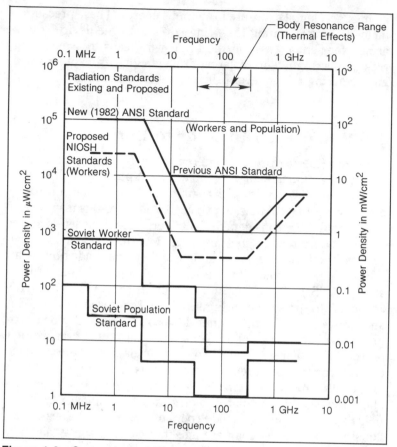

Figure 1.9—Comparison of Electromagnetic Wave Exposure Standards

Electromagnetic ambient surveys have been performed to determine the levels of radiation that humans are exposed to on a daily basis. One such ambient environmental intercept and analysis was performed within Metropolitan Washington, D.C., from 20 Hz to 10 GHz using automatic instrumentation. Data were collected at 10 typical sites including airports, shopping centers, hospitals and schools where humans congregate in significant numbers. Results of the survey indicated that the total daily RF-spectrum energy from ambients immersing humans may exceed levels of 0.1 mW/cm^2 on a steady daily dosage at certain locations.

While these levels are of the order of one-tenth to one-hundredth of those considered hazardous in the U.S.A., these levels may constitute serious threats to health and welfare if the Russian standards of safety are more nearly correct. The fact is that the whole topic of biological and central nervous system effects of RF radiation is quite controversial today. In some circles it is felt that the Russian conclusions tend to be fanciful and at times are not apparently supported by the measurements and results reported. Nevertheless, little is known about the effect on humans when exposed to lower-power densities of various frequencies, peak vs. average powers of different duty cycles and the effects of cumulative exposure times.

1.7 An Overview of EMI Control Techniques

EMI control techniques involve both hardware and methods and procedures. They may also be divided into intrasystem and intersystem EMI control. Engineers and technicians may become knowledgeable and even accomplished in intrasystem EMI control techniques and yet remain relatively naive in the other, or vice versa. This volume presents an overview of both techniques.

EMI control can be applied in the design, installation and operational stages of equipment and system deployment. The best practice is to apply EMI control in all stages of the life cycle. Thus, emitters, coupling paths and receptors should be examined in terms of the various possible EMI control techniques that can be applied to each, even though many may not be used in a given situation. To illustrate this, EMI control should consider as applicable the following alphabetical listing as a function of frequency or other variables:

1. Antenna beamwidth
2. Antenna gain, hemispheric
3. Antenna polarization
4. Bond impedance
5. Box aperture leakage
6. Box shield grounding
7. Box shielding effectiveness
8. Cable shield grounding
9. Cable shielding
10. Circuit load impedance

11. Circuit source impedance
12. Compartment shielding
13. Connector leakage
14. Emitter bandwidth
15. Emitter harmonics
16. Emitter spurious emissions
17. Filter transmission loss
18. Free-space loss
19. Gasket shielding
20. Ground impedance
21. Harness cable groupings
22. Harness cable shields
23. Non-RLOS propagation
24. Pulse duration and rep rate
25. Pulse rise and fall times
26. Receptor selectivity
27. Receptor sensitivity
28. Receptor spurious responses
29. Receptor susceptibility
30. Terrain masking
31. Twisted-wire pairs
32. Wire/cable capacitive coupling
33. Wire/cable inductive coupling
34. Wire/cable shields
35. Wire orientation

Many of the above will be included in any particular EMI control situation, but many also may not apply. By including all at the beginning, the process of EMI prediction and control then becomes one of employing design tradeoffs and manipulating the variables.

1.7.1 Intrasystem EMI Control Techniques

Figure 1.10 illustrates the basic elements of concern in an intrasystem EMI problem. The test specimen may be a single box, an equipment, subsystem or system (an ensemble of boxes with interconnecting cables). From a strictly nearsighted or selfish point of view, the only EMI concern would appear to be degradation of performance due to self-jamming such as suggested at the top of Fig. 1.10. While this is the primary emphasis of MIL-E-6051D, latent problems associated with either (1) susceptibility to outside conducted and radiated emissions or (2) the tendency to pollute the outside world from its own undesired emissions (cf. MIL-STD-461C) come under the primary classification of intrasystem EMI. Corresponding EMI-control techniques, however, address themselves to both self-jamming and emission/susceptibility in accordance with applicable EMI specifications.

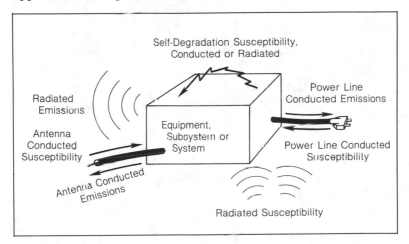

Figure 1.10—Intrasystem EMI Manifestion

Figure 1.11 presents an organization tree which groups intrasystem EMI-control techniques by five fundamental categories which often appear in literature; circuits and components, filtering, shielding, wiring and grounding.

Bonding, connectors, gasketing and other topics appear as subcategories in the figure. These categories, together with some of the subcategories, are the topics of separate chapters in this volume.

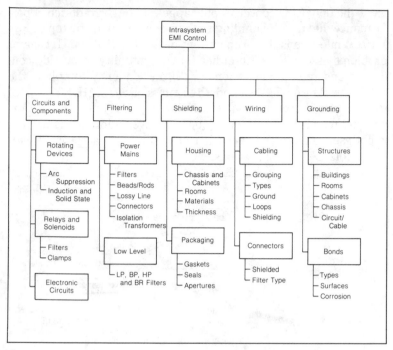

Figure 1.11—Intrasystem EMI-Control Organization Tree

1.7.2 Intersystem EMI Control Techniques

Figure 1.12 illustrates the basic elements of concern in an intersystem EMI-control problem. This type of EMI distinguishes itself by interference between two or more discrete systems or platforms which are frequently under separate user control. Culprit emissions and susceptibility situations are divided into two classes: (1) antenna entry/exit and (2) back-door* entry/exit. More than 95 percent of intersystem EMI problems involve the antenna entry/exit route of EMI. The relatively few back-door EMI situations use either

---

*Back-door intersystem EMI** is a colloquialism used to denote EMI existing between a CE transmitter-receiver pair in which either one or no antenna is involved. For example, emissions from case penetration of one source modulator may enter the antenna of a receiver, or a transmitter antenna radiation may penetrate a receiver housing and couple into the IF. Another example includes RF transmitter cable radiation coupling into the IF cable of a receiver belonging to a different system.

intrasystem or intersystem techniques, as applicable, for EMI control. The parameters measured in MIL-STD-449D and antenna conducted transmitter and receiver parameters in MIL-STD-461C constitute the principal characteristics to be controlled in intersystem EMI problems.

Figure 1.12 presents an organization tree which attempts to group intersystem EMI-control techniques by four fundamental categories: frequency management, time management, location management and direction management. System isolation/separation, antenna polarization and other control parameters appear in the figure as subcategories. These intersystem EMI control topics are the subject of Chapter 3 of this volume and Volume 7 in this handbook series.

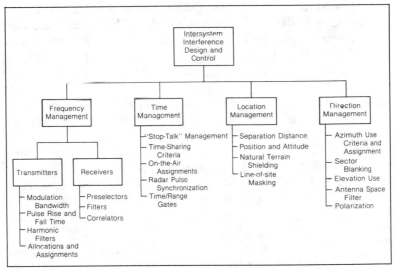

Figure 1.12—Intersystem Electromagnetic Interference Control Techniques

1.8 Bibliography

Clark, D.E., "Factors in an EM Methodology," *IEEE International EMC Symposium Record,* session I-C (New York: IEEE, 1978).

Cohen, T.J., "The Susceptibility of Home Entertainment Devices to Strong RF Fields," *IEEE International EMC Symposium Record,* session 4-A (New York: IEEE, 1975).

Cowdell, R.B., "Susceptibility on the Freeways," *IEEE International EMC Symposium Record*, session 1-B (New York: IEEE, 1976).

Dorbuck, Anthony, "RF Susceptibility Tests on Home Entertainment Devices," *IEEE International EMC Symposium Record*, session 1-B (New York: IEEE, 1976).

Duff, W.G.; Polisky, L.E. and Whitehouse, R.E., "Airborne Electromagnetic Environment Survey," *IEEE International EMC Symposium Record*, session 2B-1 (New York: IEEE, 1976).

Dvorak, T., "Electromagnetic Field Immunity—A New Parameter in Receiver Design," *IEEE Transactions on EMC*, Vol. EMC-16, no. 3, August 1974.

Engstron, J., "Susceptibility of Household AM Radio Receivers to Powerline Conducted RF Noise," *IEEE International EMC Symposium Record*, session 4B (New York: IEEE, 1977).

Engstron, J.; Malack, J.A. and Rosenbarker, I.E., "Broadband EMI Control for Data Processing and Office Equipment," Electromagnetic Compatibility 1977—Second Symposium and Technical Exhibition on EMC, Montreux, Switzerland, June 28-30, 1977.

Herman, J.R., Electromagnetic Ambients and Man-Made Noise, Vol. III, EMC Encyclopedia series (Gainesville, VA: Interference Control Technologies, Inc., 1979).

Hoff, R.J., "EMC Measurements in Hospitals," *IEEE International EMC Symposium Record*, session II (New York: IEEE, 1975).

Hsu, H.P.; Storwick, R.M.; Schlick, D.C. and Maxam, G.L., "Measured Amplitude Distribution of Automotive Ignition Noise," *IEEE Transactions on EMC*, Vol. EMC-16, no. 2, May 1974.

Malack, J., "Television Receiver Susceptibility to Broadband Noise," *IEEE International EMC Symposium Record*, session II-C (New York: IEEE, 1978).

Schulz, R.B., "A Review of Interference Criteria for Various Radio Devices," Electromagnetic Compatibility 1977—Second Symposium and Technical Exhibition on EMC, Montreux, Switzerland, June 28-30, 1977.

Skomal, E.N., "Analysis of Airborne VHF Incidental Noise Over Metropolitan Areas—Part II: Horizontal Dipole Antenna," *IEEE Transactions on EMC*, Vol. EMC-17, no. 2, May 1975.

Taylor, R.E., *RF Handbook* (NASA Goddard Space Center National Technical Information Service, 1971).

Taylor, R.E. and Hill, J.S., "0.4 to 10 GHz Airborne Electromagnetic Environment Survey over U.S.A. Urban Areas," *IEEE International EMC Symposium Record,* session 2B-1 (New York: IEEE, 1976).

Taylor, R.E. and Hill, J.S., "Airborne Urban/Suburban Noise Measured at 121.5/243 MHz," *IEEE International EMC Symposium Record,* session 2B-1 (New York: IEEE, 1977).

Taylor, R.E. and Hill, J.S., "Aircraft Measurement of Radio Frequency Noise at 121.5 MHz, 243 MHz and 406 MHz," EMC 1977—Second Symposium and Technical Exhibition on EMC, Montreux, Switzerland, June 28-30, 1977.

Tell, R.A.; Lambdin, D.L. and Mantiply, E.D., "Hospital Proximities to Nearby Broadcast Stations," *IEEE International EMC Symposium Record,* session II-C (New York: IEEE, 1978).

Toler, J.C., "Electromagnetic Interference Levels in Hospitals," *IEEE International EMC Symposium Record,* session II (New York: IEEE, 1975).

Walko, L.C.; Maxwell, K.J.; Schneider, J.G. and Serrano, A.V., "Susceptibility of Home Entertainment Equipment to High Power Interference," *IEEE International EMC Symposium Record,* session II-C (New York: IEEE, 1978).

Yamamoto, S. and Furuhashi, M., "Electrical Environmental Characteristics for Automotive Electronic Systems," *IEEE International EMC Symposium Record,* session 5B (New York: IEEE, 1977).

Zamites, C.J., Jr., and Hurburt, K.H., "Measurements of Interference Levels in the UHF Band from Aircraft Altitudes," *IEEE Transactions on EMC,* Vol. EMC-12, no. 3, August 1970.

Chapter 2

Basic Terms and Definitions

There are a number of specialized terms that are applicable to the characterization, specification or measurement of electromagnetic interference (EMI). It is particularly important that individuals responsible for ensuring that equipments or systems operate in an electromagnetically compatible manner be familiar with the basic terms and definitions that are widely used throughout the electromagnetic compatibility (EMC) community. This chapter presents a discussion of the basic terms and definitions that are important to the EMC engineer or technician.

2.1 Decibels

In order to characterize EMI, it is often necessary to deal with signal and susceptibility levels that range over many orders of magnitude. For example, receivers typically have sensitivities on the order of 10^{-13} W, whereas high-power transmitters have power outputs on the order of kilowatts or megawatts. Signals that range over many orders of magnitude such as this are usually plotted on a logarithmic scale so that the resolution may be maintained over each decade. The logarithmic representation that is often used in the EMC community is the decibel, which is defined as follows:

$$ dB = 10 \log\left(\frac{P_1}{P_2} \right) \qquad (2.1) $$

The decibel can also be expressed in terms of a voltage or current ratio as shown below:

$$\text{dB} = 10 \log \left(\frac{V_1^2/Z_1}{V_2^2/Z_2} \right) = 10 \log \left[\left(\frac{V_1}{V_2} \right)^2 \times \left(\frac{Z_2}{Z_1} \right) \right] \tag{2.2}$$

$$= 10 \log \left(\frac{V_1}{V_2} \right)^2 + 10 \log \left(\frac{Z_2}{Z_1} \right)$$

$$= 10 \log \left(\frac{V_1}{V_2} \right)^2 \quad \text{when } Z_2 = Z_1$$

$$= 20 \log \left(\frac{V_1}{V_2} \right) \tag{2.3}$$

$$\text{dB} = 10 \log \frac{(I_1^2 Z_1)}{(I_2^2 Z_2)} \tag{2.4}$$

$$= 10 \log \left(\frac{I_1}{I_2} \right)^2 \quad \text{when } Z_1 = Z_2$$

$$= 20 \log \left(\frac{I_1}{I_2} \right) \tag{2.5}$$

2.2 Conducted EMI Terminology

The term **conducted EMI** refers to EMI that is coupled between circuits, equipments or systems as a result of being conducted along an interconnecting power or signal wire or cable. The units of measure for conducted EMI are usually expressed in terms of voltage or current.

2.2.1 Conducted Voltage Reference

In many electronic and related technical disciplines the fundamental unit of signal or noise amplitude measurement is power, P. To facilitate discussion of large ranges of power, the decibel dB system is used in which the reference is the watt (1 W = 1 J/s). Thus:

$$P_{dbW} = 10 \log P_W \text{ dBW} \qquad (2.6)$$

where,

$$P_W = \text{power in watts}$$

It develops that the milliwatt (mW or, when used with dB, simply m) is used as the power reference in many applications. Some examples include signal-generator output calibrations, receiver sensitivity, path-loss analysis and the like. In units of decibels, the milliwatt is related to the watt as follows:

$$1 \text{ mW} = 10^{-3} \text{ W}$$

or, $\qquad 1 \text{ mW} = 0 \text{ dBm} = -30 \text{ dBW}$

Thus,

$$1 \text{ W} = 0 \text{ dBW} = +30 \text{ dBm}$$

Consequently, power in P_{dBm} is:

$$P_{dBm} = P_{dBW} + 30 \text{ dB} \qquad (2.7)$$

EMI specification limits, calibrations and measurements rarely use power as the reference. One reason is because signal or noise amplitude measurements are stressed and, if broadband, could either be coherent or incoherent (see Section 2.7). Direct power measurements do not identify coherence and significant errors could result in some tests involving translation of bandwidths. In any event, the EMC community uses voltage V as the basic conducted measurement reference unit.

The voltage is derived from power:

$$P = \frac{V^2}{R} \text{ watts} \tag{2.8}$$

where,

V = circuit voltage in volts

R = circuit impedance in ohms, across which V is measured

Hence, combining Eqs. (2.6), (2.7) and (2.8) yields:

$$P_{dBW} = 10 \log\left(\frac{V^2}{R}\right)$$

or,

$$P_{dBm} = 10 \log\left(\frac{V^2}{R}\right) + 30 \text{ dB} \tag{2.9}$$

The voltage ratio V_r of either two networks or one network under different conditions is obtained from their power ratios P_r, i.e.:

$$P_r = \frac{P_1}{P_2} = \frac{V_1^2/R_1}{V_2^2/R_2} = \frac{V_1^2 R_2}{V_2^2 R_1} \tag{2.10}$$

$$P_r(dB) = 10 \log\left(\frac{P_1}{P_2}\right) = 10 \log\left(\frac{V_1}{V_2}\right)^2 + 10 \log\left(\frac{R_2}{R_1}\right)$$

Thus, V_r as a ratio in dB equals P_r in dB only when $R = R_1 = R_2$:

$$V_r(dB) = 10 \log\left(\frac{V_1}{V_2}\right)^2 = 10 \log\left(\frac{P_1}{P_2}\right) \tag{2.11}$$

When V_2 = the reference voltage in volts, Eq. (2.11) becomes:

$$V_{dBV} = 20 \log V \qquad (2.12)$$

The EMC community uses the microvolt (μV) as the basic unit of reference voltage:

$$1 \; \mu V = 10^{-6} \; V = 0 \; dB\mu V \qquad (2.13)$$

Substituting Eq. (2.13) into Eq. (2.12) yields:

$$V_{dB\mu V} = 20 \log(10^6 \; V) = 20 \log V + 120 \; dB \qquad (2.14)$$

To convert from units of P_{dBm} to $V_{dB\mu V}$, Eqs. (2.9) and (2.14) are used:

$$P_{dBm} = 10 \log \left[\frac{V^2}{R} \right] + 30 \; dB \qquad (2.15)$$

$$= 20 \log V - 10 \log R + 30 \; dB \qquad (2.16)$$

$$= V_{dB\mu V} - 90 \; dB - 10 \log R \qquad (2.17)$$

$$= V_{dB\mu V} - 107 \; dB, \text{ for } R = 50 \; \Omega \qquad (2.18)$$

or,

$$V_{dB\mu V} = P_{dBm} + 107 \; dB, \text{ for } R = 50 \; \Omega$$

Equation (2.16) is plotted in Fig. 2.1 for frequently used values of R, viz., R = 50 Ω, 150 Ω, 300 Ω, 600 Ω and other impedances. Since most RF transmission line impedances are 50 Ω (coaxial cables), Eq. (2.18) is tabulated in Table 2.1 for narrowband units and yet-to-be-discussed broadband terms.

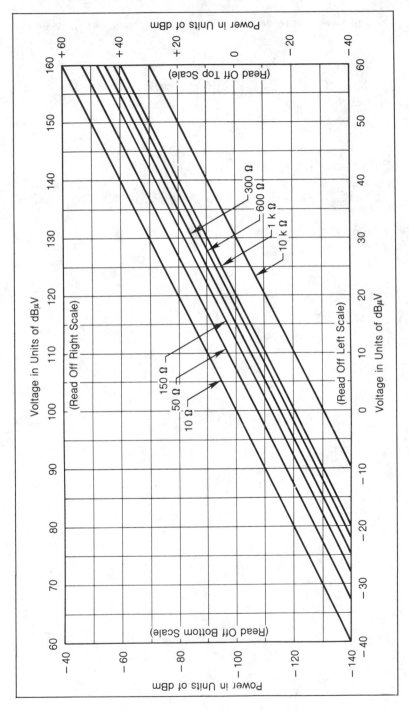

Figure 2.1—Power vs. Voltage for Several Circuit Impedances

Table 2.1—RFI/EMI Broadband and Narrowband Equivalent Terms (continued next page)

dBm	dBμV	Voltage	10 Hz	100 Hz	1 kHz	10 kHz	100 kHz	1 MHz	10 MHz
			RFI/EMI Broadband and Narrowband Equivalent Terms						
			Broadband Equivalent Signal Level* in dBμV/MHz for Indicated Receiver Impulse Bandwidth*						
+53	160	100 V	260	240	220	200	180	160	140
+48	155	56 V	255	235	215	195	175	155	135
+43	150	32 V	250	230	210	190	170	150	130
+38	145	18 V	245	225	205	185	165	145	125
+33	140	10 V	240	220	200	180	160	140	120
+28	135	5.6 V	235	215	195	175	155	135	115
+23	130	3.2 V	230	210	190	170	150	130	110
+18	125	1.8 V	225	205	185	165	145	125	105
+13	120	1.0 V	220	200	180	160	140	120	100
+ 8	115	.56 V	215	195	175	155	135	115	95
+ 3	110	.32 V	210	190	170	150	130	110	90
− 2	105	.18 V	205	185	165	145	125	105	85
− 7	100	.10 V	200	180	100	140	120	100	80
− 8	99	89 mV	199	179	159	139	119	99	79
− 9	98	79 mV	198	178	158	138	118	98	78
− 10	97	71 mV	197	177	157	137	117	97	77
− 11	96	63 mV	196	176	156	136	116	96	76
− 12	95	56 mV	195	175	155	135	115	95	75
− 13	94	50 mV	194	174	154	134	114	94	74
− 14	93	45 mV	193	173	153	133	113	93	73
− 15	92	40 mV	192	172	152	132	112	92	72
− 16	91	35 mV	191	171	151	131	111	91	71
− 17	90	32 mV	190	170	150	130	110	90	70
− 18	89	28 mV	189	169	149	129	109	89	69
− 19	88	25 mV	188	168	148	128	108	88	68
− 20	87	22 mV	187	167	147	127	107	87	67
− 21	86	20 mV	186	166	146	126	106	86	66
− 22	85	18 mV	185	165	145	125	105	85	65
− 23	84	16 mV	184	164	144	124	104	84	64
− 24	83	14 mV	183	163	143	123	103	83	63
− 25	82	13 mV	182	162	142	122	102	82	62
− 26	81	11 mV	181	161	141	121	101	81	61
− 27	80	10 mV	180	160	140	120	100	80	60
− 28	79	8.0 mV	170	159	139	119	99	79	59
− 29	78	7.9 mV	178	158	138	118	98	78	58
− 30	77	7.1 mV	177	157	137	117	97	77	57
− 31	76	6.3 mV	170	156	136	116	96	76	56
− 32	75	5.6 mV	175	155	135	115	95	75	55
− 33	74	5.0 mV	174	154	134	114	94	74	54
− 34	73	4.5 mV	173	153	133	113	93	73	53
− 35	72	4.0 mV	172	152	132	112	92	72	52
− 36	71	3.5 mV	171	151	131	111	91	71	51
− 37	70	3.2 mV	170	150	130	110	90	70	50
− 38	69	2.8 mV	169	149	129	109	89	69	49
− 39	68	2.5 mV	168	148	128	108	88	68	48
− 40	67	2.2 mV	167	147	127	107	87	67	47
− 41	66	2.0 mV	166	146	126	106	86	66	46
− 42	65	1.8 mV	165	145	125	105	85	65	45
− 43	64	1.6 mV	164	144	124	104	84	64	44
− 44	63	1.4 mV	163	143	123	103	83	63	43
− 45	62	1.3 mV	162	142	122	012	82	62	42
− 46	61	1.1 mV	161	141	121	101	81	61	41
− 47	60	1.0 mV	160	140	120	100	80	60	40
− 48	59	.89 mV	159	139	119	99	79	59	39
− 49	58	.79 mV	158	138	118	98	78	58	38
− 50	57	.71 mV	157	137	117	97	77	57	37
− 51	56	.63 mV	156	136	116	96	76	56	36
− 52	55	.56 mV	155	135	115	95	75	55	35
− 53	54	.50 mV	154	134	114	94	74	54	34
− 54	53	.45 mV	153	133	113	93	73	53	33
− 55	52	.40 mV	152	132	112	92	72	52	32
− 56	51	.35 mV	151	131	111	91	71	51	31
− 57	50	.32 mV	150	130	110	90	70	50	30
− 58	49	.28 mV	149	129	109	89	69	49	29
− 59	48	.25 mV	148	128	108	88	68	48	28
− 60	47	.22 mV	147	127	107	87	67	47	27
− 61	46	.20 mV	146	126	106	86	66	46	26
− 62	45	.18 mV	145	125	105	85	65	45	25
− 63	44	.16 mV	144	124	104	84	64	44	24
− 64	43	.14 mV	143	123	103	83	63	43	23
− 65	42	.13 mV	142	122	102	82	62	42	22
− 66	41	.11 mV	141	121	101	81	61	41	21
− 67	40	.10 mV	140	120	100	80	60	40	20

Note: − 107 dBm = 0 dBμV = 1 μV for 50 Ω load

Table 2.1—RFI/EMI Broadband and Narrowband Equivalent Terms (continued from previous page)

dBm	dBµV	Microvolts	10 Hz	100 Hz	1 kHz	10 kHz	100 kHz	1 MHz	10 MHz
− 68	39	89	139	119	99	79	59	39	19
− 69	38	79	138	118	98	78	58	38	18
− 70	37	71	137	117	97	77	57	37	17
− 71	36	63	136	116	96	76	56	36	16
− 72	35	56	135	115	95	75	55	35	15
− 73	34	50	134	114	94	74	54	34	14
− 74	33	45	133	113	93	73	53	33	13
− 75	32	40	132	112	92	72	52	32	12
− 76	31	35	131	111	91	71	51	31	11
− 77	30	32	130	110	90	70	50	30	10
− 78	29	28	129	109	89	69	49	29	9
− 79	28	25	128	108	88	68	48	28	8
− 80	27	22	127	107	87	67	47	27	7
− 81	26	20	126	106	86	66	46	26	6
− 82	25	18	125	105	85	65	45	25	5
− 83	24	16	124	104	84	64	44	24	4
− 84	23	14	123	103	83	63	43	23	3
− 85	22	13	122	102	82	62	42	22	2
− 86	21	11	121	101	81	61	41	21	1
− 87	20	10	120	100	80	60	40	20	0
− 88	19	8.9	119	99	79	59	39	19	− 1
− 89	18	7.9	118	98	78	58	38	18	− 2
− 90	17	7.1	117	97	77	57	37	17	− 3
− 91	16	6.3	116	96	76	56	36	16	− 4
− 92	15	5.6	115	95	75	55	35	15	− 5
− 93	14	5.0	114	94	74	54	34	14	− 6
− 94	13	4.5	113	93	73	53	33	13	− 7
− 95	12	4.0	112	92	72	52	32	12	− 8
− 96	11	3.5	111	91	71	51	31	11	− 9
− 97	10	3.2	110	90	70	50	30	10	− 10
− 98	9	2.8	109	89	69	49	29	9	− 11
− 99	8	2.5	108	88	68	48	28	8	− 12
− 100	7	2.2	107	87	67	47	27	7	− 13
− 101	6	2.0	106	86	66	46	26	6	− 14
− 102	5	1.8	105	85	65	45	25	5	− 15
− 103	4	1.6	104	84	64	44	24	4	− 16
− 104	3	1.4	103	83	63	43	23	3	− 17
− 105	2	1.3	102	82	62	42	22	2	− 18
− 106	1	1.1	101	81	61	41	21	1	− 19
− 107	0	1.0	100	80	60	40	20	0	− 20
− 108	− 1	.89	99	79	59	39	19	− 1	− 21
− 109	− 2	.79	98	78	58	38	18	− 2	− 22
− 110	− 3	.71	97	77	57	37	17	− 3	− 23
− 111	− 4	.63	96	76	56	36	16	− 4	− 24
− 112	− 5	.58	95	75	55	35	15	− 5	− 25
− 113	− 6	.50	94	74	54	34	14	− 6	− 26
− 114	− 7	.45	93	73	53	33	13	− 7	− 27
− 115	− 8	.40	92	72	52	32	12	− 8	− 28
− 116	− 9	.35	91	71	51	31	11	− 9	− 29
− 117	− 10	.32	90	70	50	30	10	− 10	− 30
− 118	− 11	.20	89	69	49	29	9	− 11	− 31
− 119	− 12	.25	88	68	48	28	8	− 12	− 32
− 120	− 13	.22	87	67	47	27	7	− 13	− 33
− 121	− 14	.20	86	66	46	26	6	− 14	− 34
− 122	− 15	.18	85	65	45	25	5	− 15	− 35
− 123	− 16	.16	84	64	44	24	4	− 16	− 36
− 124	− 17	.14	83	63	43	23	3	− 17	− 37
− 125	− 18	.13	82	62	42	22	2	− 18	− 38
− 126	− 19	.11	81	61	41	21	1	− 19	− 39
− 127	− 20	.10	80	60	40	20	0	− 20	− 40
− 132	− 25	.056	75	55	35	15	− 5	− 25	− 45
− 137	− 30	.032	70	50	30	10	− 10	− 30	− 50
− 142	− 35	.018	65	45	25	5	− 15	− 35	− 55
− 147	− 40	.010	60	40	20	0	− 20	− 40	− 60
− 152	− 45	.006	55	35	15	− 5	− 25	− 45	− 65

*To obtain broadband level corresponding to other impulse bandwidths, choose the next lower as bandwidth and subtract the following dB therefrom:

Bandwidth Multiplier	Subtract dB	Bandwidth Multiplier	Subtract dB	Bandwidth Multiplier	Subtract dB
1.1	1	2.2	7	4.5	13
1.3	2	2.5	8	5.0	14
1.4	3	2.8	9	5.6	15
1.6	4	3.2	10	6.3	16
1.8	5	3.5	11	7.1	17
2.0	6	4.0	12	7.9	18
				8.9	19

EXAMPLE: Determine equivalent broadband signal level corresponding to a 10 mV signal and a bandwidth of 20 kHz. From the chart, it is seen that a 10 mV (80 dBµV) signal and a 10 kHz bandwidth yields an equivalent broadband level of 120 dBµV/MHz. Since 20 kHz is 2 times 10 kHz, the value to be subtracted from the above table is 6 dB. Thus, the answer is 120 dBµV/MHz − 6 dB or 114 dBµV/MHz.

2.2.2 Conducted Current Reference

Several EMI conducted specification limits (e.g., MIL-STD-461) are given in units of current, viz., the microampere (μA). This might suggest that a small resistor R is added in series with the test lead, and the voltage drop across the resistor is measured with an EMI receiver to determine the unknown current:

$$I = V/R \qquad (2.19)$$

where,

$$I = \text{current in microamps}$$
$$V = \text{voltage in microvolts}$$
$$R = \text{resistance in ohms}$$

or,

$$I = V - 20 \log R \qquad (2.20)$$

where,
$$I = \text{current in dB}\mu\text{A}$$
$$V = \text{voltage in dB}\mu\text{V}$$
$$R = \text{resistance in ohms}$$

The above practice is rarely done since it disturbs the test item and is not practical where many cable wires are involved. Consequently, a current probe is used.

2.2.3 Transfer Impedance

In some situations, EMI current in a test sample wire is measured with the EMI receiver acting as a tunable voltmeter and the current probe as the sensing device. Here, a two-terminal pair transfer impedance Z_T is defined for the current probe:

$$Z_T = \frac{V_{out}}{I_{in}} \qquad (2.21)$$

where,

$$V_{out} = \text{output voltage across the current probe when terminated in 50 } \Omega \text{ (the EMI receiver)}$$
$$I_{in} = \text{unknown input current flow in the wire(s) around which the probe is snapped}$$

In units of dB, Eq. (2.21) becomes:

$$Z_{dB\Omega} = V_{dB\mu V} - I_{dB\mu A} \qquad (2.22)$$

or the unknown EMI current is:

$$I_{dB\mu A} = V_{dB\mu A} - Z_{dB\Omega} \qquad (2.23)$$

The manufacturer furnishes the transfer impedance $Z_{dB\Omega}$ of his current probe as the transducer calibration and the operator measures the voltage $V_{dB\mu V}$ by substitution. Thus, the unknown current is obtained.

2.3 Radiated EMI Terminology

The term **radiated EMI** refers to EMI that is coupled between circuits, equipments or systems via electromagnetic fields that are radiated from an EMI source and picked up by susceptible circuits, equipments or systems. The units of measure for radiated EMI are usually expressed in terms of power density or field strength.

2.3.1 Near and Far Fields

Before discussing radiated units in terms of power density, electric field intensity and magnetic field intensity it is necessary to review the concept of near and far fields. The latter is sometimes referred to as **plane waves** or a **plane-wave field**.

The power flux flow (or simply power density) P_D in units of watts per square meter is:

$$P_D = E \times H \qquad (2.24)$$

where,

    E = electric field intensity in volts per meter

    H = magnetic field intensity in amps per meter

The electric and magnetic field intensities are related by the wave impedance Z in ohms:

$$Z = E/H \qquad (2.25)$$

As shown in following text, $Z = 120\pi \; \Omega = 377 \; \Omega$ for far-field conditions only. Thus, for plane waves, the electric and magnetic fields are uniquely related by 377 Ω. Such a unique relation, however, does not exist in the near field. In fact, it will be shown that Z may assume any value, e.g., a small fraction of 377 Ω for magnetic fields (sometimes called low-impedance fields, i.e., low with respect to 377 Ω), or many times 377 Ω for electric fields (sometimes called high-impedance fields, i.e., high with respect to 377 Ω). Note that Eq. (2.25) still applies in the near field. With any electric field, there exists a corresponding magnetic field and vice versa, as long as the frequency is not dc.

The following discussion treats the subject of near and far fields with respect to the size D of the field-producing element (or aperture dimension) in terms of a wavelength λ. When $D \ll \lambda$, the near/far-field interface distance r is defined as:

$$r = \lambda/2\pi, \text{ for } D \ll \lambda \tag{2.26}$$

$$r = D^2/2\lambda, \text{ for } D \geqslant \lambda/2 \tag{2.27}$$

Note that when $D = \lambda/2$, Eq. (2.27) becomes $r = \lambda/8$ which nearly equals Eq. (2.26). These two situations are discussed spearately in the following sections.

2.3.2 Small Dimension, $D \ll \lambda$

The purpose of this section is to present some explanation about magnetic, electric and electromagnetic fields as pertinent background to understanding and applying field theory. Since the literature is replete with excellent discussions of Maxwell's equations and field theory, only a few aspects are presented here. The electric (E_θ E_r) and magnetic (H_ϕ) fields existing about an oscillating doublet (tiny dipole in which $D \ll \lambda$) are obtained from applying Maxwell's equations:

$$E_\theta = \frac{Z_0 I D \pi \sin\theta}{\lambda^2} \left[-\left(\frac{\lambda}{2\pi r}\right)^3 \cos\psi - \left(\frac{\lambda}{2\pi r}\right)^2 \sin\psi \right.$$

$$\left. + \left(\frac{\lambda}{2\pi r}\right) \cos\psi \right] \tag{2.28}$$

$$E_r = \frac{2Z_0 I D \pi \cos\theta}{\lambda^2} \left[\left(\frac{\lambda}{2\pi r}\right)^3 \cos\psi + \left(\frac{\lambda}{2\pi r}\right)^2 \sin\psi \right] \tag{2.29}$$

$$H_\phi = \frac{I D \pi \sin\theta}{\lambda^2} \left[\left(\frac{\lambda}{2\pi r}\right)^2 \sin\psi + \left(\frac{\lambda}{2\pi r}\right) \cos\psi \right] \tag{2.30}$$

where,

Z_0 = free-space impedance (for $r \gg \lambda/2\pi$) = 377 Ω

I = current in short wire (doublet)

D = length of short wire (doublet)

θ = zenith angle to r

λ = wavelength corresponding to frequency f

ω = radial frequency = $2\pi f$

r = distance from short wire doublet to measuring point

$\psi = 2\pi r/\lambda - \omega t$

t = time

Several observations can be made about the near and far fields from Eqs. (2.28) and (2.30):

1. When the multiplier $\lambda/2\pi r$ = 1 in the electric-field and magnetic-field terms, all coefficients of either the sine or cosine are unity and equal. Thus, when $r = \lambda/2\pi$ (about one-sixth wavelength), this corresponds to the transition-field condition or boundary between the near field (first term of equations) and far field (last term).

2. When r $\gg \lambda/2\pi$ (far-field conditions), only the last term of Eqs. (2.28) and (2.30) is significant (E_r is dropped from further discussion here). For this condition the wave impedance $Z_0 = E_\theta/H_\phi = 377\ \Omega$. This is called the **radiation field** (plane waves) and both E_θ and H_ϕ are in time phase ($\cos\psi$) although in directional quadrature.

3. When r $\ll \lambda/2\pi$ (near-field conditions), only the first term of each equation is significant. For this condition, the wave impedance $E_\theta H_\phi = Z_0/2\pi r$. Note that the wave impedance is now $\gg Z_0$ since $\lambda/2\pi r \gg 1$. This is sometimes called simply an electric field or a high-impedance field, i.e., high relative to a plane-wave impedance. It is also the induction field, and E_θ and H_ϕ are in both phase and directional quadrature.

4. Had the oscillating source not been a small straight wire doublet exhibiting high circuit impedance but, rather, a small wire loop exhibiting low circuit impedance, the first term appearing in Eqs. (2.28) and (2.29) would vanish, but a similar first term would appear in Eq. (2.30). For this condition, the wave impedance in the near field, $E_\theta/H_\phi = Z_0\ 2\pi r/\lambda$. Note that the wave impedance is now $\ll Z_0$. This is sometimes called a magnetic field or a low-impedance field, i.e., low relative to Z_0, the plane-wave (radiation) impedance.

Figure 2.2 illustrates the first three observations for the amplitude of each of the electric-field terms in Eq. (2.28). Note that the quasistationary field is the largest term in the near field and the induction term is next largest, whereas the radiation term is the largest in the far field. For r $= \lambda/2\pi$ all terms are equal.

Figure 2.3 illustrates conceptually the above third and fourth observations in the near or induction field. Figure 2.3a shows a monopole or straight wire in which the RF current is low. Consequently, the source or circuit impedance is high. The wave impedance close-in is also high, being made up predominantly of the electric field. The electric field attenuates more rapidly ($1/r^3$) with an increase in distance than the magnetic field ($1/r^2$) in the induction region, [cf. Eqs. (2.28) and (2.30)]. Thus, the wave impedance decreases with an increase in distance where it asymptotically approaches $Z_0 = 377\ \Omega$ in the far or radiation field (r $\gg \lambda/2\pi$).

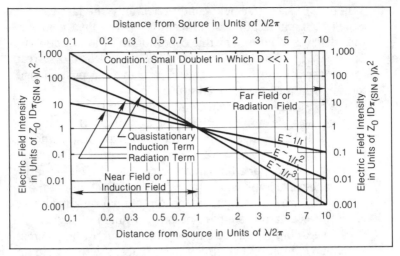

Figure 2.2—Electric Field Intensity vs. Source Distance

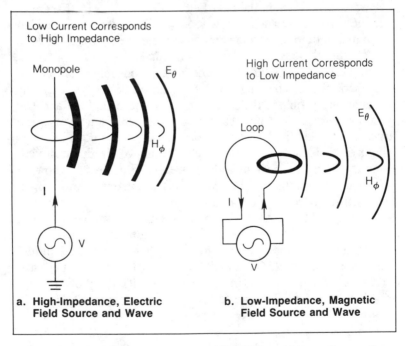

Figure 2.3—Conceptual Illustration of Field Intensities vs. Source Type and Distance

The converse applies for the situation in Fig. 2.3b wherein a low-impedance source or circuit creates a low-impedance wave predominantly the magnetic-field component. This impedance increases with distance where it asymptotically approaches 377 Ω in the far field. Figure 2.4 illustrates these impedances of both fields as a function of distance r.

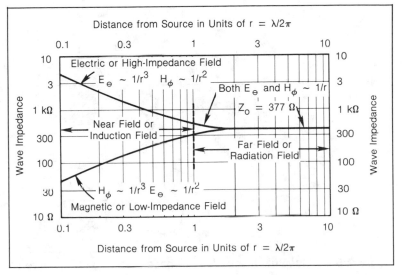

Figure 2.4—Wave Impedance as a Function of Source Distance

2.3.3 Near and Far Fields, $D \geqslant \lambda/2$

When the dimension D of an emission source (e.g., an antenna) becomes an appreciable fraction of a wavelength, the expressions presented in Eqs. (2.28) through (2.30) no longer apply. Different relations then must be used since the curvature of the arriving wave front no longer permits the incremental elements of an antenna to be in phase. This is illustrated in Fig. 2.5 where the wave front first intercepts the center of the antenna. The outer extremes of the antenna represent an increasing phase lag off axis. Thus, the resulting addition of each incremental element must be integrated to achieve the net vector amplitude.

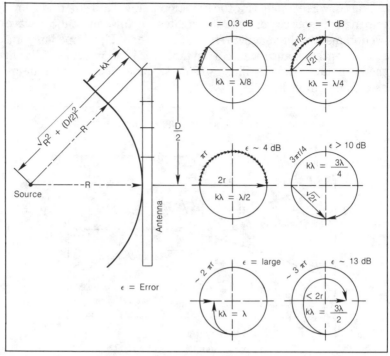

Figure 2.5—Conceptual Illustration of Phase Error From Curvature of Wave Front

Rather than employing calculus here, this addition is illustrated in Fig. 2.5 by numerical integration in which k = λ/8, λ/4, λ/2, 3 λ/4, λ and 3 λ/2. The results of this are shown in Fig. 2.6 in which the relative antenna gain is plotted as a function of distance. Note the oscillatory performance in the near field with a decreasing envelope as the distance from source to antenna is decreased. The envelope results from a decrease in the projected wave front element upon the antenna element as one moves out toward the antenna extremes.

To define the near-to-far field interface R it remains to determine the allowable error ϵ in dB by which the gain is constant as one moves from R to infinity (see Fig. 2.6). Different disciplines use different values. Antenna and propagation disciplines often use kλ = λ/16, which corresponds to an error of about 0.1 dB in antenna gain. The EMC community uses either k = λ/8 (0.3 dB error) or k = λ/4 (1 dB error), depending upon the application. To determine the

2.16

distance R, the Pythagorean Theorem is used in Fig. 2.5:

$$(R + k\lambda)^2 = R^2 + (D/2)^2 \qquad (2.31)$$

$$2Rk\lambda + (k\lambda)^2 = (D/2)^2$$

Thus, $2Rk\lambda \approx (D/2)^2$, or $R = D^2/8k\lambda$ $\qquad$ (2.32)

Since, $2Rk\lambda \gg (k\lambda)^2$

When $k = \lambda/4$ is chosen (i.e., 1 dB error in gain), Eq. (2.32) becomes:

$$R = D^2/2\lambda, \text{ for a 1 dB error} \qquad (2.33)$$

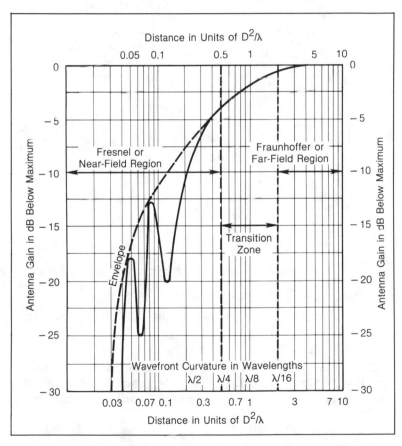

Figure 2.6—Relative Antenna Gain vs. Source to Antenna Distance

2.3.4 Electric-Field Reference

An approach similar to that discussed in an earlier section regarding power versus voltage is also developed here. Power density P_D previously defined in Eq. (2.24), is used as the basic unit of power flux flow by the microwave community. Here, far-field conditions generally apply at higher frequencies. The EMC and broadcast communities, however, prefer the field intensity term to the power density. The EMC community also rates its EMI specification limits in units of field intensity. The two are related as follows [cf. Eqs. (2.15) through (2.18)]:

$$P_D = E^2/Z, \text{ in W/m}^2 \tag{2.34}$$

$$P_{dBW/m^2} = 20 \log E_{V/m} - 10 \log Z \tag{2.35}$$

or,

$$P_{dBm/m^2} = E_{dBV/m} - 10 \log Z + 30 \text{ dB}$$

$$= E_{dB\mu V/m} - 90 \text{ dB} - 10 \log Z \tag{2.36}$$

$$= E_{dB\mu V/m} - 116 \text{ dB, for } Z = 377 \text{ } \Omega$$

or,

$$E_{dB\mu V/m} = P_{dBm/m^2} + 116 \text{ dB, for } Z = 377 \text{ } \Omega \tag{2.37}$$

where,

$$E = \text{electric field intensity in volts per meter}$$

$$E_{dB\mu V/m} = E \text{ in units of dB}\mu\text{V/m}$$

$$Z = \text{wave impedance} = 120\pi = 377 \text{ } \Omega \text{ for far-field conditions only}$$

Equation (2.37) is tabulated in Table 2.2 for various units. Note that Eqs. (2.17) and (2.36) are nearly identical; the former involves conducted voltages and the latter applies to radiated electric fields.

Table 2.2—Field Intensity and Power Density Relationships
(Related by Free-Space Impedance = 377 Ω)

Volts/m	dBμV/m	Watts/M²	dBW/²	Watts/cm²	dBW/cm²	mW/cm²	dBm/cm²
10,000	200	265,000	+54	27	+14	26,500	+44
7,000	197	130,000	+51	13	+11	13,00	+41
5,000	194	66,300	+48	6.6	+8	6,630	+38
3,000	190	23,900	+44	2.4	+4	2,390	+34
2,000	186	10,600	+40	1.1	0	1,060	+30
1,000	180	2,650	+34	.27	−6	265	+24
700	177	1,300	+31	.13	−9	130	+21
500	174	663	+28	.066	−12	66	+18
300	170	239	+24	.024	−16	24	+14
200	166	106	+20	.011	−20	11	+10
100	160	27	+14	27×10^{-4}	−26	2.7	+4
70	157	13	+11	13×10^{-4}	−29	1.3	+1
50	154	6.6	+8	6.6×10^{-4}	−32	.66	−2
30	150	2.4	+4	2.4×10^{-4}	−36	.24	−6
20	146	1.1	0	1.1×10^{-4}	−40	.11	−10
10	140	.27	−6	27×10^{-5}	−46	.027	−16
7	137	.13	−9	13×10^{-6}	−49	.013	−19
5	134	.066	−12	6.6×10^{-6}	−52	66×10^{-4}	−22
3	130	.024	−16	2.4×10^{-6}	−56	24×10^{-4}	−26
2	126	.011	−20	1.1×10^{-6}	−60	11×10^{-4}	−30
1	120	27×10^{-4}	−26	27×10^{-8}	−66	2.7×10^{-4}	−36
0.7	117	13×10^{-4}	−29	13×10^{-8}	−69	1.3×10^{-4}	−39
0.5	114	6.6×10^{-4}	−32	6.6×10^{-8}	−72	66×10^{-4}	−42
0.3	110	2.4×10^{-4}	−36	2.4×10^{-8}	−76	24×10^{-6}	−46
0.2	106	1.1×10^{-4}	−40	1.1×10^{-8}	−80	11×10^{-6}	50
0.1	100	27×10^{-6}	−46	27×10^{-10}	−80	2.7×10^{-6}	−56
70×10^{-3}	97	13×10^{-6}	−40	13×10^{-10}	−89	1.3×10^{-6}	−59
50×10^{-3}	94	6.6×10^{-6}	−52	6.6×10^{-10}	−92	66×10^{-8}	−62
30×10^{-3}	90	2.4×10^{-6}	−56	2.4×10^{-10}	−96	24×10^{-8}	−66
20×10^{-3}	86	1.1×10^{-6}	−60	1.1×10^{-10}	−100	11×10^{-8}	−70
10×10^{-3}	80	27×10^{-8}	−66	27×10^{-12}	−106	2.7×10^{-8}	−76
7×10^{-3}	77	13×10^{-8}	−69	13×10^{-12}	−109	1.3×10^{-8}	−79
5×10^{-3}	74	6.6×10^{-8}	−72	6.6×10^{-12}	−112	66×10^{-10}	−82
3×10^{-3}	70	2.4×10^{-8}	−76	2.4×10^{-12}	−116	24×10^{-10}	−86
2×10^{-3}	66	1.1×10^{-8}	−80	1.1×10^{-12}	−120	11×10^{-10}	−90
1×10^{-3}	60	27×10^{-10}	−86	27×10^{-14}	−126	2.7×10^{-10}	−96
700×10^{-6}	57	13×10^{-10}	−89	13×10^{-14}	−129	1.3×10^{-10}	−99
500×10^{-6}	54	6.6×10^{-10}	−92	6.6×10^{-14}	−132	66×10^{-12}	−102
300×10^{-6}	50	2.4×10^{-10}	−96	2.4×10^{-14}	−136	24×10^{-12}	−106
200×10^{-6}	46	1.1×10^{-10}	−100	1.1×10^{-14}	−140	11×10^{-12}	−110
100×10^{-6}	40	27×10^{-12}	−106	27×10^{-16}	−146	2.7×10^{-12}	−116
70×10^{-6}	37	13×10^{-12}	−109	13×10^{-16}	−149	1.3×10^{-12}	−119
50×10^{-6}	34	6.6×10^{-12}	−112	6.6×10^{-16}	−152	66×10^{-14}	−122
30×10^{-6}	30	2.4×10^{-12}	−116	2.4×10^{-16}	−156	24×10^{-14}	−126
20×10^{-6}	26	1.1×10^{-12}	−120	1.1×10^{-16}	−160	11×10^{-14}	−130
10×10^{-6}	20	27×10^{-14}	−126	27×10^{-18}	−166	2.7×10^{-14}	−136
7×10^{-6}	17	13×10^{-14}	−129	13×10^{-18}	−169	1.3×10^{-14}	−139
5×10^{-6}	14	6.6×10^{-14}	−132	6.6×10^{-18}	−172	66×10^{-16}	−142
3×10^{-6}	10	2.4×10^{-14}	−136	2.4×10^{-18}	−176	24×10^{-16}	−146
2×10^{-6}	6	1.1×10^{-14}	−140	1.1×10^{-18}	−180	11×10^{-16}	−150
1×10^{-6}	0	27×10^{-16}	−146	27×10^{-20}	−186	2.7×10^{-16}	−156

2.3.5 Magnetic Field Reference

From Eq. (2.25), the magnetic field intensity in A/m is defined in terms of the electric field:

$$H_{A/m} = \frac{E_{V/m}}{Z_{\Omega}} \tag{2.38}$$

or,

$$H_{\mu A/m} = \frac{E_{\mu V/m}}{Z_{\Omega}} \tag{2.39}$$

$$H_{dB\mu A/m} = E_{dB\mu V/m} - 20 \log Z \tag{2.40}$$

$$= E_{dB\mu V/m} - 52 \text{ dB for free space} \tag{2.41}$$

As it happens, the EMC community specifies magnetic-flux density B in its specifications (e.g., MIL-STD-461) rather than magnetic-field intensity:

$$B = \mu H \text{ tesla } (1 \text{ tesla} = 1 \text{ weber/m}^2 = 10^4 \text{ gauss}) \tag{2.42}$$

$$= 4\pi \times 10^{-7} \text{ h/m} \times H_{A/m}$$

where,

μ = absolute permeability of medium in henries per meter (h/m)

Thus,

$$B_{dBT} = H_{dBA/m} - 118 \text{ dB} \tag{2.43}$$

$$= H_{dB\mu A/m} - 238 \text{ dB} \tag{2.44}$$

Since the tesla or dBT is a large unit of magnetic flux density, the EMC community has chosen to use the picotesla (10^{-12} T) as its basic unit. Consequently,

$$B_{dBpT} = B_{dBT} + 240 \text{ dB} \tag{2.45}$$

Combining Eqs. (2.43) and (2.45):

$$B_{dBpT} = H_{dBA/m} + 122 \text{ dB} \tag{2.46}$$

Combining Eqs. (2.38), (2.42) and (2.46) yields:

$$B = \mu E/Z \tag{2.47}$$

or,

$$B_{dBpT} = E_{dBV/m} + 70 \text{ dBpT/v/m, for free space} \tag{2.48}$$

$$= E_{dB\mu V/m} + 190 \text{ dBpT/}\mu\text{V/m, for free space} \tag{2.49}$$

Finally, it is useful to develop a few other magnetic flux density relations, since these conversions may be used on occasion when interfacing with other disciplines. Since $1 \text{ T} = 10^4 \text{ G}$:

$$B_{dBpT} = B_{dBgauss} + 160 \text{ dB} \tag{2.50}$$

Because 1 gamma $= 10^{-9}$ tesla and 1 milligama $= 1$ pT:

$$B_{dBpT} = B_{dBgamma} + 60 \text{ dB} \tag{2.51}$$

$$= B_{dBmgamma} \tag{2.52}$$

2.3.6 Antenna Factor

Antenna factor is a term used by the EMC community to define the antenna transducer calibration relation for making radiated emission measurements. Thus, antenna factor (AF) is:

$$AF = E/V \tag{2.53}$$

where,

 E = unknown electric field to be measured, in V/m

 V = voltage at output terminals of measuring antenna, in V or μV

The units of AF from Eq. (2.53) are 1/m. Expressed in dB, Eq. (2.53) is:

$$AF_{dB/m} = AF_{dB} = E_{dB\mu V/m} - V_{dB\mu V} \tag{2.54}$$

or,

$$E_{dB\mu V/m} = V_{dB\mu V} + AF_{dB} \tag{2.55}$$

The antenna factor 1/m unit is dropped in the above equations, following the rather careless practice of manufacturers and others. As a substitute, the antenna factor is added in dB, corresponding to the measurement frequency as shown in Fig. 2.7.

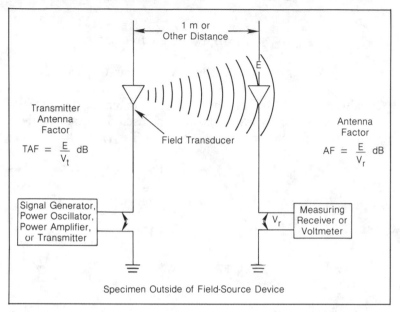

Figure 2.7—Antenna Factors (Emission and Susceptibility)

Antenna factors are also measures of the figure of merit of the antenna transducer. As seen from Eq. (2.53), if a given E produces a high V, the transducer is sensitive and the antenna factor is small. On the other hand, if a low V resulted, the transducer is insensitive and AF is large. Typical range of antenna factors is from about 0 to +60 dB. Table 2.3 lists antenna factors for typical antennas used in measuring radiated EMI emissions.

Another definition of antenna factor involves the effective height of the antenna and its efficiency in delivering the induced voltage to the antenna load:

$$AF = 1/h_e A_e \qquad (2.56)$$

or,

$$AF_{dB} = -h_{edB} - A_{edB} \qquad (2.57)$$

where,

h_e = antenna electrical height in meters   (2.58)

A_e = antenna efficiency or ratio of V_L/V_o

V_o = antenna induced voltage, i.e., available or
      open-circuit voltage

V_L = antenna induced voltage delivered to a load
      (i.e., a 50 Ω EMI receiver) terminating the antenna

Table 2.3—Range of Antenna Factors of Receiving Antennas

Antenna	Below 1 MHz	1 - 30 MHz	30 - 200 MHz
Capacitive Probe	NA	NA	NA
Passive 41" Rod	58 to 35 dB	35 to 22 dB	NA
Passive 81" Rod	52 to 29 dB	29 to 16 dB	NA
Active 41" Rod	+6 dB	+6 dB	NA
Active 6" Probe	+23 dB	+23 dB	+23 dB
Tunable Dipole	NA	NA	−2 to +14 dB
Broadband Dipole	NA	NA	0 to +18 dB
Bi-Conical	NA	NA	7 to 18 dB
Conical Log Sp.	NA	NA	NA
Ridged Guide	NA	NA	NA

Antenna	0.2 - 1 GHZ	1 - 10 GHZ
Capacitive Probe	NA	NA
Passive 41" Rod	NA	NA
Passive 81" Rod	NA	NA
Active 41" Rod	NA	NA
Active 6" Probe	NA	NA
Tunable Dipole	14 to 28 dB	NA
Broadband Dipole	NA	NA
Bi-Conical	NA	NA
Conical Log Sp.	17 to 26 dB	25 to 48 dB
Ridged Guide	11 to 18 dB	21 to 40 dB

The term **electrical height** means the effective height (or length) of the antenna in coupling to an electric field. It does not mean the height of the antenna above the earth, although this height also affects reception.

The effective height of a rod or whip antenna above a ground plane is equal to one-half its mechanical or physical height because the induced voltage increment is zero at the base and increases linearly to ΔV, the increment per unit length at the top. Then integrated over the mechanical height of a rod, the electric field induces a voltage of (V/2)h, or V × h/2. Thus, a 1 m (41") rod has an h_e of 0.5 m. The h_e for a half-wave dipole is λ/π m.

When Eq. (2.58) is substituted into Eq. (2.56) and the result substituted into Eq. (2.53), there results:

$$AF = \frac{E}{V_L} = \frac{1}{h_e A_e} = \frac{1}{h_e\,(V_L/V_o)} = \frac{V_o}{h_e V_L} \qquad (2.59)$$

or,

$$E_{dB\mu V/m} = V_{odB\mu V/m} + h_{edB\ meter} \qquad (2.60)$$

$$V_{odB\mu V/m} = E_{dB\mu V/m} + h_{edB\ meter} \qquad (2.61)$$

Equation (2.61) is the expression for antenna induced voltage. It is the electric-field intensity corrected by the height of the antenna.

The antenna factor may be developed either theoretically or experimentally. Either approach, however, is based on far-field conditions and applies to antennas loaded by a 50 Ω receiver. The experimental approach for determining AF at a 1 m distance from the test sample is not valid below about 50 MHz since far-field conditions then do not exist. The theoretical antenna factor is:

$$AF_{dB} = 10\ \log \frac{9.7}{\lambda\sqrt{G_r}} \qquad (2.62)$$

where, G_r = antenna power gain

Equation (2.62) is plotted in Fig. 2.8 as a function of frequency and antenna gain.

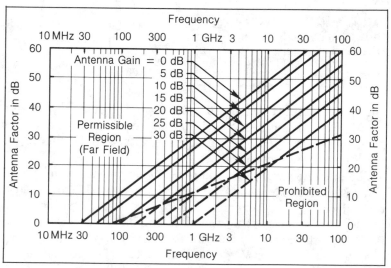

Figure 2.8—Antenna Factor vs. Frequency for Indicated Antenna Gain

2.4 Representation of Signals in the Time and Frequency Domains

In general, EMI signals can be represented in terms of their characteristics in either the time or frequency domains, and Laplace or Fourier analysis may be used to transform signals from one domain to the other. This section presents the basic Laplace and Fourier analysis relationships and describes their application to some typical EMI signals.

2.4.1 Laplace Transforms

There are many situations where transient conditions, such as a sudden change in voltage or current, cause EMI in electronic equipments and systems. This type of transient condition which occurs as a result of a change from one state to another can be represented by a step function. The spectral content of a step function is given by the Laplace transform $\mathcal{L}[v(t)]$, which is defined as follows:

$$\mathcal{L}[v(t)] = F(s) = \int_0^\infty v(t)\, e^{-st}\, dt \qquad (2.63)$$

where,

$$
\begin{aligned}
v(t) &= \text{function of time t} \\
s &= \sigma + j\omega \\
\sigma &= \text{convergence factor} \\
\omega &= \text{frequency radians}
\end{aligned}
$$

Alternatively, if the Laplace transform is known, the time waveform is given as the inverse transform as shown below.

$$v(t) = \mathcal{L}^{-1}\{\mathcal{L}[v(t)]\} = \mathcal{L}^{-1}[V(s)] \qquad (2.64)$$

2.4.2 Fourier Series

A periodic function of time v(t) having a fundamental period T_0 can be represented as an infinite sum of sinusoidal waveforms. This summation, called a Fourier series, may be written in several forms. One such form is the following:

$$v(t) = A_0 + \sum_{n=1}^{\infty} A_n \cos \frac{2\pi nt}{T_0} + \sum_{n=1}^{\infty} B_n \sin \frac{2\pi nt}{T_0}$$

(2.65)

The constant A_0 is the average value of $v(t)$ given by:

$$A_0 = \frac{1}{T_0} \int_{-T_0/2}^{T_0/2} v(t)\, dt$$

(2.66)

while the coefficients A_n and B_n are given by:

$$A_n = \frac{2}{T_0} \int_{-T_0/2}^{T_0/2} v(t) \cos \frac{2\pi nt}{T_0}\, dt$$

(2.67)

and

$$B_n = \frac{2}{T_0} \int_{-T_0/2}^{T_0/2} v(t) \sin \frac{2\pi nt}{T_0}\, dt$$

(2.68)

The exponential form of the Fourier series finds extensive application in communication theory. This form is given by:

$$v(t) = \sum_{n=-\infty}^{\infty} V_n e^{j2\pi nt/T_0}$$

(2.69)

where V_n is given by:

$$V_n = \frac{1}{T_0} \int_{-T_0/2}^{T_0/2} v(t) e^{-j2\pi nt/T_0}\, dt$$

(2.70)

The Fourier series of a periodic function is thus seen to consist of a summation of harmonics of a fundamental frequency $f_0 = 1/T_0$. The coefficients V_n are called spectral amplitudes; that is, V_n is the amplitude of the spectral component at frequency nf_0.

2.4.3 Fourier Transform

A periodic waveform may be expressed as a sum of spectral components. These components have finite amplitudes and are separated by finite frequency intervals $f_0 = 1/T_0$. The normalized power of the waveform is finite, as is also the normalized energy of the signal in an interval T_0. Now suppose the period T_0 of the waveform is increased without limit. In this case, a single-pulse nonperiodic waveform eventually would result.

As T_0 approaches infinity, the spacing of spectral components becomes infinitesimal. The frequency of the spectral components, which in the Fourier series was a discontinuous variable with a one-to-one correspondence with the integers, instead becomes a continuous variable. The normalized energy of the nonperiodic waveform remains finite, but, since the waveform is not repeated, its normalized power becomes infinitesimal. The spectral amplitudes similarly become infinitesimal. The Fourier series for the periodic waveform:

$$v(t) = \sum_{n = -\infty}^{\infty} V_n e^{j2\pi n f_0 t} \qquad (2.71)$$

becomes:

$$v(t) = \int_{-\infty}^{\infty} V(f) e^{j2\pi ft}\, df \qquad (2.72)$$

The finite spectral amplitudes V_n are analogous to the infinitesimal spectral amplitudes $V(f)df$. The quantity $V(f)$ is called the amplitude spectral density or more generally the Fourier transform of $v(t)$. The Fourier transform is given by:

$$V(f) = \int_{-\infty}^{\infty} v(t) e^{-j2\pi ft}\, dt \qquad (2.73)$$

2.5 Transients

This section discusses transients because they appear so often in EMC technology in general and EMI measurements in particular. Furthermore, an understanding of transients and their amplitude spectrum occupancy and phase relations are paramount to an understanding of broadband emissions discussed in the next section. As presented there, broadband emissions may be coherent (e.g., a transient or impulse) or incoherent (e.g., bandwidth-limited white noise). The former results in a 20 dB/decade bandwidth relation while incoherent broadband emissions result in a 10 dB/decade bandwidth dependency.

2.5.1 Transient Sources

When either an emitting EMI source or a potential victim receptor performs over a broadband of frequencies, it is likely that it develops or responds, respectively, to transients. Transients distinguish themselves by having a low duty cycle and fast rise and/or fall times. The duty cycle δ, of an emitting source is defined as:

$$\delta = \tau \times f_r$$

where,

τ = equivalent pulse or impulse width at the 50 percent height

f_r = pulse repetition rate, or average number of pulses or impulses per second for random occurrences

Most transients from incidental emitting sources correspond to duty cycles which are very small, i.e., less than 10^{-5}. Table 2.4 lists some approximate duty cycles identified to the nearest order of magnitude corresponding to a few transient sources. When the duty cycle becomes significantly greater than 10^{-5}, such as 10^{-3} for radar or 0.5 for a computer clock, the emitting source is no longer regarded as a transient. However, it still may exhibit fast rise times and, therefore, broadband emissions.

Transients have become a major problem because of the many

emitting sources in operation and because computers, digital and control devices, among others, are especially susceptible.

Table 2.4—Typical Transient Sources

Emitting Transient Source	Repetition Rate	Impulse Width	Duty Cycle
Fluorescent Lamps	100 pps	10^{-7} s	10^{-5}
Ignition Systems:			
Idle Speed	100 pps	10^{-8} s	10^{-6}
Fast Speed	10^3 pps	10^{-8} s	10^{-5}
Relays and Solenoids:			
Casual Use	10^{-3} pps	10^{-7} s	10^{-10}
Pinball Machine	1 pps	10^{-7} s	10^{-7}
Teletype	10 pps	10^{-7} s	10^{-6}
Brush-Commutator Motor	10^3 pps	10^{-8} s	10^{-5}
On-Off Switches:			
Wall Switch	10^{-4} pps	10^{-6} s	10^{-10}
Lathe	10^{-3} pps	10^{-7} s	10^{-10}
Copy Machine	10^{-3} pps	10^{-7} s	10^{-10}

2.5.2 Spectrum Occupancy

A transient is a current or voltage amplitude versus time which is made of two different level states. Two examples are shown in Fig. 2.9 for an approximation of a transient:

1. A step function with finite rise or fall time in which two different levels exist on either side of the transition (transient), either of which may take on any amplitude including zero.
2. A pulse or impulse with finite rise and fall times (not necessarily the same) in which a different level exists with reference to the mid-pulse level of the transition (transient), and in which the preceding and subsequent levels may be any amplitude, including zero. Thus, the pulse or impulse is essentially a back-to-back step function of the same or different rise/fall times.

2.5.2.1 Step Functions

By using either the Fourier integral or Laplace transform, the spectrum occupancy of a transient may be determined in the frequency domain from its structure in the time domain. For the step function shown in Fig. 2.9:

$$\text{Step Function} = \frac{\Delta e}{\tau_r} U(t)t - \frac{\Delta e}{\tau_r} U(t - \tau_r)t$$

$$\text{Laplace Transform} = \frac{\Delta e}{\tau_r s^2} (1 - e^{-\tau_r s}) \qquad (2.74)$$

$$\leqslant \frac{2\Delta e}{\tau_r s^2} = 0.05 \, \Delta e / \tau_r f^2, \text{ for } f > 1/\tau_r \qquad (2.75)$$

where,

$$s = j\omega = j2\pi f$$

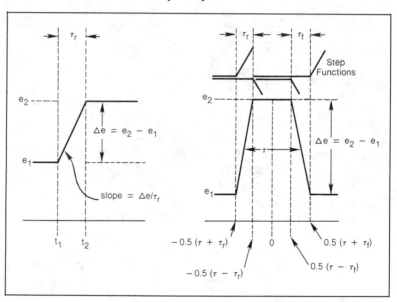

Figure 2.9—Step Function and Impulse Transients

2.30

Equation (2.74) is plotted in Fig. 2.10. The envelope of its amplitude, developed in Eq. (2.75), is also shown in the figure. The envelope falls off inversely with frequency squared (40 dB/decade) for a finite rise time and for $f > 1/\tau_r$. Should the rise time become arbitrarily large:

$$\lim_{\tau_r \to \infty} \frac{0.05\Delta e}{\tau_r^2} = 0, \text{ for } f > 1/\tau_r$$

Thus, to reduce the amplitude of a step function in the frequency domain, its transition time (rise or fall time) should be made as large and smooth as possible. (If the transition is a smooth function rather than an abrupt one, it can be shown that the slope falls off at the rate of 60 dB/decade or faster for $f > 1/\tau_r$).

Conversely, when the rise time becomes arbitrarily small Eq. (2.74) becomes:

$$\lim_{\tau_r \to 0} \frac{\Delta e}{\tau_r s^2} (1 - e^{-\tau_r s}) = \lim_{\tau_r \to 0} \frac{\Delta e \times e^{-\tau_r s}}{2s} = \frac{\Delta e}{2s}$$

$$= 0.08\Delta e/f \qquad (2.76)$$

Equation (2.76), in which L'Hopitals rule was applied, shows that the amplitude of a pure step function (no rise time) in the frequency domain falls off inversely with frequency at 20 dB/decade. The amplitude also becomes arbitrarily large as the frequency approaches zero.

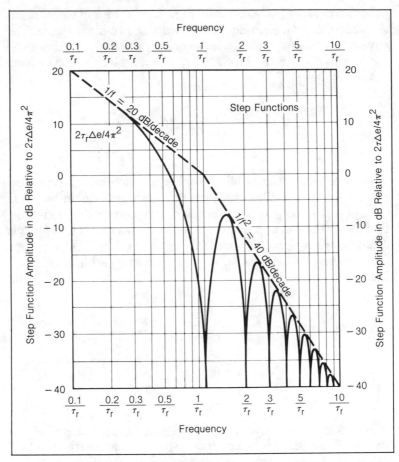

Figure 2.10—Time-Domain Responses of Step and Pulse Functions With Finite Rise Times (continued next page)

2.32

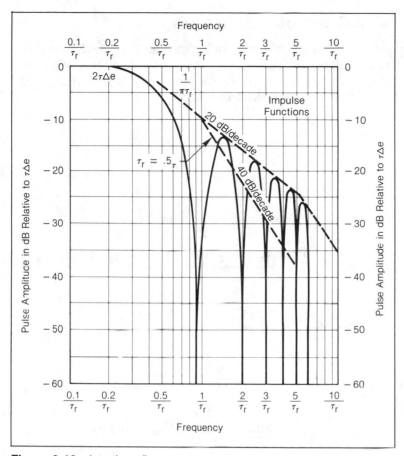

Figure 2.10—(continued)

2.33

2.5.2.2 Impulse Functions

The development of a pulse or impulse-like transient having finite rise and fall times (see Fig. 2.9) follows a similar mathematical procedure to the preceding. The pulse function is made up of four step functions (SF) as shown in the figure.

$$SF = \frac{\Delta e}{\tau_r} \{(U[t + 0.5 (\tau + \tau_r)]t - U[t + 0.5(\tau - \tau_r)]t\}$$

$$- \frac{\Delta e}{\tau_f} \{U[t - 0.5 (\tau - \tau_f)]t - U[t - 0.5(\tau + \tau_f]t\}$$

The Laplace transform $\mathcal{L}$ of the four step functions (i.e., the pulse) is:

$$\mathcal{L}(SF) = \frac{\Delta e}{s^2} \left\{ \frac{e^{s\tau/2}(e^{s\tau_r/2} - e^{-s\tau_r/2})}{\tau_r} - \frac{e^{-s\tau/2}(e^{s\tau_f/2} - e^{-s\tau_f/2})}{\tau_f} \right\}$$

$$= \frac{2\Delta e}{s^2} \left\{ \frac{e^{s\tau/2}\sin\pi f\tau_r}{\tau_r} - \frac{e^{-s\tau/2}\sin\pi f\tau_f}{\tau_f} \right\} \qquad (2.77)$$

When the rise and fall times are equal, i.e., when $\tau_r = \tau_f$, Eq. (2.77) becomes:

$$\mathcal{L}(SF) = \frac{2\Delta e}{s^2} \left\{ (e^{s\tau/2} - e^{-s\tau/2}) \frac{\sin \pi f\tau_r}{\tau_r} \right\}$$

$$= \tau\Delta e \frac{\sin \pi f\tau}{\pi f\tau} \times \frac{\sin \pi f\tau_r}{\pi f\tau_r} \qquad (2.78)$$

Equation (2.78) approaches an amplitude density of $\tau\Delta e$ volt seconds, or V/Hz as f approaches 0. However, since the negative frequency domain does not exist, the amplitude approaches $2\tau\Delta e$.

The dashed line in Fig. 2.10 represents the envelope A of the function in which:

$$A = 2\tau\Delta e, \text{ for } 0 \leqslant f \leqslant 1/\pi\tau$$

$$= \frac{2\Delta e}{\pi f}, \text{ for } 1/\pi\tau \leqslant f \leqslant 1/\pi\tau_r \qquad (2.79)$$

$$= \frac{2\Delta e}{\pi^2 f^2 \tau_r}, \text{ for } f \geqslant 1/\pi\tau_r \qquad (2.80)$$

Between $f = 1/\pi\tau$ and $1/\pi\tau_r$, the slope is 20 dB/decade. Above $f = 1/\pi\tau_r$, the slope becomes 40 dB/decade. For $\tau_r = \tau_f = 0$, Eq. (2.79) becomes:

$$\mathcal{L}(SF) = \tau\Delta e \ \frac{\sin \pi f\tau}{\pi f\tau} \qquad (2.81)$$

This is the classical (sin x)/x function so often appearing in EMC literature. Its slope beyond $f > 1/\pi\tau$ is 20 dB/decade.

When $\tau_r = \tau/2$, the impulse is a triangular wave which is also shown in Fig. 2.10. Its 40 dB/decade slope breaks close in. Thus, to reduce EMI, make the rise and fall times approximately equal, and τ_r should be as large as possible.

2.5.2.3 The EMP — A Triangular Impulse

EMI problems and testing associated with the electromagnetic pulse (EMP) can become significant. The EMP may be approximated by a triangular pulse of $\tau_r = 10$ ns and $\tau_f = 500$ ns. Thus, the pulse width, $\tau = (\tau_r + \tau_f)/2 = 255$ ns ($\tau \approx \tau_f/2$).

The spectrum distribution for this pulse was previously indicated in Eq. (2.77). It is rewritten here somewhat differently:

$$\mathcal{L}(SF) = \left(\frac{e^{j\pi f\tau}\sin \pi f\tau_r}{\pi f\tau_r} - \frac{e^{-j\pi f\tau}\sin \pi f\tau_r}{\pi f\tau_r} \right) \qquad (2.82)$$

The notch frequencies of its spectrum envelope are:

$$A = 2\tau\Delta e = \tau_f \Delta e \text{ V/Hz for } 0 \leqslant f \leqslant 1/\pi\tau_r \qquad (2.83)$$

$$= \frac{\Delta e}{\pi f} \text{ for } 1/\pi\tau_f \leqslant f \leqslant 1/\pi\tau_r \qquad (2.84)$$

$$= \frac{\Delta e}{\pi^2 f^2 \tau_r} \text{ for } f \geqslant 1/\pi\tau_r \qquad (2.85)$$

Equations (2.83) to (2.85) are plotted in Fig. 2.11. Here, all values are increased by 10^3 so that the ordinate reference is now V/kHz. To determine the EMI amplitude in a bandwidth B_{kHz}, add 20 log B_{kHz} to the value shown in Fig. 2.11.

2.5.2.4 Lightning Stroke Impulse

Lightning strokes also create EMI problems. They can be simulated by a pulse width τ of about 50 μs and a 10 to 90 percent rise time τ_r of about 500 ns. The average stroke is about 30 kA. Thus, the rate of rise is about 60 kA/μs. The spectral intensity is $2\tau A \approx 3$ A/Hz = 3 kA/kHz = 190 dBA/kHz, and the first notch frequency, $1/\pi\tau$, is 6.3 kHz. The second notch frequency is 637 kHz. Figure 2.12 shows the current spectral density of the stroke in the left ordinate and the magnetic flux density at a distance of 100 m. To calculate the magnetic flux density at other distances, R (in meters), add dB = 20 log(R/100).

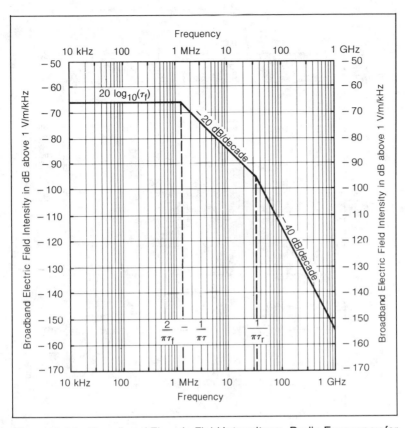

Figure 2.11—Broadband Electric Field Intensity vs. Radio Frequency for Simulated EMP

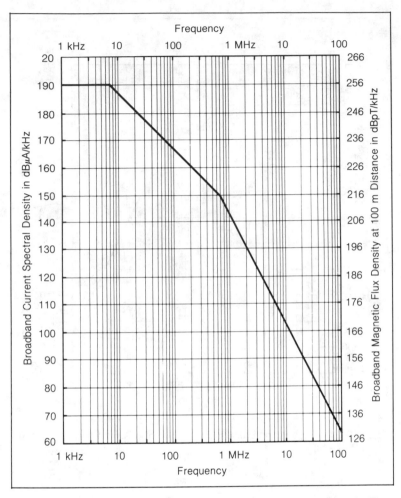

Figure 2.12—Broadband Current Spectral Density and Magnetic Flux Density from a Lightning Stroke

2.6 Narrowband Emissions

The term **narrowband emission** indicates that the emission bandwidth is narrower than some reference bandwidth. Here, the reference bandwidth may be that associated with a potentially susceptible victim receptor. More specifically, the reference bandwidth is that of an EMI measurement receiver. Thus, an emission source is narrowband when its 3 dB bandwidth is smaller than that of the EMI measurement receiver's 3 dB bandwidth. As discussed in a later section, the definition of broadband emission is just the reverse.

To illustrate the above, consider a signal which is neither CW nor exhibits a wide bandwidth. For convenience of discussion, a single voltage pulse emission having a carrier frequency f_c is selected as shown in Fig. 2.13. The (sin x)/x distribution centered about f_c is recognized with the x-axis crossings at $f_c \pm 1/\tau$, $f_c \pm 2/\tau$, etc. Its greatest amplitude at f_c is $A\tau$ volt seconds or V/Hz.

Figure 2.13 also shows an EMI receiver RF selectivity response having a bandwidth B_n centered about f_c. By inspection of the figure, one concludes that the pulse emission occupancy is narrowband since its 3 dB bandwidth B_e is less than (narrow) with respect to the receiver bandwidth B_n. In other words, $B_e < B_n$.

To be useful in performing EMI measurements and emission recognition, there must exist one or more tests for broadband or narrowband. One such test is the tuning test and another is the bandwidth change test.

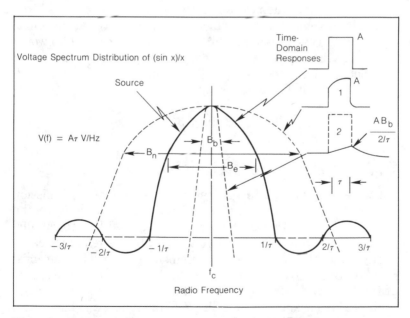

Figure 2.13—Narrowband and Broadband Transients Relative to the Measuring Receiver Bandwidth

2.6.1 Narrowband Tuning Test

If the receiver with bandwidth B_n in Fig. 1.13 is tuned up or down in frequency by an amount equal to its own 3 dB bandwidth, and if the output level (Δ/V) changes by more than 3 dB, then the emission source is narrowband. If there is a very large change (say, greater than 20 dB), then the emission source is very narrowband with respect to the receiver bandwidth. If the change is about 3 dB, however, the emission source has a transitional bandwidth, i.e., transitional between narrowband and broadband conditions. Thus, the tuning test will indicate narrowband (NB) when:

$$NB_{tuning} \quad \Delta V > 3 \text{ dB} \qquad (2.86)$$

2.6.2 Narrowband Bandwidth Test

The second test available for narrowband emission identification involves a change in the bandwidth of the EMI receiver. If a second bandwidth in the receiver with bandwidth B_n in Fig. 2.13 is selected such that the new bandwidth is at least 2 B_n, and if the output level V changes by an amount less than 3 dB, then the emission source is narrowband. A further increase in bandwidth would result in little or no perceptible change in output. If the change had been about 3 dB, the emission would be transitional. Thus, the bandwidth test will indicate narrowband when:

$$NB_{bandwidth} \quad \Delta V < 3 \text{ dB} \qquad (2.87)$$

2.7 Broadband Emissions

The term **broadband emission** indicates that the emission bandwidth is broader than some reference bandwidth. Here, the reference bandwidth may be that associated with a potentially-susceptible victim receptor. More specifically the reference bandwidth is often that of an EMI measurement receiver. Thus, an emission source is broadband when its 3 dB bandwidth exceeds that of the 3 dB EMI receiver bandwidth.

Figure 2.13 is again used to illustrate the tuning and bandwidth test criteria. The EMI receiver now has an RF response as shown with bandwidth B_b centered about the carrier f_c. By inspection of the figure, one concludes that the pulse emission is broadband since its 3 dB bandwidth B_e is greater (broader) with respect to the receiver bandwidth. In other words, $b_e > B_b$. The preceding two tests for determining if the signal is broadband or narrowband will again be applied.

2.7.1 Broadband Tuning Test

If the receiver with bandwidth B_b is tuned up or down in frequency by an amount equal to its own 3 dB bandwidth, and if the output level ΔV changes by less than 3 dB, then the emission source is broadband. If there is no perceptible change at all, the emission source is extremely broadband relative to the receiver bandwidth. If the change is about 3 dB, however, the emission source has a transitional bandwidth, i.e., transitional between narrowband and broadband conditions. Thus, the tuning test will indicate broadband (BB) when:

$$BB_{tuning} \; \Delta V < 3 \text{ dB} \tag{2.88}$$

2.7.2 Broadband Bandwidth Test

The second test available for broadband emission identification involves a change in the bandwidth of the EMI receiver. If a second bandwidth in the receiver with bandwidth B_b in Fig. 2.13 is selected such that the new bandwidth is at most $B_b/2$, and if the output level ΔV changes by an amount greater than 3 dB, then the emission source is broadband. If the change had been about 3 dB, the emission would be transitional. Thus, the bandwidth test will indicate broadband when:

$$BB_{bandwidth} \; \Delta V > 3 \text{ dB} \tag{2.89}$$

2.7.3 Summary of Narrowband and Broadband Tests

The foregoing may be summarized in a simple matrix as illustrated in Table 2.5. Special situations may develop when the change in test receiver output is approximately 3 dB, viz., (1) transitional situations and (2) broadband incoherent. There is not much which can be done for a transitional situation, although its impact in terms of identifying the emission type for EMI specification limit compliance can be significant. For example, if an emission is identified as either narrowband or broadband (i.e., transitional situation), it may be within specifications for one situation and out of specifications for another. While the test engineer could theroretically select the more favorable situation here (if his objective were to simply pass the test sample), a better approach would be to select a different receiver bandwidth and perform the RF tuning test.

**Table 2.5—Summary of Narrowband and Broadband
Emission Identification Criteria**

Type of Emission Type of Test	Narrowband	Broadband	Notes
RF Tuning	> 3 dB	< 3 dB	(1)
Bandwidth Change	< 3 dB	> 3 dB	(2)

Notes:
(1) Up or down frequency change equals the EMI receiver bandwidth.
(2) For a narrowband test, increase bandwidth by at least two times. For a broadband test, decrease bandwidth to no more than one-half.

The second special situation to be mentioned involves identifying that an emission may be or is broadband but that the receiver output level ΔV changes in the bandwidth change test by any of the following:

$$\Delta V = 20 \log(B_{new}/B_{old}), \text{ for coherent BB} \qquad (2.90)$$

$$\Delta V = 10 \log(B_{new}/B_{old}), \text{ for incoherent BB} \qquad (2.91)$$

$$\Delta V = \text{somewhere between Eqs. (2.90) and (2.91)} \qquad (2.92)$$

For example, if B_{old} in Fig. 2.13 is B_b, and if B_{new} were $B_b/2$, then Eq. (2.90) would indicate a 6 dB change (broadband coherent emission) while Eq. (2.91) would indicate a 3 dB change (broadband incoherent emission which could be mistaken as transitional). These special situations are discussed in the following sections.

2.7.4 Coherent and Incoherent Broadband Emissions

A signal or emission is said to be **coherent** when neighboring frequency increments are related or well defined in both amplitude and phase. For broadband situations, neighboring amplitudes are both equal and in phase. Examples of coherent broadband emission sources are transients such as listed in Table 2.4 and pulsed sources such as computer clocks, radar and pulse code modulation (PCM) telemetry as long as the conditions first confirm that the emission is broadband.

A signal or emission is said to be **incoherent** when it is not coherent, viz., when neighboring frequency increments are random or pseudo random (bandwidth limited) in either phase or in both amplitude and phase. Examples of incoherent broadband emission sources are gas lamps (dc energized), noise diodes, black bodies including internal receiver noise, and corona discharge from high-voltage sources.

2.7.4.1 Coherent Broadband Emissions

In examining a transient such as previously shown in Eq. (2.81) for a rectangular pulse, the amplitude is flat within 1.3 dB for $0 \leqslant f \leqslant 1/\pi\tau$ and there is no phase change at all from $0 \leqslant f \leqslant 1/\tau$. Thus, this qualifies as a coherent emission. Consequently, the voltage developed under the $(\sin x)/x$ curve V_{BC} within a receiver bandwidth B* for $f < 1/\pi\tau$ such as shown in Fig. 2.10 is simply the area under the curve:

$$V_{BC} \cong 2\tau\Delta eB, \text{ for } f_B \leqslant 1/\pi\tau \qquad (2.93)$$

or,

$$V_{dBV} = 20 \log 2\tau\Delta e + 20 \log B \qquad (2.94)$$

All coherent broadband voltages are proportional to their receiver bandwidths, and any change in bandwidth yields a corresponding change in EMI receiver voltage level equal to that presented in Eq. (2.90).

---

*The bandwidth is somewhat different from the 3 dB bandwidth. It is called the **impulse bandwidth.**

2.7.4.2 Incoherent Broadband Emissions

When the voltage phase term is random from neighboring frequency increment to increment, the incremental voltages do not add in phase but add in an rms fashion. This incoherent emission within a bandwidth B is then:

$$V_{BI} = \left\{ \int_0^B (2\tau\Delta e)^2 dB \right\}^{1/2} \quad \text{for } f_B \leqslant 1/\pi\tau \qquad (2.95)$$

$$= \left\{ (2\tau\Delta e)^2 B \right\}^{1/2} = 2\tau\Delta e\sqrt{B} \qquad (2.96)$$

and, $\quad V_{dBV} = 20 \log 2\tau\Delta e + 10 \log B \qquad (2.97)$

All incoherent broadband voltages are proportional to the square root of their bandwidths, and any change in bandwidth yields a corresponding change in EMI receiver voltage level equal to that presented in Eq. (2.91). This is further illustrated by thermal noise or bandwidth-limited white noise in receivers. The receiver noise power N is:

$$N = FKTB \text{ watts} \qquad (2.98)$$

$$V = \sqrt{4RN} \text{ volts}$$

$$= \sqrt{4RFKTB} \qquad (2.99)$$

Again, incoherent broadband noise voltage is proportional of the square root of bandwidth.

2.8 Frequency and Wavelength

Sometimes the term **wavelength** instead of frequency is used. To convert from frequency f in Hz to wavelength λ (length of one cycle of frequency) in meters, the velocity of propagation in air is used:

$$\lambda f = C; \quad \lambda = C/f \text{ or } f = C/\lambda \tag{2.100}$$

where, $\quad\quad C \approx 3 \times 10^8 \text{ m/s in air}$

thus, $\quad\quad \lambda_m = 3 \times 10^8/f_{Hz} \text{ meters}$

$$= 300/f_{MHz} \tag{2.101}$$

where, $\quad\quad f_{Hz} = \text{frequency in Hz}$

$$f_{MHz} = \text{frequency in MHz}$$

Equation (2.100) is plotted in Fig. 2.14 from 10 Hz to 100 GHz and for λ in units of centimeters, inches, meters, kilometers and miles. The arrows on the graphic lines instruct which axis to read from (right or left distance axis, or top or bottom frequency axis).

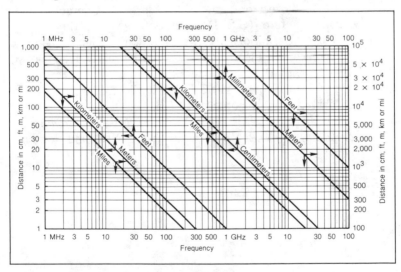

Figure 2.14—Wavelength in Air vs. Radio Frequency

2.9 Bibliography

Apollo Program NHB 5320.3, *Electromagnetic Compatibility Principles and Practices* (NASA, October 1965).

Compliance Engineering, 1985-6 (Boxborough, MA: Dash, Straus and Goodhue).

MIL-D-18300D (WP), "Design Data Requirements for Avionic Equipment (U.S. Dept. of Defense, December 1961).

MIL-D-8706B (AS), "Data and Tests, Engineering: Contract Requirements for Aircraft Weapon Systems (U.S. Dept. of Defense, August 1968).

Mil-D-8708 (AS), "Demonstration Requirements for Airplanes" (U.S. Dept. of Defense, January 1969).

MIL-E-6051D, "Military Specification, Electromagnetic Compatibility Requirements, Systems (U.S. Dept. of Defense, September 1967).

MIL-STD-461, "Electromagnetic Interference Characteristics, Requirements for Equipment (U.S. Dept. of Defense, August 1968).

MIL-STD-462, "Electromagnetic Interference Characteristics, Measurements of (U.S. Dept. of Defense, July 1967).

MIL-STD-463, "Definitions and System of Units, Electromagnetic Interference and Electromagnetic Compatibility Technology," (U.S. Dept. of Defense, June 1977).

USAF Design Handbook, AFSC DH 1-4, Electromagnetic Compatibility (U.S. Air Force, WPAFB, Ohio).

Violette, J.L.N.; White, D.R.J. and Violette, M.F., *Electromagnetic Compatibility Handbook* (New York: Van Nostrand Reinhold Col, 1987).

Chapter 3

EMC Design of Telecommunication Systems

Our society relies on the ability to establish and maintain extensive reliable communications. In general, the requirement for use of the electromagnetic spectrum for communication, navigation and radar systems has been rapidly increasing. Our military strategy is based on the rapid deployment of dynamic forces supported by an extensive Command, Control, Communications and Intelligence (C^3I) network to provide the information required for Battle Management. In the civilian sector, our communications requirements have increased drastically as a result of the mobility of our society and our dependence on computers. The cellular telephone has significantly increased the capacity of our mobile communications and fixed point-to-point microwave and satellite communication systems provide an extensive data transmission network for computer systems.

One of the most important considerations in the design, installation and operation of a communication-electronic (CE) system is that of achieving and maintaining EMC between the system and the other CE equipments in the immediate vicinity. EMC is the ability of equipments or systems to function as designed without degradation or malfunction in an intended operational electromagnetic environment. The equipment or system should not adversely affect the operation of, or be adversely affected by, any other equipment or system.

To succeed in achieving EMC and to permit efficient use of the frequency spectrum, it is essential that engineers, technicians and users responsible for the planning, design, development, installation and operation of CE equipments employ suitable analysis techniques. These techniques permit them to identify, localize and define EMI problem areas before incurring expenditures of time, effort and dollars. More timely and economical corrective measures then may be taken.

The primary purpose of this chapter is to provide analysis techniques and tools that may be used in planning, designing, installing and operating communication equipments or systems which are free of EMI problems. Careful application of these techniques at appropriate stages in the system life cycle will ensure EMC without either the wasteful expense of overengineering or the uncertainties of underengineering.

3.1 The Communication System EMI Problem

In a typical communication situation, the receiver must be able to pick up its intended signal, which is probably relatively weak, while operating in the presence of a number of relatively strong potentially interfering signals which result from other CE systems operating in close proximity. Conversely, the transmitter must be able to transmit a relatively strong signal without causing interference to nearby sensitive receivers.

The basic EMC requirement is to plan, specify and design systems, equipments and devices that can be installed in their operational environments without creating or being susceptible to interference. To help satisfy this requirement, careful consideration must be given to a number of factors that influence EMC. In particular, it is necessary to consider major sources of EMI, modes of coupling and points or conditions of susceptibility. The EMC technologist should be familiar with the basic tools (including analysis, measurement, control, suppression, specifications and standards) that are used to achieve EMC.

This chapter presents a methodology for EMC design of telecommunication systems and describes analysis techniques that may be used to identify and define potential EMI problems. The techniques are specifically oriented toward EMI signals that are generated by potentially interfering transmitters, propagated and received via antennas and cause EMI in receivers associated with telecommunication systems.

3.2 Major EMI Interactions between Transmitters and Receivers

In the planning and design of a communication system, it is important to recognize that there are several different means by which EMI may occur. For each situation, the appropriate types of EMI must be considered. The important types of EMI, which are shown in Fig. 3.1, may be considered to be in one of three basic categories: co-channel, adjacent-signal or out-of-band.

These categories are defined as follows:

Co-channel EMI refers to interference resulting from signals that exist within the narrowest passband of the receiver. For superheterodyne receivers (which are used for many applications) the frequency of co-channel interference must be such that the interference is translated to the intermediate frequency (IF) passband in the same manner as the desired signal. This requires the frequency of co-channel interfering signals to equal the tuned radio frequency, plus or minus one-half the narrowest IF bandwidth. Although the receiver is most sensitive to this type of interference, it is usually easily controlled by avoiding co-channel assignments within a relatively large control zone over which this type of interference may occur.

Adjacent-signal EMI refers to potentially interfering signals that exist within or near the receiver radio frequency (RF) passband but fall outside of the IF passband after conversion. The most significant adjacent-signal EMI effects result from intermodulation and transmitter noise.

The adjacent-signal EMI region may extend over a considerable range of frequencies on each side of the tuned frequency. For example, for a typical UHF communication transceiver having 25 kHz channel spacing, the adjacent-signal EMI region may include 400 channels (i.e., 10 MHz) on each side of the desired channel. Although the adjacent-signal EMI region includes a relatively wide range of frequencies, the receiver is not particularly sensitive to these signals. As a result, adjacent-signal EMI is usually limited to co-site situations involving transceivers which are located within 1.5 or 3 km (1 or 2 miles) of each other.

Out-of-band EMI refers to signals having frequency components which are significantly outside of the widest receiver passband. The most significant out-of-band EMI effects result from transmitter harmonics interfering with receiver fundamentals or transmitter fundamentals interfering with receiver spurious responses. EMI between transmitter harmonics and receiver spurious responses are also possible but extremely unlikely. Because of the power levels involved, out-of-band EMI is usually restricted to co-site situations.

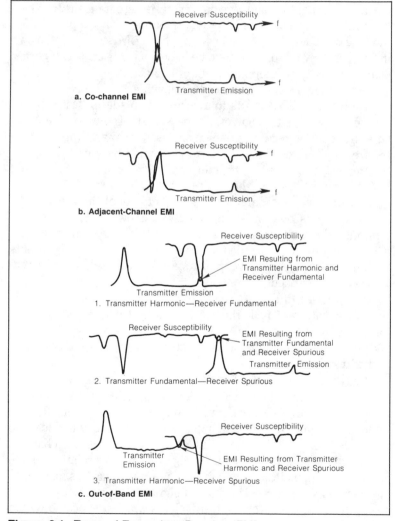

Figure 3.1—Types of Transmitter-Receiver EMI

3.3 Basic EMC Analysis Equation

To determine whether an EMI problem exists between a potentially interfering transmitter and a receiver, it is necessary to consider the susceptibility of the receiver to both the design and spurious outputs (individually and collectively) of the potentially interfering transmitters. The factors that must be included in the analysis for each transmitter output (or group of transmitter outputs) include:

1. Transmitter power (P_T)
2. Transmitting antenna gain in the direction of the receiver (G_{TR})
3. Propagation loss between the transmitter and receiver (L)
4. Receiver antenna gain in the direction of the transmitter (G_{RT})
5. The amount of power required to produce interference in the receiver (P_R) in the presence of the desired signal

Factors that must be considered in interference analysis include the **design** (intentional) and operational performance characteristics of equipment and as well as **nondesign** (unintentional) and non-operational characteristics. This chapter discusses equipment characteristics that are considered in EMC design and analysis. It also describes techniques that are employed for representing these equipment characteristics in the form of general mathematical models for analysis. The necessity of considering parameters such as transmitter spurious output emissions, receiver spurious responses, antenna side-lobe and back-lobe radiation and unintentional propagation paths introduces complications because it is now necessary to obtain information on equipment non-design characteristics. Unlike equipment design characteristics (which are usually well defined and may be readily obtained from equipment specifications), equipment spurious characteristics are not usually identified or described in equipment specifications. Therefore, it is difficult to obtain information on the spurious characteristics of specific equipments.

For situations in which specific detailed data are not available, several different sources of input information may be used to derive "default models." This chapter presents equipment EMC default models that have been derived from statistical summaries of measured equipment characteristics and from MIL-STD-461 limits.

The procedure that is used for each transmitter output emission can be demonstrated by considering the interference situation that

exists between a particular output of one of a number of potentially interfering transmitters and a specimen receiver. For the case
of a particular transmitter output (which may be either a fundamental or a spurious emission), the power available at the receiver is
given by:

$$P_A(f,t,d,p) = P_T(f,t) + C_{TR}(f,t,d,p) \qquad (3.1)$$

where,

$P_A(f,t,d,p)$ = power available at the receiver (in dBm) as a
function of frequency (f), time (t), distance
separation (d) and direction (p), of both
transmitter and receiver and their antennas

$P_T(f,t)$ = transmitter power (in dBm)

$C_{TR}(f,t,d,p)$ = transmission coupling between transmitter and
receiver (in dB)

In problems involving interference coupled from a transmitting
antenna to a receiving antenna, the transmission coupling function
is represented by:

$$C_{TR}(f,t,d,p) = G_{TR}(f,t,d,p) - L(f,t,d,p) + G_{RT}(f,t,d,p) \qquad (3.2)$$

where,

$G_{TR}(f,t,d,p)$ = the transmitting-source antenna gain in the
direction of the receiver in dB

$L(f,t,d,p)$ = the propagation loss function in dB

$G_{RT}(f,t,d,p)$ = the receiving antenna gain in the direction of
the transmitter in dB

By comparing the power available at the receiver input terminals
to the power required at the input to produce interference in the
receiver at the frequency in question, $P_R(f,t)$, it is possible to determine the interference situation for the particular transmitter output being considered. The requirement for EMC is that the power
available at the receiver be less than the power required to produce
interference in the receiver. Thus, the condition for electromagnetic
compatibility is:

$$P_A(f,t,d,p) < P_R(f,t) \qquad (3.3)$$

3.6

On the other hand, if the power available at the receiver input terminals is equal to or greater than the power required to produce interference in the receiver, an electromagnetic interference problem may exist, viz.,

$$P_A(f,t,d,p) \geqslant P_R(f,t) \tag{3.4}$$

When $P_A = P_R$, EMC is marginal and an EMI problem may or may not exist.

An indication of the magnitude of a potential interference problem may be obtained by considering the difference between the power available and the susceptibility threshold. This difference is termed **interference margin** (IM) and provides a measure of the total contribution to interference, i.e.,

$$IM(f,t,d,p) = P_A(f,t,d,p) - P_R(f,t) \tag{3.5}$$

The interference margin is defined such that there is a potential interference problem if the margin is positive and there is little to no chance of interference if the interference margin is negative.

The expression IM(f,t,d,p) in Eq. (3.5) can be considered to represent an equivalent on-tune interference-to-noise (I/N) ratio at the receiver input terminals. If the expressions for $P_A(f,t,d,p)$ and $P_R(f,t)$ are expanded, Eq. (3.5) becomes:

$$
\begin{aligned}
IM(f,t,d,p) = I/N = & \; P_T(f_E) + G_{TR}(f_E,t,d,p) \\
& - L\,(f_E,t,d,p) + G_{RT}(f_E,t,d,p) \\
& - P_R(f_R) + CF(B_T,B_R,\,\Delta f)
\end{aligned} \tag{3.6}
$$

where,

$P_T(f_E)$ = power transmitted in dBm at emission frequency (f_E)

$G_{TR}(f_E,t,d,p)$ = transmitter antenna gain in dB at emission frequency (f_E) in the direction of receiver

$L(f_E,t,d,p)$ = propagation loss in dB at emission frequency (f_E) between transmitter and receiver

$G_{RT}(f_E,t,d,p)$ = receiver antenna gain in dB at emission frequency (f_E) in direction of transmitter

$$P_R(f_R) \quad = \quad \text{receiver susceptibility threshold in dBm at response frequency } (f_R)$$

$$CF(B_T, B_R, \Delta f) \quad = \quad \text{factor in dB that accounts for transmitter and receiver bandwidths, } B_T \text{ and } B_R, \text{ respectively and the frequency separation } (\Delta f) \text{ between transmitter emission and receiver response.}$$

The final term in Eq. (3.6), $CF(B_T, B_R, \Delta f)$, takes into account the relative bandwidths, transmitter modulation envelope, receiver selectivity curve and the frequency separation, if any, between the transmitter output and the receiver response. The procedure used for determining $CF(B_T, B_R, \Delta f)$ is illustrated by considering the various possibilities that may exist between particular output response pairs as shown in Fig. 3.2.

First, if the output and response occur at the same center frequency (i.e., $f = 0$), there are two basic co-channel possibilities that may be considered:

1. Receiver bandwidth is either equal to or larger than the transmitter bandwidth ($B_R > B_T$). For this case, all the power associated with the transmitter output is received, and no correction is necessary (i.e., $CF(B_T, B_R, \Delta f) = 0$)
2. Receiver bandwidth is less than the transmitter bandwidth ($B_R < B_T$). For this case, only a portion of the power associated with the emission output is received, and it is necessary to apply a bandwidth correction factor, CF, to account for the bandwidth differences. This correction for $\Delta f = 0$ is dependent on the bandwidth ratios and is of the form:

$$CF(\Delta f = 0) = K \log(B_R / B_T) \text{ dB} \qquad (3.7)$$

where,

$$B_R \quad = \quad \text{receiver 3 dB bandwidth in Hz}$$

$$B_T \quad = \quad \text{transmitter 3 dB bandwidth in Hz}$$

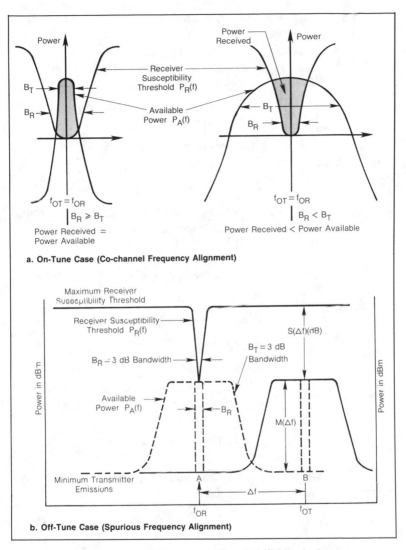

a. On-Tune Case (Co-channel Frequency Alignment)

b. Off-Tune Case (Spurious Frequency Alignment)

Figure 3.2—Illustration of Frequency Bandwidth Analysis

A constant for a particular emission-response combination, K, can be represented as:

$$K = 0 \text{ for } B_R \geqslant B_T \text{ and co-channel frequency alignment}$$

$$K = 10 \text{ for noise-like signals for which rms levels apply and } B_R < B_T$$

$$K = 20 \text{ for pulse signals for which peak levels apply and } B_R < B_T$$

$$(3.8)$$

As the transmitter and receiver center frequencies are separated, the transmitter power can enter the receiver by either of two other possible means (see Fig. 3.1):

1. The transmitter emission modulation sidebands can enter the receiver at the main-response frequency. For this case, the correction factor is:

$$CF_R(\Delta f) = [K \log (B_R/B_T) + M(\Delta f)] \text{ dB} \qquad (3.9)$$

where,

$$M(\Delta f) = \text{modulation sideband level in dB above transmitter power at frequency separation } (\Delta f)$$

$$K = \text{as defined in Eq. (3.8)}$$

2. The power at the transmitter main output frequency can enter the receiver off-tune response. For this case, the correction factor is:

$$CF_T(\Delta f) = -S(\Delta f) \text{ dB} \qquad (3.10)$$

where,

$$S(\Delta f) = \text{receiver selectivity in dB above receiver fundamental susceptibility at frequency separation } \Delta f$$

The final bandwidth correction factor which must be applied to the interference margin due to nonalignment of the transmitter output and receiver response is either $CF_R(\Delta f)$ or $CF_T(\Delta f)$, whichever is larger.

The prediction equations previously presented are applicable to various types of interference problems. In most cases the major difficulty is to determine the parameters in the equations. Although this may appear to be a relatively simple undertaking where transmitting and receiving equipments are involved, it is not. This occurs because each transmitter produces a number of undesired spurious emissions, each receiver has a number of spurious responses and information is not usually available on spurious characteristics.

Furthermore, it is necessary to consider radiation in unintended directions via unintended propagation paths. Interactions between transmitters and receivers having totally different operational functions, purposes and technical characteristics also must be determined. Hence, for the simple case of an EMI prediction involving a single transmitter and receiver pair, information must be obtained for each transmitter output and receiver response, and the basic prediction equation must be applied for each output-response combination.

The following sections describe transmitter, receiver, antenna and propagation characteristics that may be used for EMC analysis.

3.4 Transmitter Emission Characteristics

The primary function of a transmitter is to generate RF power containing direct or latent intelligence within a specified frequency band. In addition to the desired power, transmitters produce numerous unintentional emissions at spurious frequencies as illustrated in Fig. 3.3. A **spurious emission** is any radiated output that is not required for transmitting the desired information. Desired and undesired RF power generated by transmitters may produce EMI in receivers or other equipments. Therefore, in evaluating EMC, it is necessary to consider all transmitter emissions as potential sources of interference.

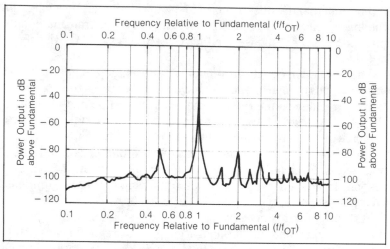

Figure 3.3—Transmitter Output Spectrum Resulting from Composite of Broadband Noise and Discrete Emissions

3.4.1 Fundamental Emissions

To consider the transmitter fundamental output in EMC analysis, it is necessary to define the transmitter operating frequency, the fundamental power output, the bandwidth associated with the fundamental emission and the modulation envelope in the vicinity of the fundamental emission.

The operating frequency is obtained from frequency assignment data, operational information or is defined as part of the statement of the problem. The transmitter fundamental power output and bandwidth are nominal data that should be available from the manufacturers specifications on the transmitter. The modulation envelope describes the relative power in the sidebands around the carrier frequency and may be represented as described in the following paragraphs.

The transmitter fundamental output is not actually confined to a single frequency; it is distributed over a range of frequencies around the fundamental. The characteristics of the power distribution in the vicinity of the fundamental are determined primarily by the baseband modulation characteristics of the transmitter. The resulting spectral components are termed modulation sidebands. The power distribution in the modulation sidebands is represented by a modulation envelope function. In general, the modulation envelopes are described by specifying bandwidths or frequency ranges and functional relationships which describe the variation of power with frequency, $M(\Delta f)$. The modulation envelope model is:

$$M(\Delta f) = M(\Delta f_i) + M_i \log(\Delta f/\Delta f_i) \qquad (3.11)$$

where,

Δf = separation from reference frequency

Δf_i = frequency of applicable region

M_i = slope of modulation envelope for applicable region in dB/decade

An example of the resulting functional relationship is shown in Fig. 3.4. The parameters that are required to specify the modulation envelope are the bandwidths of applicable regions of constant slope and the rate at which the envelope falls off over the frequency region of interest.

Table 3.1 summarizes modulation envelope parameter values for some of the more commonly used types of modulation. The off-tune transmitter emission level is given by:

$$P_T(f_{OT} \pm \Delta f) \text{ dBm/channel} = P_T(f_{OT}) \text{ dBm} + M(\Delta f) \text{ dB} \qquad (3.12)$$

For adjacent-signal frequencies that are sufficiently removed from the transmitter tuned frequency, the major source of interference may result from the broadband noise generated by the transmitter. This transmitter noise may be considered to be included in the modulation envelope and may be represented as a noise floor that extends over a large portion of the frequency spectrum.

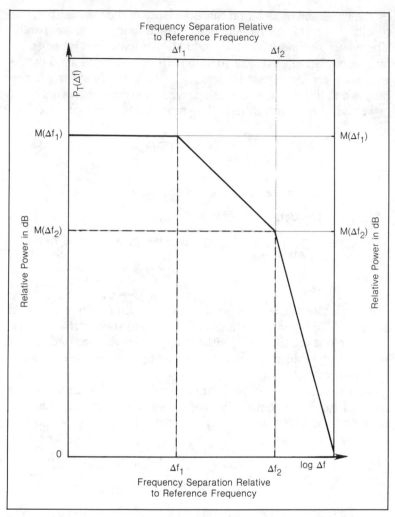

Figure 3.4—Modulation Envelope Representation

Table 3.1—Constants for Modulation Envelope Model

Type of Modulation	i	Δf_i	$M(\Delta f_i)$ (dB above fundamental)	M_i^* (dB/decade)
AM Communication and CW Radar	0	$0.1\,B_T$	0	0
	1	$0.5\,B_T$	0	133
	2	B_T	-40	67
AM Voice	0	1 Hz	-28	0
	1	10 Hz	-28	-28
	2	100 Hz	0	7
	3	1000 Hz	-11	60
FM	0	$0.1\,B_T$	0	0
	1	$0.5\,B_T$	0	333
	2	B_T	-100	0
Pulse**	0	$\dfrac{1}{10\tau}$	0	0
	1	$\dfrac{1}{\pi(\tau+\Delta\tau)}$	0	20
	2	$\dfrac{1}{\pi\Delta\tau}$	$-20\log\left(1+\dfrac{\tau}{\Delta\tau}\right)$	40

3.4.2 Transmitter Intermodulation

Intermodulation is the process by which two or more undesired signals mix in a nonlinearity to produce additional undesired signals at frequencies which are the sum or difference of the input frequencies or their harmonics. In general, intermodulation may occur in both transmitters and receivers. To determine which type intermodulation predominates for a given EMI situation, it is necessary to calculate the equivalent interference level which results from both transmitter and receiver intermodulation and consider the case which results in the largest potential interference.

3.15

As a rule, the most serious problems result from third order intermodulation and will result from mixing products that are given by:

$$f_{IM} = 2f_1 - f_2 \tag{3.13}$$

or,

$$f_{IM} = 2f_2 - f_1 \tag{3.14}$$

where,

f_{IM} = the resulting frequency of the intermodulation product

The transmitter third-order intermodulation problem is illustrated in Fig. 3.5. Referring to the figure, it is shown that intermodulation will occur in both of the two transmitters. The predominant transmitter intermodulation situation depends on the geometry and the power levels and frequencies of the two transmitters. In general, it will be necessary to consider both transmitter intermodulation situations to determine which one produces the most significant signal at the receiver.

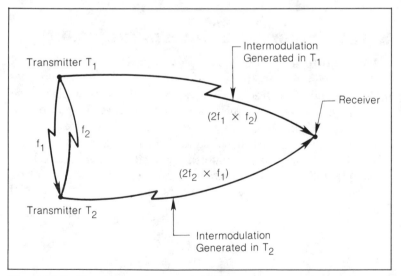

Figure 3.5—Transmitter Intermodulation

For cases where the frequency separation (Δf) between the transmitters is less than or equal to one percent of the transmitter frequency, the equivalent transmitter intermodulation power (P_E) may be approximated by Equation (3.15):

$$P_E(dBm) \quad = \quad P_1(dBm) - 10 \text{ dB} \qquad\qquad (3.15)$$

where,

$\quad$ $P_1(dBm)$ $\quad$ = $\quad$ interfering power available at the transmitter where the intermodulation occurs

For cases where the frequency separation is greater than 1 percent, PE may be approximated by Equation (3.16):

$$P_E(dBm) \quad = \quad P_1(dBm) - 10 \text{ dB} - 30 \log \Delta f(\text{percent}) \ (3.16)$$

It should be noted that P_E is the intermodulation signal level at the transmitter where the intermodulation occurs. To determine the level at a receiver, it is necessary to include the effects of propagation loss.

3.4.3 Harmonic Emission Levels

Referring to Fig. 3.3, it may be observed that transmitter emissions are present at frequencies which are harmonically related to the transmitter fundamental frequency. For the example illustrated in Fig. 3.3, there are other outputs (of lesser amplitude) present at frequencies which are harmonics of the master oscillator frequency. However, because of their reduced amplitude, these master oscillator harmonics do not usually create EMI problems. The harmonic frequencies of the fundamental output are given by:

$$f_{NT} = N f_{OT} \qquad\qquad (3.17)$$

where,

$\quad$ f_{NT} $\quad$ = $\quad$ frequency of Nth harmonic of transmitter

$\quad$ N $\quad$ = $\quad$ integer associated with harmonic

$\quad$ f_{OT} $\quad$ = $\quad$ operating frequency of transmitter

The general math model that is used to describe transmitter harmonic emission levels is:

$$P_T(f_{NT}) \text{ dBm} = P_T(f_{OT}) \text{ dBm} + [(A \log N) + B] \qquad (3.18)$$

where,

A = slope of harmonic levels in dB/decade

B = intercept in dB relative to fundamental emission

If data on transmitter harmonic emission outputs are available from spectrum signature measurements or other information sources, they should be used to determine specific harmonic output models. Conversely, in many instances, specific data are not available. Thus, it is necessary to employ other techniques for determining specific models to be used in EMC analysis.

3.4.3.1 Harmonic Emission Levels Based on MIL-STD-461

One source of information regarding transmitter spurious output levels is the specification or standard associated with the particular CE equipment. Transmitter specifications impose a limit on spurious outputs, and for certain types of problems it may be desirable to use these levels in performing an EMC analysis. If this approach is used, the resulting transmitter harmonic amplitude models would be obtained by setting A to zero, and B to the specification limit. Thus, for example, if transmitter harmonic amplitude models were based on MIL-STD-461, the constants for the model would be:

A = 0

B = as indicated in Table 3.2

Table 3.2—Values for B Based on MIL-STD-461

Transmitter Power in dBm	B in dB Above Transmitter Power
20	−38
50	−80
70	−100
100	−118

3.4.3.2 Statistical Summary Harmonic Amplitude

To provide transmitter harmonic amplitude models that may be used in the absence of specific measured data, statistical summary models have been derived from available spectrum signature data. The results obtained by summarizing data for approximately 100 different transmitter nomenclatures are presented in Table 3.3. The specific values of A and B that correspond to the harmonic emission levels in Table 3.3 are −70 dB/decade and −30 dB respectively. The resulting math model for the harmonic emission level is:

$$P_T(f_{NT}) \text{ dBm } = P_T(f_{OT}) \text{ dBm } - 70 \log N - 30 \qquad (3.19)$$

Table 3.3—Harmonic Average Emission Levels

Harmonic	2	3	4	5	6	7	8	9	10
Average Emission Level (dB Above Fundamental)	−51	−64	−72	−79	−85	−90	−94	−97	−100

3.5 Receiver Susceptibility Characteristics

Receivers are designed to respond to certain types of electromagnetic signals within a predetermined frequency band. However, receivers also respond to undesired signals having various modulation and frequency characteristics. Thus it is necessary to treat a receiver as potentially susceptible to all transmitter emissions.

There are a number of interference effects that an undesired signal can produce in a receiver. To represent receiver composite susceptibility, it is necessary to consider these effects and to determine which effect dominates within a given range of frequencies.

Figure 3.6 is a functional diagram useful in discussing various receiver EMI effects. A superheterodyne receiver generally employs RF stages which provide frequency selectivity or amplification and one or more mixers which translate the RF signal to intermediate frequencies (IFs). It also contains IF stages which provide further frequency selectivity and amplification, a detector which recovers the modulation and post-detection stages that process the signal and drive one or more output displays. Since tuned-radio-frequency (TRF) and crystal-video receivers do not use the superheterodyne principle, they do not contain mixers and IF amplifiers.

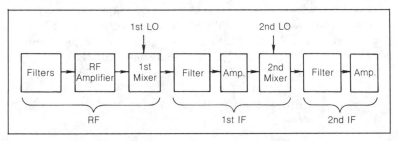

Figure 3.6—Representation for Superheterodyne Receiver

In specifying receiver susceptibility, it is necessary to consider the effects of an interfering signal on each of these stages. The resulting susceptibility function (see Fig. 3.7) represents a composite of the most significant effects.

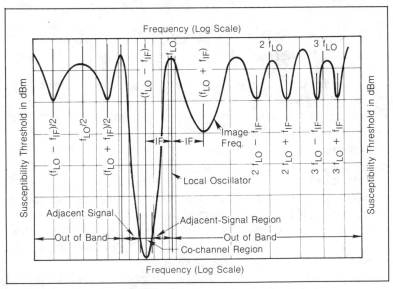

Figure 3.7—Receiver Susceptibility Characteristics

3.5.1 Co-channel Interference

Co-channel interfering signals are amplified, processed and detected in the same manner as the desired signal. Thus, the receiver is particularly vulnerable to these emissions. Co-channel EMI may either desensitize the receiver or override or mask the desired signal. It may also combine with the desired signal to cause serious distortion in the detected output or cause the automatic-frequency control circuitry to retune to the frequency of the interference, if this is applicable.

For co-channel signals, the receiver susceptibility threshold may be represented by the receiver (or environment) noise (i.e., signals which are below the noise can be considered to be noninterfering). The receiver noise level is directly related to the receiver sensitivity, which may be obtained from nominal data on the receiver.

3.5.2 Receiver Adjacent-Signal Interference

Adjacent-signal interference can produce any of several effects in a receiver. The interference may be translated through the receiver together with the desired signal and both appear at the input to an IF stage. In this case, the IF selectivity and the adjacent-signal emission spectrum will both influence the relative level of the interfering signal appearing at the input to the detector. Alternately, one or more interfering emissions may produce nonlinear effects such as desensitization, cross modulation or intermodulation in the RF amplifier or mixer.

Desensitization is a reduction in the receiver gain to the desired signal as a result of an interfering emission producing automatic gain control (AGC) action or causing one or more stages of the receiver to operate nonlinearily due to saturation. **Cross modulation** is the transfer of the modulation from an undesired emission to the desired signal as a result of the former causing one or more stages of the receiver to operate nonlinearily. **Intermodulation** is the generation of undesired signals from the nonlinear combination of two or more input signals which produce frequencies existing at the sum or difference of the input frequencies or their harmonics.

Although desensitization and cross modulation effects can occur in receivers, recent improvements in receiver design have significantly reduced EMI problems due to these effects. In many cases, transmitter noise and transmitter or receiver intermodulation are the limiting factors in adjacent-signal operation. Because intermodulation is often the most serious receiver nonlinear adjacent-signal effect, the models for only this effect will be discussed in this section.

3.5.2.1 Receiver Selectivity

The receiver selectivity determines the amount of attenuation or rejection provided to off-tuned signals by the receiver. In general, the receiver susceptibility threshold for off-tuned signals is increased by the receiver selectivity for the frequency separation in question. The mathematical model used to represent receiver IF selectivity $S(\Delta f)$ is expressed as a piecewise linear function of the logarithm of frequency separation, Δf.

$$S(\Delta f) = S(\Delta f_i) + S_i \log (\Delta f / \Delta f_i) \tag{3.20}$$

for,

$$\Delta f_i < \Delta f < \Delta f_{i+1}$$

where,

S_i = slope of selectivity curve for applicable region

Δf_i = initial frequency of applicable region

Δf = $|f - f_{OR}|$

This model can be used by specifying the frequency deviations associated with the 3 dB and 60 dB selectivity levels. The resulting selectivity model is shown in Fig. 3.8. Notice that a maximum value of 100 dB is assumed for receiver selectivity. This implies that any emission source greater than 100 dB above receiver sensitivity may penetrate and become a source of EMI.

One good indicator for the selectivity characteristics is given by the shape factor; the ratio of the 60 dB bandwidth to the 3 dB bandwidth. Applying the shape factor (SF) concept to Eq. (3.20), the IF selectivity relation yields:

$$S(\Delta f) \, dB = 60 \, \frac{\log (\Delta f/\Delta f_1)}{\log (SF)} \, dB \qquad (3.21)$$

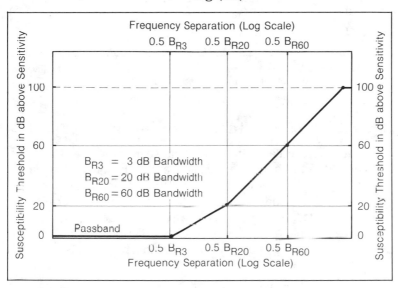

Figure 3.8—Receiver Selectivity Model

When $\Delta f/\Delta f_1$ is chosen to equal the shape factor, Eq. (3.21) yields 60 dB.

A typical value for receiver shape factor is 4. When this value is substituted into Eq. (3.21), the selectivity model parameters can be determined. The resulting values are summarized in Table 3.4. The receiver susceptibility to narrowband off-tune signals is given by:

$$P_R(f_{OR} \pm \Delta f) \, dBm = P_R(f_{OR}) \, dBm + S(\Delta f) \, dB \qquad (3.22)$$

Table 3.4—Summary of Receiver Selectivity Parameters

i	Δf_i	Constants for IF Selectivity Model $S(f_i)$ dB	$S_i{}^*$ dB/decade
0	0.1 B_R	0	0
0	0.5 B_R	0	100
2	5 B_R	100	0

*Note: The slope, S_i, in dB/decade is positive on the upper side and negative on the lower side of the receiver tuned frequency.

3.5.2.2 Receiver Intermodulation

For an intermodulation product to cause interference, it must be transformed to a frequency within or near the IF passband for detection to occur. The method considered here is intermodulation in the RF amplifiers and first mixer which results in an intermodulation frequency at or near the receiver tuned frequency, f_{OR}. Signals which are capable of producing intermodulation interference in a receiver must satisfy the following relationship:

$$mf_1 \pm nf_2 - f_{OR} \leqslant B_R/2 \tag{3.23}$$

where,

f_1 and f_2 = frequencies of two interfering emissions

f_{OR} = receiver tuned frequency

B_R = IF bandwidth in which intermodulation products are significant

m and n = integers

The only signals that are potentially serious sources of intermodulation are those which are in the vicinity of the receiver frequency and produce intermodulation products which fall within the receiver operating or immediately adjacent channels.

The following equations present the frequency criteria which two interfering signals must meet to satisfy these constraints:

$f_N \pm f_F - f_{OR} \leqslant B_R/2$ (second order)

$2f_N - f_F - f_{OR} \leqslant B_R/2$ (third order)

$3f_N - 2f_F - f_{OR} \leqslant B_R/2$ (fifth order)

$4f_N - 3f_F - f_{OR} \leqslant B_R/2$ (seventh order)

where,

f_{OR} = receiver RF tuned frequency

f_N = frequency of intereferring emission nearest to f_{OR}

f_F = frequency of interfering emission farthest from f_{OR}

Equation 3.23 may be normalized to the receiver fundamental frequency and solved to show the relationship between two culprit signals which will produce an intermodulation product at the receiver fundamental frequency:

$$m \frac{f_1}{f_{OR}} \pm n \frac{f_2}{f_{OR}} = 1 \qquad (3.24)$$

Figure 3.9, obtained from Equation (3.24), shows the resulting chart for second- and third-order intermodulation products. Intermodulation signal combinations falling on or near one of the lines are capable of generating an intermodulation product in the vicinity of the receiver tuned frequency.

The area on the chart marked "Region of Major Significance" is particularly important because of the proximity of the signals to the receiver tuned frequency. Signals within this region will, in general, experience less RF selectivity (rejection) than will signals outside of the region. Thus, they are more likely to produce significant intermodulation products. The extent of this region is in general a function of RF selectivity, but the area indicated is representative of typical receivers.

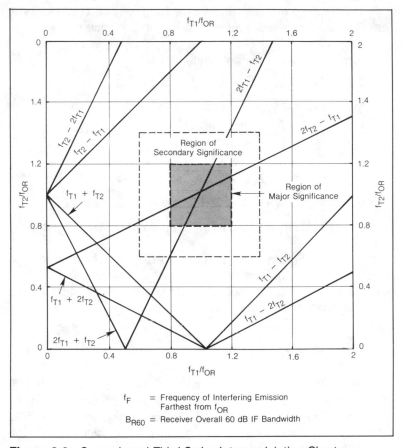

Figure 3.9—Second- and Third-Order Intermodulation Chart

To evaluate the impact of receiver intermodulation, it is convenient to express the effect in terms of an equivalent interference margin. This corresponds to the margin resulting from two interfering signals that produce an intermodulation product that falls within the receiver overall 3 dB passband. If the intermodulation product is off-tuned from the receiver tuned frequency, the IF selectivity can be applied to determine the resulting off-tune interference margin. If the input signals producing the intermodulation do not produce hard saturation in the receiver front end, and the desired signal and the resulting intermodulation do not exceed the receiver automatic gain control (AGC) threshold, the equivalent interference margin (IM) resulting from intermodulation is:

$$IM(dB) = mP_N + nP_F + IMF - P_R(f_{OR}) \qquad (3.25)$$

where,

P_N and P_F = power in dBm at receiver input resulting from interfering signals at frequencies f_N and f_F

m and n = constants associated with intermodulation order (m corresponds to the harmonic of the near signal and n corresponds to the harmonic of the far signal that are mixing to produce the intermodulation product)

IMF = intermodulation factor which depends on receiver nonlinearity and RF selectivity

From an EMI standpoint, third-order intermodulation is usually the most serious offender. For this case, the equivalent interference margin is:

$$IM(dB) = 2P_N + P_F + IMF - P_R(f_{OR}) \qquad (3.26)$$

To use Eq. (3.26) in an EMC analysis, it is necessary to determine the value of the intermodulation factor (IMF). If measured data on receiver intermodulation characteristics are available these data may be used to evaluate IMF. If measured data are not available, IMF may be evaluated from MIL-STD-461 limits to provide a default model as described in the next section.

3.5.2.3 Intermodulation Models from MIL-STD-461

Intermodulation measurements made in accordance with MIL-STD-461 are performed in a manner such that the two interfering signals are equal in amplitude and the resulting intermodulation product produces a standard response in the receiver. The MIL-STD-461 limits (CS03) for conducted susceptibility to intermodulation interference specify that no intermodulation responses shall be observed when the interfering signals are 66 dB above the on-tune level required to produce a response. The resulting MIL-STD-461 default model for third-order intermodulation interference is:

$$IM(dB) = 2P_N + P_F - 3P_R(f_{OR}) - 198 \qquad (3.27)$$

3.5.3 Receiver Spurious Responses

Strong out-of-band interference may produce spurious responses in a receiver. The superheterodyne receiver is most susceptible to those out-of-band signals that mix with local oscillator harmonics to produce a signal at the IF. Spurious responses in such a receiver usually occur at specific frequencies, and other out-of-band frequencies are attenuated by the receiver IF selectivity. For a tuned-RF or crystal-video receiver, the receiver will be susceptible to those out-of-band interfering signals that are not adequately rejected by the RF selectivity.

There are several means by which an out-of-band emission can be translated to one of the passband frequencies of a superheterodyne receiver. The most significant of these occurs in the first mixer stage. Here, the desired signal is heterodyned with the local oscillator (LO) to translate the incoming signal to the intermediate frequency. In addition to desired signals, interfering emissions at many different frequencies are capable of being heterodyned with the LO or other signals and translated to the receiver IF. Amplitude of responses produced in this manner is directly proportional to the strength of the original signals. The level of the LO is typically on the order of 120 dB greater than both desired and interfering signals which are present at the input to the first mixer stage. Therefore, heterodyne products which involve the LO are much larger in amplitude than those heterodyne products which do not involve the LO. Thus, superheterodyne receivers are most susceptible to out-of-band signals that heterodyne with the LO to produce a product in or near the IF passband.

In this section, the term **spurious response**, when applied to superheterodyne receivers, refers specifically to those undesired responses that result from the mixing of a LO with an undesired emission. Those input interfering frequencies which are capable of appearing at the IF as a result of mixing with the LO are known as **spurious-response frequencies**. The amount of power necessary to cause interference at any particular spurious-response frequency is a function of receiver susceptibility to the response.

The frequencies for which spurious responses will occur are given by the following expression:

$$f_{SR} = (pf_{LO} \pm f_{IF})/q \tag{3.28}$$

where,

f_{SR} = spurious response frequencies

p and q = integers associated with the local oscillator and interference signal

f_{LO} = local oscillator frequency

f_{IF} = intermediate frequency

Figure 3.7 illustrates receiver spurious response susceptibility. In general, the most significant responses are those for which q is equal to 1. Higher values of q do not need to be considered for most EMI situations. The general math model that describes receiver spurious response susceptibility for a given value of q is:

$$P_R(f_{SR}) = P_R(f_{OR}) + I \log P + J \tag{3.29}$$

where,

I = slope of spurious response susceptibility in dB/decade

J = intercept in dB relative to fundamental susceptibility

3.5.3.1 Receiver Response Models Based on MIL-STD-461

If specific information on the spurious response characteristics of a receiver is not available, it may be desirable to use "default models" that are based on the spurious response limits specified in CS04 of MIL-STD-461. These limits may be used to solve for I and J of Eq. (3.29) for the various regions of interest. The resulting default models are provided in Table 3.5.

Table 3.5—MIL-STD-461 Models for Spurious Response

For interfering signals within the receiver 80 dB bandwidth (i.e., $f_o - BW/2 < f_{SR} < f_o + BW/2$):

$$P(f_{SR})dBm = P_R(f_{OR})dBm + \frac{160}{BW}(f_{SR} - f_o)$$

For interfering signals outside the receiver 80 dB bandwidth but within the overall tuning range of the receiver (i.e., $f_L \leqslant f_{SR} \leqslant f_o - BW/2$ or $f_o + BW/2 \leqslant f_{SR} \leqslant f_H$):

$$P_R(f_{SR})\ dBm = P_R(f_{OR})\ dBm + 80\ dB$$

For interfering signals outside the tuning range of the receiver (i.e., for $f_{SR} < f_L$ or $f_{SR} > f_H$:

$$P_R(f_{SR}) = 0\ dBm$$

where,
f_o = receiver tuned frequency
BW = receiver 80 dB bandwidth
P_R = receiver sensitivity
f_L = lowest tuned frequency of receiver
f_{II} = highest tuned frequency of receiver

3.5.3.2 Statistical Summary of Receiver Spurious Response Levels

When specific receiver measured data are not available, one alternative for obtaining an out-of-band susceptibility model is to derive statistical summaries from data on receivers. Statistical summary models have been evaluated from available spectrum signature data, and the specific values for I and J are 35 dB/decade and 75 dB, respectively. The corresponding spurious response model is:

$$PR(f_{SR}) = P_R(f_{OR}) + 35 \log P + 75 \tag{3.30}$$

Table 3.6 presents the average spurious response susceptibility levels obtained from measured data.

Table 3.6—Summary of Spurious Response Average

Susceptibility (q = 1)										
Local Oscillator Harmonic (p)	1 (Image)	2	3	4	5	6	7	8	9	10
Average Susceptibility Level (dB above Fundamental Sensitivity	75	82	92	96	99	102	105	107	108	110

3.6 Antenna Radiation Characteristics

Antennas are designed to radiate or receive signals over a specific solid angle and within a specified frequency range. For land mobile or broadcast applications, the antenna is usually designed to radiate or receive uniformly over all sectors surrounding the antenna. Other systems such as fixed point-to-point communication, radar and certain telemetry systems are designed to confine the functional radiated or received signals to certain limited sectors.

In practice, however, it is not possible to accomplish perfect discrimination with antennas in either the spatial or frequency domain. Thus, antennas that are intended to restrict radiation to specific regions also radiate into or receive signals from other unintentional regions. In addition, undesired signals at nondesign frequencies are inadvertently radiated or received by antennas, and the spatial characteristics of an antenna for spurious frequencies are significantly different from characteristics at the design frequency.

3.6.1 Design Frequency and Polarization

Figure 3.10 illustrates the design frequency and polarization radiation characteristics for a number of typical antenna types. Refer-

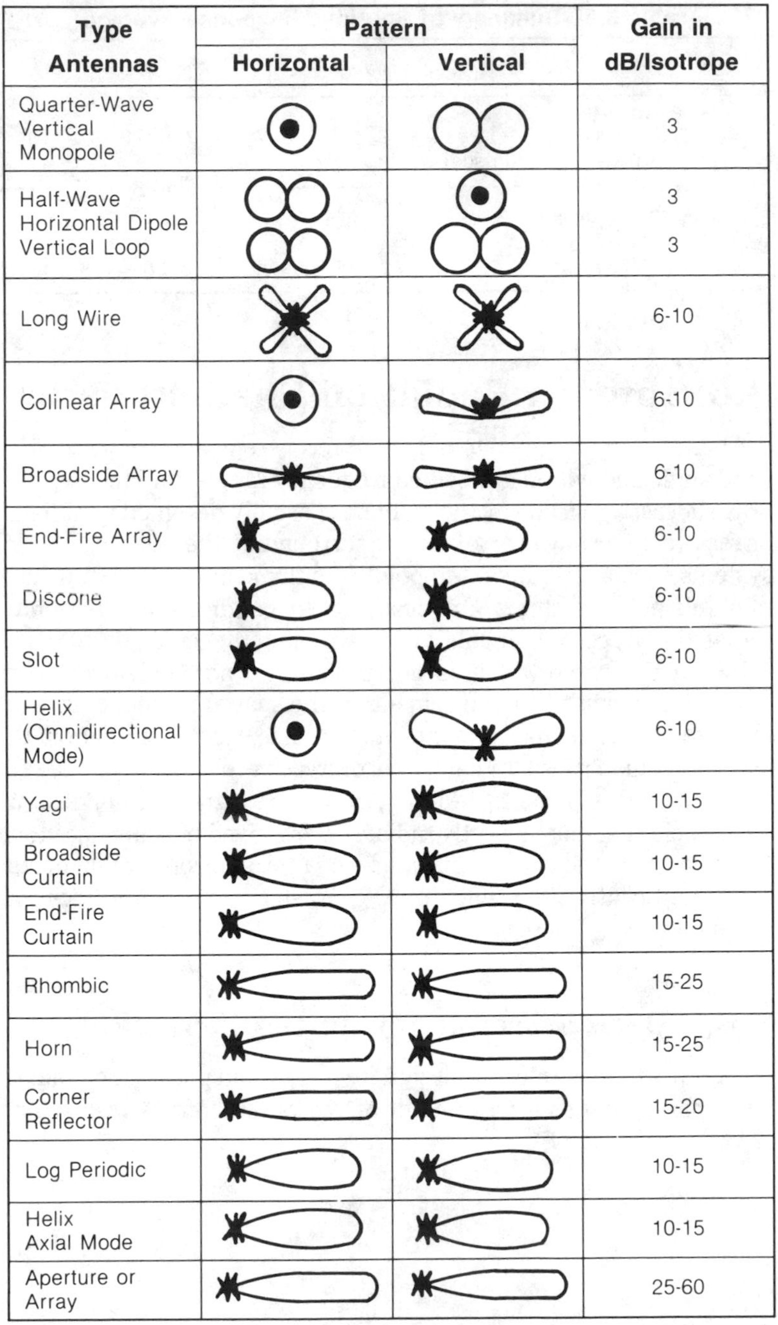

| Type | Pattern | | Gain in |
Antennas	Horizontal	Vertical	dB/Isotrope
Quarter-Wave Vertical Monopole			3
Half-Wave Horizontal Dipole Vertical Loop			3 3
Long Wire			6-10
Colinear Array			6-10
Broadside Array			6-10
End-Fire Array			6-10
Discone			6-10
Slot			6-10
Helix (Omnidirectional Mode)			6-10
Yagi			10-15
Broadside Curtain			10-15
End-Fire Curtain			10-15
Rhombic			15-25
Horn			15-25
Corner Reflector			15-20
Log Periodic			10-15
Helix Axial Mode			10-15
Aperture or Array			25-60

Figure 3.10—Radiation Characteristics For Typical Antennas

3.32

ring to Fig. 3.10, the radiation characteristics for each antenna may be considered to consist of intentional and unintentional radiation regions. Typical gains in the intentional radiation region (for the design frequency and polarization) are given in the column on the right. Antennas are often categorized according to these gains (G) as follows:

1. Low gain: $G < 10$ dB

2. Medium gain: 10 dB $\leqslant G \leqslant 25$ dB

3. High gain: $G > 25$ dB

For the unintentional radiation region, typical mean gain levels relative to an isotrope would typically be:
1. -3 dB for low-gain antennas

2. -10 for medium- and high-gain antennas

Gain levels at a specific orientation may exhibit large variations from these levels.

3.6.2 Polarization Dependence

If an antenna is linearly polarized, there will be a significant difference between antenna gain, in the intentional radiation region, for vertical and horizontal polarizations. This effect will be most pronounced at the design frequency, and the gain will be maximum for the predominant mode of polarization. In general, the discrimination afforded by using antennas which are orthogonally polarized will be on the order of 16 dB to 20 dB, and this provides one means of reducing the probability of interference between different users (e.g., land mobile applications typically use vertical polarization, whereas television broadcast utilizes horizontal polarization).

3.6.3 Nondesign Frequencies

For nondesign frequencies, the antenna gain in the intentional radiation region would typically be reduced by the following:
1. 13 dB for high-gain antennas

2. 10 dB for medium-gain antennas

3. 0 dB for low-gain antennas

The antenna gain at specific nondesign frequencies may exhibit variations from the values specified above. The overall characteristics of the unintentional radiation region are not significantly affected by frequency.

3.7 Propagation Effects

In discussing concepts regarding propagation it is helpful to begin with a discussion of free-space propagation between lossless isotropic antennas. Once the principles governing propagation under these conditions are understood, it is easier to follow the concept of propagation between either omnidirectional or directional antennas in the presence of earth and reflecting and scattering objects such as buildings, trees, etc.

Because many EMI situations involve transmitters and receivers that are co-located or located in close proximity, free-space propagation conditions are often assumed for the purpose of performing an EMC analysis. If a transmitted signal is radiated from an isotropic antenna in free space, the signal spreads uniformly in all directions. Thus, at a distance, d, from the source, the power density is:

$$P_D = P_T/4\pi d^2 \qquad (3.31)$$

where,

P_D = power density (i.e., power per unit area)

P_T = transmitted power

d = distance from antenna to observation point

The power available at the terminals of a lossless receiving antenna having an area A_R and a gain G is:

$$
\begin{aligned}
P_R &= P_D A_R = P_D(G\lambda^2/4\pi) \\
&= P_T\lambda^2/(4\pi d)^2 \text{ for } G = 1 \text{ (isotropic)} \qquad (3.32)
\end{aligned}
$$

where,

λ = wavelength in same units as d

3.34

The above relationship can be expressed in terms of frequency in MHz (f_{MHz}), and distance in statute miles (d_{mi}) or kilometers (d_{km}) by substituting for λ:

$$\lambda(km) = \frac{0.3 \text{ km/s}}{f_{MHz}} \tag{3.33}$$

or,

$$\lambda(miles) = \frac{984}{f_{MHz}}$$

Then,

$$P_T/P_R = \frac{(4\pi)^2}{(0.3)^2} f_{MHz}^2 d_{km}^2$$

$$= 1.75 \times 10^3 f_{MHz}^2 d_{km}^2$$

or,

$$P_T/P_R = \frac{(4\pi)^2 (5,280)^2}{(984)^2} f_{MHz}^2 d_{mi}^2$$

$$= 4,560 f_{MHz}^2 d_{mi}^2$$

Therefore, the free-space attenuation in dB between lossless isotropic antennas for far-field conditions is:

$$L(f,d) = 10 \log (P_T/P_R)$$

$$= 32 + 20 \log f_{MHz} + 20 \log d_{km}$$

or,

$$= 37 + 20 \log f_{MHz} + 20 \log d_{mi}$$

$$\tag{3.35}$$

3.8 Sample EMC Analysis

There are many EMC analysis problems for which only a few transmitter-receiver pairs need to be considered, and the prediction is either performed manually or with the aid of a small computer program which may be run on a personal computer or a time-share terminal. This section presents a step-by-step process for performing a manual EMC analysis through the use of a special form.

Although the particular form presented in this section was designed for analyzing AM and FM analog voice communication systems such as those used for land mobile applications, similar forms may be used for other types of communication systems.

3.8.1 Transmitter Noise

Consider the case of a land mobile receiver operating at 150 MHz. Determine whether EMI will result if a land mobile transmitter, operating at 150.1 MHz, is installed 122 m (400 ft) from the receiver. The pertinent transmitter and receiver characteristics are:

Transmitter power, P_T = 50 dBm

Transmitter antenna gain G_T = 3 dB

Receiver antenna gain, G_R = 3 dB

Receiver sensitivity = −107 dBm

Allowable degradation = 0 dB

This is clearly a co-site, adjacent-signal situation, and the primary cause of potential interference would be transmitter noise. The completed short form is provided for this example. The results indicate that a +8 dB interference margin will be obtained, and a marginal interference situation exists.

EMC Analysis Form for Analog Voice Systems

Form A—Transmitter Noise

Adjacent Signal Interference*		
Transmitter Noise		
1. Transmitter Power, P_T (dBm/Channel)	50	
2. Noise Constant	56	
3. 20 log Δf_{TR} (kHz)	40	
4. Noise per Channel dBm/Channel) (1) − (2) − (3)	− 46	
5. Transmitter Antenna Gain, G_{TR} (dB)	3	
6. Effective Radiated Noise Power (dBm/Channel); (4) + (5)	− 43	
7. Propagation Constant	32	
8. 20 log d_{TR} (km)	− 18	
9. 20 log f_R (MHz)	44	
10. Propagation Loss, L (dB): (7) + (8) + (9)	58	
11. Receiver Antenna Gain, G_{RT} (dB)	3	
12. Noise Power Available, P_A (dBm); (6) − (10) + (11)	− 98	
13. Receiver Sensitivity Level (dBm)	− 107	
14. Allowable Degradation of Receiver Sensitivity (dB)	0	
15. Receiver Susceptibility Level, P_R (dBm); (13) + (14)	− 107	
16. Interference Margin (dB); (12) − (15)	9	
Third Order Intermodulation		
Frequency Check		
• Select Receiver fo Analysis		
17. Receiver/Frequency, f_R (MHz)		
• Select Cosite Transmitter, T_1, with Frequency Nearest to f_R		
18. Transmitter Frequency, f_{T_1} (MHz)		
19. Frequency Separation ΔF_{TR} (MHz); (18) − (17)		
20. Frequency, f_{T_2}, for Intermodulation; (18) + (19)		
21. Channel Width, (MHz)		
22. Band for Intermodulation; (20) ± (21)	(−)	(+)

• Check Other Cosite Transmitters for Frequency within Band Specified by (22). If one is found, continue with analysis. If none, eliminate selected transmitter from consideration and repeat process with another transmitter.

Interference Margin < 0.10 dB, EMI Highly Improbable
10 dB < Interference Margin < 10 dB, EMI Marginal
Interference Margin > 10 dB, EMI Probable.

*Applies to co-site transmitters and receivers with frequency separations (Δf)

3.8.2 Intermodulation

Consider the case of a land mobile receiver operating at 450 MHz in the vicinity (12 m, or 40 ft) of a land mobile transmitter at 451 MHz. Determine whether an intermodulation problem will result if a second transmitter operating at 452 MHz is located 30.5 m (100 ft) from the receiver on a site which is 24.5 m (80 ft) from the first transmitter. The pertinent transmitter and receiver characteristics are:

Transmitter power (T_1 and T_2) = 50 dBm

Transmitter antenna gain (G_{T1} and G_{T2}) = 3 dB

Receiver antenna gain, G_R = 3 dB

Receiver sensitivity = −107 dBm

Allowable degradation = 0 dB

Channel width = 50 kHz

This situation could result in either transmitter or receiver third-order intermodulation. To determine whether third-order intermodulation is possible, it is first necessary to perform the frequency check indicated on the short form. This has been performed on the accompanying form, and the results indicate that an intermodulation problem may occur.

Next it is necessary to calculate the interference margin resulting from both receiver and transmitter intermodulation situations to determine the corresponding interference potential. These calculations, which are straightforward, have been performed on the appropriate form. The calculations indicate that receiver intermodulation results in a +30 dB interference margin and transmitter intermodulation results in a +57 interference margin. For this situation, transmitter intermodulation will predominate and EMI is probable.

EMC Analysis Form for Analog Voice Systems

Form B—Intermodulation (continued next page)

Adjacent Signal Interference*	
Transmitter Noise	
1. Transmitter Power, P_T (dBm/Channel)	
2. Noise Constant	56
3. 20 log Δf_{TR} (kHz)	
4. Noise per Channel dBm/Channel) (1) − (2) − (3)	
5. Transmitter Antenna Gain, G_{TR} (dB)	
6. Effective Radiated Noise Power (dBm/Channel); (4) + (5)	
7. Propagation Constant	32
8. 20 log d_{TR} (km)	
9. 20 log f_R (MHz)	
10. Propagation Loss, L (dB): (7) + (8) + (9)	
11. Receiver Antenna Gain, G_{RT} (dB)	
12. Noise Power Available, P_A (dBm); (6) − (10) + (11)	
13. Receiver Sensitivity Level (dBm)	
14. Allowable Degradation of Receiver Sensitivity (dB)	
15. Receiver Susceptibility Level, P_R (dBm); (13) + (14)	
16. Interference Margin (dB); (12) − (15)	

Third Order Intermodulation

Frequency Check

• Select Receiver fo Analysis		
17. Receiver/Frequency, f_R (MHz)		450
• Select Cosite Transmitter, T_1, with Frequency Nearest to f_R		
18. Transmitter Frequency, f_{T_1} (MHz)		451
19. Frequency Separation ΔF_{TR} (MHz); (18) − (17)		+1
20. Frequency, f_{T_2}, for Intermodulation; (18) + (19)		452
21. Channel Width, (MHz)		.050
22. Band for Intermodulation; (20) ± (21)	(−) 451.95	(+) 452.05

• Check Other Cosite Transmitters for Frequency within Band Specified by (22). If one is found, continue with analysis. If none, eliminate selected transmitter from consideration and repeat process with another transmitter.

Interference Margin < 0.10 dB, EMI Highly Improbable
10 dB < Interference Margin < 10 dB, EMI Marginal
Interference Margin > 10 dB, EMI Probable.

*Applies to cosite transmitters and receivers with frequency separations (Δf)

EMC Analysis Form for Analog Voice Systems

Form B—(continued)

Adjacent Signal Interference*	T_1	T_2
Receiver Intermodulation		
23. Transmitter Power, P_T (dBm)	50	50
24. Transmitter Antenna Gain, G_{TR} (dB)	3	3
25 Effective Radiated Power (dBm) (23) + (24)	53	53
26. Propagation Constant	32	32
27. 20 log d_{TR} (km)	−38	−38
28. 20 log f_T (MHz)	53	53
29. Propagation Loss (dB); (26) + (27) + (28)	47	55
30. Receiver Antenna Gain, (dB)	3	3
31. Power Available at Receiver, (dBm); (25) − (29) + (30)	9	1
32. Multiply T_1 Power Available, Line (31), by Two	18	
33. T_2 Power Available, Line (31)		1
34. Intermodulation Constant		−93
35. Frequency Separation, $\Delta\infty/o$ [19) ÷ (17)] × 100		0.22
36. 60 log $\Delta\infty/o$ or 0		0
37. Equivalent Intermodulation Power (dBm); (32) + (33) + (34) − (36)		−74
38. Receiver Susceptibility Level, P_R (dBm)		−107
39. Interference Margin, (dB); (37) − (38)		+33
Transmitter Intermodulation		
40. Power of T_2 (dBm)		50
41. T_2 Antenna Gain (dB)		3
42. T_2 Effective Radiated Power (dBm), (40) + (41)		53
43. Propagation Constant		32
44. 20 log $d_{T_1 T_2}$ (km)		−32
45. 20 log f_{T_2} (MHz)		53
46. Propagation Loss L (dB); (43) + (44) + (45)		53
47. T_1 Antenna Gain (dB)		3
48. T_2 Signal at T_1 (dBm); (42) − (46) + (47)		3
49. Intermodulation Constant		10
50. 30 log ($\Delta\infty/o$, (line 35), or 0; Whichever Is Larger		0
51. Intermodulation Power at T_1 (dBm); (48) − (49) + (50)		−7
52. T_1 Antenna Gain (dB)		3
53. Intermodulation ERP (dBm); (51) + (52)		−4
54. Propagation Constant (dB)		32
55. 20 log $d_{T_1 R}$ (km)		−38
56. 20 log f_R (MHz)		53
57. Intermodulation Propagation Loss (dB); (54) + (55) + (56)		47
58. Receiver Antenna Gain (dB)		3
59. Intermodulation Power at Receiver (dBm); (53) − (57) + (58)		−48
60. Receiver Susceptibility Level (dBm)		−107
61. Interference Margin (dB)		59

Interference Margin < .10 dB, EMI Highly Improbable
− 10 dB < Interference Margin < 10 dB, EMI Marginal
Interference Margin > 10 dB, EMI Probable.

3.8.3 Out-of-Band EMI

Consider that an industrial user desires to operate a land mobile base receiver at 158.1 MHz. The receiving antenna will be located on top of a building, and a survey of the immediate vicinity reveals that there is a public safety transmitter operating at 39.525 MHz and a land transportation transmitter operating at 452.9 MHz. The separations between the industrial receiver, public safety and land transportation transmitter are 30.5 m (100 ft) and 6 m (20 ft), respectively. Determine whether an EMI problem exists if the system characteristics are as follows:

Industrial receiver:
    Frequency = 158.1 MHz
    Intermediate frequency = 10.7 MHz
    Local oscillator = 147.4 MHz
    Fundamental sensitivity = −107 dBm
    Antenna gain = 3 dB
Public safety transmitter:
    Frequency = 39.525 MHz
    Power output = 100 watts
    Antenna gain = 0 dB
Land transportation transmitter:
    Frequency = 452.9 MHz
    Power output = 50 watts
    Antenna gain = 6 dB

These two potential interference situations are clear examples of out-of-band EMI. The most probable causes of interference for these situations would be a harmonic of the public safety transmitter interfering with the industrial receiver fundamental and a spurious response of the industrial receiver being interfered with by the fundamental of the land transportation transmitter. The calculations have been performed on the accompanying forms. The results indicate that both of these transmitters pose a potential EMI problem to the receiver.

Form C—EMI from Public Safety Transmitter

Out of Band Interference*	
Transmitter Harmonic to Receiver Fundamental; $f_R > f_{Tq}$	
1. Receiver Frequency, f_R (MHz)	158.1†
2. Transmitter Frequency, f_T (MHz)	39.525†
3. (1) ÷ (2) and Round Off to Nearest Integer, N	4
4. Transmitter Harmonic Frequency, Nf_T (MHz); (3) × (2)	158.1
5. Frequency Separation, | (4) − (1) |, (MHz)	0
6. Receiver Bandwidth	0.015†
• If (5) > (6) No Harmonic Interference If (5) < (6) Continue	
7. Transmitter Power, P_T (dBm)	50
8. Harmonic Correction, (dB); from Table 8.2	−72
9. Harmonic Power (dBm); (7) + (8)	−22
10. Propagation Constant	32
11. 20 log d_{TR} (km)	−30
12. 20 log f_R (MHz)	44
13. Propagation Loss, L, (dB) (10) + (11) + (12)	46
14. Receiver Antenna Gain, G_R (dB)	3
15. Power Available at Receiver (dBm); (9) − (13) + (14)	−65
16. Receiver Susceptibility Level, P_R (dBm)	−107
17. Interference Margin, (dB); (15) − (16)	+42
Transmitter Fundamental to Receiver Spurious: $f_T > f_R$	
18. (2) ÷ (1) and Round Off to Nearest Integer, P	
19. Local Oscillator Frequency, f_{LO} (MHz)	
20. Intermediate Frequency, f_{IF} (MHz)	
21. $\|Pf_{LO} \pm f_{IF} - f_T\|$;(18) × (19) ± (20) − (2)|	
If (21+) or (21−) > (6) No Spurious Interface If (21+) or (21−) < (6) Continue	
22. Transmitter Power, P_T(dBm)	
23. Transmitter Antenna Gain, G_T (dB)	
24. Propagation Constant	32
25. 20 log d_{TR} (km)	
26. 20 log f_T (MHz)	
27. Propagation Loss, L (dB); (24) + (25) + (26)	
28. Power Available at Receiver, (dBm); (22) + (23) − (27)	
29. Receiver Fundamental Susceptibility, P_R (dBm)	
30. Spurious Correction, from Table 8.3	
31. Spurious Susceptibility, (dBm); (29) + (30)	
32. Interference Margin, (dB); (28) − (31)	

Interference Margin < − 10 dB, EMI Highly Improbable
− 10 dB < Interference Margin < 10 dB, EMI Marginal
Interference Margin > 10 dB, EMI Probable.

*Applies to cosite transmitters and receivers with frequency separations (Δf) greater than 10% of operating frequency.
†These entries are also required for transmitter fundamental to receiver spurious.

Form D—EMI from Land Transportation Transmitter

Out of Band Interference*	
Transmitter Harmonic to Receiver Fundamental; $f_R > f_{Tq}$	
1. Receiver Frequency, f_R (MHz)	158.1†
2. Transmitter Frequency, f_T (MHz)	452.9†
3. (1) ÷ (2) and Round Off to Nearest Integer, N	
4. Transmitter Harmonic Frequency, Nf_T (MHz; (3) × (2)	
5. Frequency Separation, | (4) − (1) |, (MHz)	
6. Receiver Bandwidth	0.015†
• If (5) > (6) No Harmonic Interference	
If (5) < (6) Continue	
7. Transmitter Power, P_T (dBm)	
8. Harmonic Correction, (dB); from Table 8.2	
9. Harmonic Power (dBm); (7) + (8)	
10. Propagation Constant	32
11. 20 log d_{TR} (km)	
12. 20 log f_R (MHz)	
13. Propagation Loss, L, (dB) (10) + (11) + (12)	
14. Receiver Antenna Gain, G_R (dB)	
15. Power Available at Receiver (dBm); (9) − (13) + (14)	
16. Receiver Susceptibility Level, P_R (dBm)	
17. Interference Margin, (dB); (15) − (16)	
Transmitter Fundamental to Receiver Spurious: $f_T > f_R$	
18. (2) ÷ (1) and Round Off to Nearest Integer, P	3
19. Local Oscillator Frequency, f_{LO} (MHz)	147.4
20. Intermediate Frequency, f_{IF} (MHz)	10.7
21. $\|Pf_{LO} \pm f_{IF} - f_T\|$;(18) × (19) ± (20) − (2)| (+) 0	(−) 21.4
If (21 +) or (21 −) > (6) No Spurious Interface	
If (21 +) or (21 −) < (6) Continue	
22. Transmitter Power, P_T(dBm)	47
23. Transmitter Antenna Gain, G_T (dB)	6
24. Propagation Constant	32
25. 20 log d_{TR} (km)	− 44
26. 20 log f_T (MHz)	53
27. Propagation Loss, L (dB); (24) + (25) + (26)	41
28. Power Available at Receiver, (dBm); (22) + (23) − (27)	− 12
29. Receiver Fundamental Susceptibility, P_R (dBm)	− 107
30. Spurious Correction, from Table 8.3	92
31. Spurious Susceptibility, (dBm); (29) + (30)	− 15
32. Interference Margin, (dB); (28) − (31)	+ 27

Interference Margin < − 10 dB, EMI Highly Improbable
− 10 dB < Interference Margin < 10 dB, EMI Marginal
Interference Margin > 10 dB, EMI Probable.

*Applies to cosite transmitters and receivers with frequency
separations (Δf) greater than 10% of operating frequency.
†These entries are also required for transmitter fundamental to receiver
spurious.

3.9 Computer EMC Analysis

The previous section described forms which may be used to perform a manual EMC analysis. All of the operations indicated on the forms may be easily programmed on a computer or a calculator to assist the system designer in performing an EMC analysis. If one is to be involved in the planning and design of a large system (e.g., a statewide public safety system) it is recommended that a computer or calculator be used to assist in the many calculations that will be required to perform an EMI analysis. Also, it is suggested that a computer data base be established and maintained on all other users in the area.

3.10 Bibliography

Acton, F.S., *Analysis of Straight Line Data* (New York: John Wiley & Sons, Inc., 1953).

Duff, W.G., "Broadband Nontunable Receiver for EMI Measurements," *1984 IEEE EMC Symposium Record* (New York: IEEE, 1984).

Duff, W.G., "EMC Design of Telecommunications Systems," *EMC Expo 1986 Symposium Record* (Gainesville, Virginia: Interference Control Technologies, Inc., 1986).

Duff, W.G., A Handbook on Mobile Communications (Gainesville, Virginia: Interference Control Technologies, Inc., 1976).

Duff, W.G. and Edwards, J.H., "Summary of Equipment EMC Characteristics," *1970 IEEE Regional EMC Symposium Record* (New York: IEEE, 1970).

Duff, W.G. and Heisler, K.G., Jr., et. al., "Voice Communication Degradation Study," RADC-TR-67-556, February 1968.

Duff, W.G., and Heisler, K.G., Jr., "The Effects of Sites Upon the Radiation Characteristics of Antennas," *Proceedings of the Tenth Tri-Service Conference on EMC*, November 1964.

Duff, W.G., and Moore, R.M., "Graphical-Numerical Prediction of Tuned RF Amplifier Output Spectrum: IRE Convention," 1961.

Duff, W.G. and White, D.R.J., Handbook Series on Electromagnetic Interference and Compatibility, Vol. 5, *EMI Prediction and Analysis Techniques* (Gainesville, Virginia: Interference Control Technologies, Inc., 1972).

Duff, W.G., et. al., "Adjacent Signal Interference," *Communication Designer's Digest,* December 1968.

Duff, W.G., et. al., "An Electromagnetic Compatibility Figure of Merit (EMC FOM) for Single-Channel, Voice Communications Equipment," *IEEE Transactions on EMC,* Vol. EMC-17, No. 1, February 1975.

Duff, W.G., et. al., "Compatibility Prediction Accuracy as a Function of Spectrum Signature Data Inputs," *1966 IEEE EMC Symposium Record* (New York: IEEE, 1966).

Duff, W.G., et. al., "Detecting and Locating Sources of Intermodulation Interference," *IEEE International EMC Symposium Record* (New York: IEEE, 1984).

Duff, W.G., et. al., "Determination of Receiver Susceptibility Parameters," *IEEE International EMC Symposium Record* (New York: IEEE, 1970).

Duff, W.G., et. al., "EMC Design Criteria," *Southeastern Regional EMC Symposium Record* (New York: IEEE, 1969).

Duff, W.G., et. al., "Intrasystem EMI Prediction and Analysis," *1973 IEEE EMC Symposium Record* (New York: IEEE, 1973).

Duff, W.G., et. al., "Nonlinear Effects Models for the Intrasystem Electromagnetic Compatibility/Intrasystem Analysis Program," *1979 IEEE EMC Symposium Record* (New York: IEEE, 1979).

Duff, W.G., et. al., "Radar EMI to Voice Communications Receivers," *IEEE International EMC Symposium Record* (New York: IEEE, 1972).

Duff, W.G., et. al., "The Application of Spectrum Signature Data to Interference Analysis," *IEEE International EMC Symposium Record* (New York: IEEE, 1966).

Duff, W.G., et. al., "Transmitter and Receiver FOM Scoring," *IEEE International EMC Symposium Record* (New York: IEEE, 1974).

"Electromagnetic Compatibility Principles and Practices," (NASA Office of Manned Space Flight, Apollo Program, October 1965).

Hald, A., *Statistical Theory with Engineering Applications* (New York: John Wiley & Sons, 1952).

Hebrand, F.B., *Introduction to Numerical Analysis* (New York: McGraw-Hill Book Co., Inc., 1961).

Heisler, K.G., Jr., "Preparation of Statistical Input Functions for Interference prediction," *Proceedings of the Seventh Armour Research Foundation Conference,* 1961.

Jansky and Bailey, a Division of Atlantic Research Corp., *Interference Notebook, Vol. 2,* contract AF 30(602)-68-C-0050, RADC-TR-66-1.

"Nonlinear System Modeling and Analysis with Applications to Communications Receivers," Signatron, RADC-TR-73-178, June 1978.

Spagon, J. and Morrison, E.L., Jr., "System Analysis, Prediction, Hardware Implications and Program Control," *IEEE International EMC Symposium Record* (New York: IEEE, 1984).

Spina, J.F. and Weiner, D.D., *Sinusoidal Analysis and Modeling of Weakly Nonlinear Circuits* (New York: Van Nostrand Reinhold Co., 1980).

Volterra, V., *Theory of Functionals and of Integral and Integro-Differential Equations* (London: Blackie and Sons, 1930).

Wiener, N., "Response of a Non-Linear Device to Noise," M.I.T. Radiation Laboratory Report V-165, April 1942.

Chapter 4

EMC Design of Electronic Equipment and Systems

This chapter discusses the problems resulting from electromagnetic interference (EMI) effects in electronic equipments and systems. The chapter presents a number of examples of typical EMI effects on electronic equipments and systems, defines the basic elements of an EMI situation and describes methods for EMC design.

Electromagnetic compatibility (EMC) is a necessary condition for effective electronic equipment or system performance. EMC is the ability of equipments and systems to function as designed in their intended operational environment without adversely affecting the operation of, or being affected adversely by, other equipments or systems. Thus, the manner in which modern life is conducted and its efficiency depends on the ability to achieve and maintain EMC.

The basic EMC requirement is to plan, specify and design systems, equipments and devices that can be installed in their operational environments without creating or being susceptible to interference. To help satisfy this requirement careful consideration must be given to a number of factors that influence EMC. In particular, it is necessary to consider major sources of EMI, modes of coupling and points or conditions of susceptibility. The electronic equipment or system designer should be familiar with the basic tools (including prediction, analysis, measurement, control, suppression, specifications and standards) that are used to achieve EMC.

4.1 Effects of EMI

EMI may directly influence the performance of an equipment or system and it can indirectly affect the overall accomplishment of an operation or mission. Examples of **direct influences** of EMI on electronic equipment and system performance are:

1. False targets and missed targets in a radar display system
2. Erroneous navigation data or landing system errors in an aircraft
3. Lost or garbled messages in a communication system
4. False commands to a missile or electro-explosive device
5. False indications in an automatic braking control system
6. False commands to a system controlling the electronic ignition and fuel injection in automobile.

Some resulting **indirect effects** corresponding to the above include:

1. (a) False alerts in an air defense system as a result of false targets or (b) surprise enemy attacks as a result of missed targets
2. (a) Aircraft mid-air collisions as a result of navigation errors or (b) aircraft crashes while landing because of altitude or glide slope errors
3. Ineffective control of riots or fires because of lost or garbled emergency fire or police communications
4. Accidental launching of missiles or detonation of explosives because of erroneous electrical commands
5. Accidents resulting from faulty operation of automatic braking systems
6. Loss of power and performance in vehicles resulting from EMI to vehicle electronics

All of these effects, both direct and indirect, have occurred as a result of EMI. They can recur and, with the increase of EMI sources and receptors every year, the incidence will likely become greater.

4.2 Basic Elements of EMI Problems

Three basic elements are common to all EMI situations. These three are: a source of EMI, a transfer or coupling medium and a susceptible device. Figure 4.1 illustrates the three basic elements of an EMI situation and identifies various possible sources of EMI, modes of coupling and potentially susceptible devices. To effectively suppress and control EMI problems, it is necessary to develop an awareness of the role that each of these basic elements play, assess potential EMI problems (which requires quantitative information on EMI levels produced by sources, coupling from source to victim and victim susceptibility) and understand how to minimize the resulting EMI impact on potentially susceptible devices.

EMI Sources	Coupling Media	Susceptible Devices
Radio Transmitters (Broadcast, Communications, Navigation, Radars)	Radiated Antenna-to-Antenna Case Radiation Case Penetration Field-to-Wire Wire-to-Field Wire-to-Wire	Radio Receivers Analog Sensors and Amplifiers
Receiver Local Oscillators		Industrial Control Systems
Motors, Switches, Fluorescent Lights, Diathermy, Dielectric Heaters, Arc Welders	Conducted Common Ground Impedance Power Line Interconnecting Cable	Computers Ammunition and Ordnance
Engine Ignition		Human Beings (Biological Hazards)
Computers & Peripherals		
Naturals Sources: Lightning, Galactic Noise, Electrostatic Discharge		

Figure 4.1—Three Basic Elements of an Emission Susceptibility Situation

4.3 Sources of EMI

Any electrical, electromechanical or electronic device is a potential source of EMI. In general, EMI sources can be classified either as transmitters (i.e., equipment whose primary function is to intentionally generate or radiate electromagnetic signals) or incidental sources (i.e., equipments that generate electromagnetic energy as an unintended by-product in the process of performing their primary function). Sometimes sources of EMI are divided into natural and man-made sources. Figure 4.2 shows such an organization. This section will be concerned with only man-made sources of EMI.

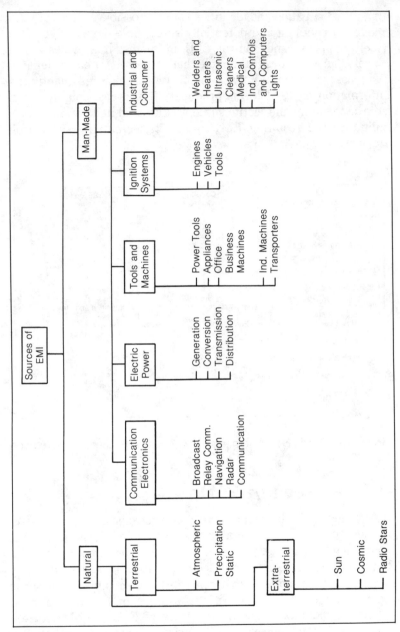

Figure 4.2—Sources of Electromagnetic Interference

The energy generated by EMI sources either can be radiated from the source into the surrounding environment and then picked up by potentially susceptible devices or conducted from the source into potentially susceptible devices via power leads, signal leads or any other interconnecting wires or cables. In general, it is necessary to consider both radiated and conducted emissions from an EMI source.

The emissions generated by EMI sources can be categorized as either narrowband or broadband. Figure 4.3 illustrates these two emission categories. The term **narrowband emission** means that the emission bandwidth is narrow relative to some reference bandwidth which is usually that of an EMI measurement receiver. Examples of narrowband emissions would be a signal from a sinusoidal oscillator, an amplitude or frequency modulated communications signal, etc.

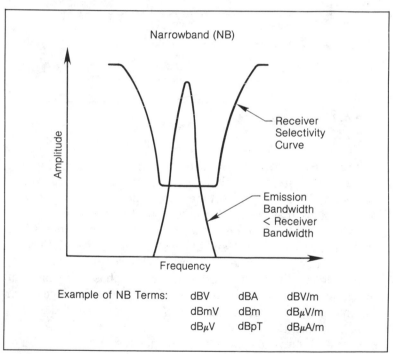

Figure 4.3—Narrowband and Broadband Emissions: Effective Radiated Power (ERP) = Power Output × Antenna Gain (continued next page)

4.5

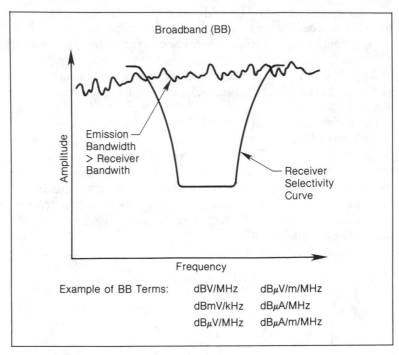

Figure 4.3—(continued)

The term **broadband emission** refers to EMI with emission bandwidths that are broad relative to a reference bandwidth which, again, is usually that of an EMI measurement receiver. Broadband EMI emissions may be further categorized as **coherent** or **incoherent**. A signal or emission is said to be coherent when neighboring frequency increments are related or well defined in both amplitude and phase. For broadband coherent situations, neighboring amplitudes are both equal and in phase. Examples of coherent emission sources are transients and pulsed sources such as computer clocks, radar and PCM telemetry as long as the emission is broadband.

A signal or emission is said to be incoherent when it is not coherent, i.e., when neighboring frequency increments are random or pseudorandom (bandwidth limited) in either phase or both amplitude and phase. Examples of incoherent broadband emission sources are gas lamps (dc energized), noise diodes, black bodies (including internal receiver noise) and corona discharge from high-voltage sources.

The amplitude of narrowband conducted emissions may be expressed in terms of voltage or current. Narrowband radiated emission are expressed in terms of power density (e.g., W/m^2) or field strength (e.g., V/m). With broadband emissions, it is necessary to specify the signal levels per unit of bandwidth. Thus, broadband conducted emissions are specified in terms of voltage or current per unit of bandwidth (e.g., V/MHz). Broadband radiated emissions are specified in terms of radiated levels per unit of bandwidth (e.g., V/m/MHz). For coherent broadband emissions, the received voltage is proportional to the receiver bandwidth, whereas for incoherent broadband emissions, the voltages are proportional to the square root of the receiver bandwidth.

Although any source of EMI can produce radiated emissions, radio transmitters are intentionally designed to generate and radiate electromagnetic signals. Thus, they usually represent the most serious threat from a radiated emission standpoint. Transmitters may cause EMI problems in other equipments that are located within several (or in some cases many) kilometers of the source. Other equipments can cause EMI as a result of their radiated emissions, but they will usually cause problems only in their immediate vicinity.

Figure 4.4 displays the frequency bands allocated for various radio and communication services and indicates the maximum effective radiated power allowed for each service. The levels shown in Fig. 4.4 represent the maximum effective radiated power that will be produced by the fundamental (or intentional) output from the transmitters. Because these fundamental power outputs are relatively high power, they exhibit a serious potential for causing interference problems to electronic equipments or systems located within several kilometers of the transmitters.

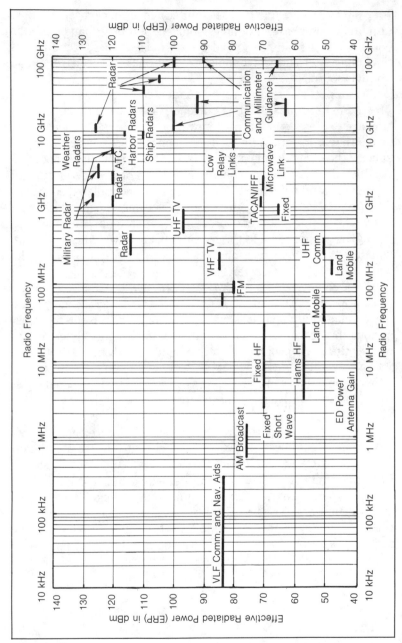

Figure 4.4—U.S. and Canadian Frequency Allocations and Maximum Effective Radiated Powers

4.8

Transmitters generate electromagnetic energy not only in the fundamental or intended frequency range, but also over a wide range of other frequencies on both sides of the fundamental carrier, harmonics of the fundamental and other undesired or spurious frequencies. These undesired emissions result from carrier spreading by the baseband transmitter modulation spectrum, production of broadband noise in the output stages and generation of harmonics of the fundamental as a result of nonlinearities in the equipment output stages. Additionally, because of transmitter nonlinearities, signals from two or more transmitters can heterodyne in the output stages of one to produce additional signals at totally different frequencies. This is called **transmitter intermodulation**. Transmitter spurious emissions are typically at least 60 dB below the fundamental outputs and, because of the low power associated with these spurious emissions, they normally represent an EMI threat only to communication receivers and other very sensitive, frequency-selective electronic equipments or systems.

Any electrical or electronic equipment can be a potential source of EMI. In general, the EMI levels radiated from electrical or electronic equipment are relatively low in power; therefore, these equipments usually pose an EMI threat only to communication receivers or sensitive electronic equipment or systems operated near the source. In general, it is difficult to define the radiated EMI levels that result from the many different types of electrical or electronic equipment. However, if the equipment was required to conform to an EMI specification or standard, then the radiated limit imposed by the standard may be used to provide an upper bound on the radiated emission that will be produced by the device.

Figure 4.5 shows typical narrowband and broadband radiated emission limits imposed by MIL-STD-461 at a distance of 1 m from the test specimen. These limits may be relaxed by 10 dB for certain types of electronic equipments or systems used in specific applications.

Computing devices that are used in nonmilitary applications will be required to conform to the Federal Communications Commission (FCC) Part 15, Subpart J. The FCC radiated emission limits for computing devices are given in Table 4.1. Radiation from computing devices can cause EMI to radio receivers and other nearby sensitive electronic equipment.

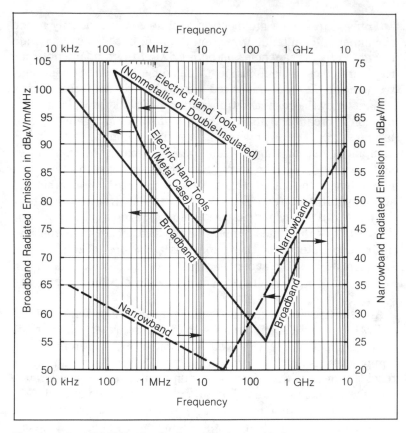

Figure 4.5—MIL-STD-461 Radiated Emission Limits

Table 4.1—FCC Radiation Limits for Computers—Part 15.J

Class A Radiation Limit
(Computers for Use in Industry/Commercial Areas)

f(MHz)	d(m)	E(μV/m)	E (dBμV/m)
30-88	30	30	30
88-216	30	50	34
216-1,000	30	70	37

Class B Radiation Limit
(Computers for Use in Residential Areas)

f(MHz)	d(m)	E(μV/m)	E (dBμV/m)
30-88	3	100	40
88-216	3	150	43
216-1,000	3	200	46

4.10

All electrical equipments can be potential sources of incidental radiation. Although the levels associated with these sources are usually relatively low, they often are the cause of interference because of their broadband characteristics. Here, significant emissions occupy several octaves or more of the frequency spectrum. Some of the more important sources include: power lines, automobile engine ignition systems, fluorescent lamps, electrical motors, switches and relays. Incidental radiation may cause EMI in communication receivers or other sensitive electronic equipments or systems. Figure 4.6 illustrates the typical EMI levels that result from the combined effects of all sources of man-made incidental noise as found in a typical environment.

EMI can be conducted from a source to a potentially susceptible device via power leads, signal leads or any other interconnecting wires or cables. Although any electrical or electronic device can produce conducted EMI, electrical power systems are often the most serious sources of conducted interference. As electrical circuits loads are switched on and off, large transients may be produced. These transients can cause EMI in electronic equipment or systems. Typical transients in unprotected electrical power systems may be as large as 10 times the normal line voltage (i.e., 1,150 V transients in a 115 V electrical power system). To avoid EMI problems in susceptible electronic equipments or systems, it is necessary to provide protection to control the transients resulting from surges in the electrical system.

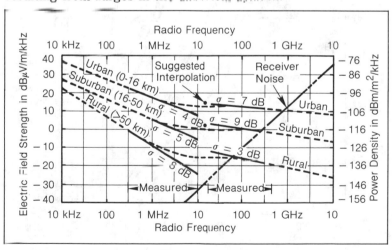

Figure 4.6—Median Incidental Man-Made Noise Based on Lossless Omnidirectional Antenna Near Surface

Equipment-generated EMI can also be conducted along power leads, control leads, signal leads, externally connected leads and interconnecting cables. This conducted EMI can also cause problems in susceptible devices that are connected to an EMI source, either directly or through a common ground. In general, it is difficult to determine the conducted EMI levels generated by various sources. However if the equipment was required to conform to MIL-STD-461 or FCC Part 15.J, the conducted EMI limits imposed by the standards may be used to provide an upper bound on the conducted emissions that will be produced by the device.

Figure 4.7 shows typical broadband and narrowband conducted emission limits for power leads and control and signal leads as required by MIL-STD-461. Table 4.2 shows conducted emission limits for computing devices as specified in FCC Part 15.J.

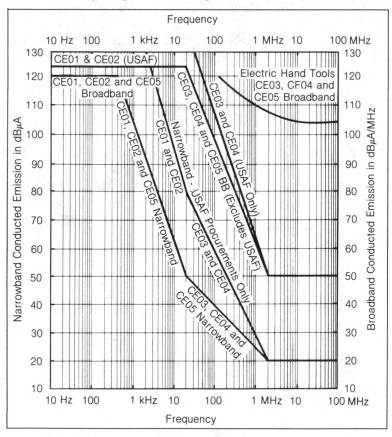

Figure 4.7—MIL-STD-461 Conducted Emission Specification Limits

4.12

Table 4.2—FCC Conducted Limits for Computers—Part 15.J

Class A Conduction Limit		
f(MHz)	RF Voltage (µV)	V (dBµV)
0.45 - 1.6	1,000	60
1.6 - 30	3,000	70
Class B Conduction Limit		
f(MHz)	RF Voltage (µV)	V(dBµV)
0.45 - 30	250	48

Note: For Conducted Limtis, a 13 dB Reduction is Allowed If the Noise is Demonstrated to Be Impulsive Broadband

4.4 Modes of Coupling

Emissions may be coupled by one or more paths from the interference source to the susceptible receiving device(s). Basically, these paths are classified as either (a) **conduction paths**, which include all forms of direct hard-line, wire or cable coupling, or (b) **radiation paths**, which involve propagation through the environment or induction (near field) therein.

Conducted interference may enter a receptor or receiver as a result of directly-coupled wiring leads between the receptor and some source of electrical disturbance. Typical conducted paths include interconnecting cables, power leads and control and signal cables.

Radiating interference includes situations in which emissions (a) enter via a receiving system antenna, if applicable, (b) penetrate a shielded housing at the openings and couple into low-level circuitry, and (c) couple into various signal, control or power leads of a receptor via radiated paths.

The mode(s) of coupling an emitter to a receptor can become very complicated. In general, the coupling paths are extensive and may not be well defined. Coupling can also result from a combination of paths, such as conducted from an emitter to a point of radiation, then picked up by induction and reconducted to the victim.

Some idea of EMI coupling paths is suggested in Fig. 4.8, where both radiation and conducted paths are illustrated. While not all-inclusive, these paths account for, perhaps, 98 percent of all intrasystem EMI situations. The object is to classify each potential EMI situation into one or more of the coupling paths illustrated.

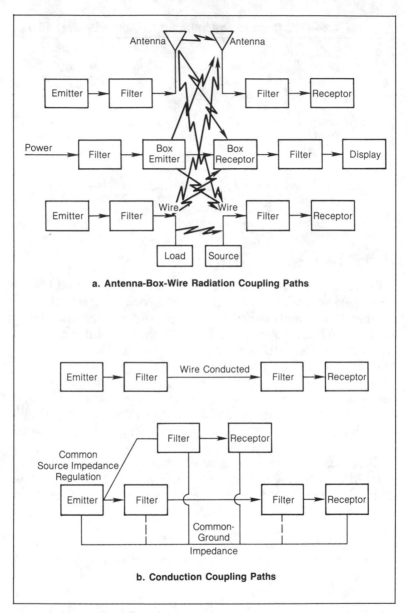

Figure 4.8—Principal EMI Coupling Paths

The radiation paths are:
1. Antenna-to-antenna
2. Wire-to-antenna
3. Antenna-to-box
4. Wire-to-box
5. Antenna-to-wire
6. Wire-to-wire
7. Box-to-antenna
8. Box-to-box
9. Box-to-wire

The conduction paths are:
1. Wire-to-wire
2. Filters
3. Common-ground impedance
4. Common-source impedance

In discussing concepts regarding coupling of EMI, it is helpful to begin with a discussion of free-space propagation between lossless isotropic antennas. Once the principles governing propagation under these conditions are understood, it is easier to follow the concept of propagation between either omnidirectional or directional antennas in the presence of earth, and reflecting and scattering objects such as buildings, trees, etc., and to understand some of the concepts governing radiation and reception of EMI by equipments and circuits.

If a transmitted signal is radiated from an isotropic antenna in free space, the signal spreads uniformly in all directions as illustrated in Fig. 4.9. Thus, at a distance, d, from the source, the power density is:

$$P_D = \frac{P_T}{4\pi d^2} \qquad (4.1)$$

where,

P_D = power density (i.e., power per unit area)

P_T = transmitter power

d = distance from antenna to observation point

The electric field strength, E, radiated from an isotropic antenna may be calculated as follows:

$$E = \sqrt{P_D Z_O} \tag{4.2}$$

where,

E = electric field strength in volts/unit length

Z_o = characteristic impedance of free space = 120π

$$E = \frac{\sqrt{30\ ERP}}{d} \tag{4.3}$$

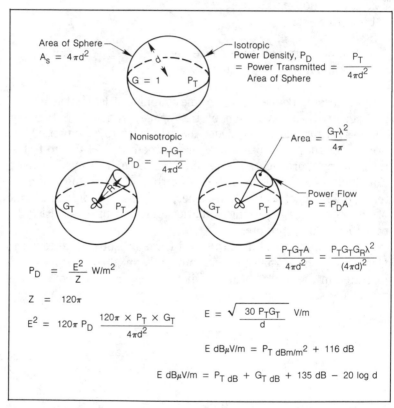

Figure 4.9—Three-Dimensional Geometry Illustrating Gain of Antenna

4.16

The effective radiated power levels generated by various sources were presented in Fig. 4.4. Equation (4.2) can be used to calculate the field strength at a given distance, d, from the source. Figure 4.10 illustrates field strengths as a function of effective radiated power and distance from the source.

The power available at the terminals of a lossless isotropic receiving antenna having an area A_R and a gain G is:

$$P_R = P_D A_R = P_D \ \frac{G\lambda^2}{4\pi} \tag{4.4}$$

$$= \frac{P_T\lambda^2}{(4\pi d)^2} \ \text{for G = 1 (isotropic)}$$

where,

λ = wavelength in the same units as d

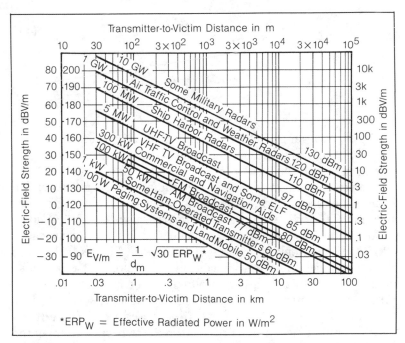

Figure 4.10—Free-Space Electric Field Strength vs. Transmitter Distance and ERP

The above relationship can be expressed in terms of frequency in MHz (f_{MHz}), and distance in statute miles (d_{mi}) or kilometers (d_{km}) by substituting for λ:

$$\lambda(km) = \frac{0.3 \text{ km/s}}{f_{MHz}} \tag{4.5}$$

or,

$$\lambda(miles) = \frac{984}{f_{MHz}}$$

Then,

$$P_T/P_R = \frac{(4\pi)^2}{(0.3)^2} f_{MHz}^2 d_{km}^2$$

$$= 1,750 \, f_{MHz}^2 \, d_{km}^2$$

or,

$$P_T/P_R = \frac{(4\pi)^2 (5,280)^2}{(984)^2} f_{MHz}^2 d_{mi}^2 \tag{4.6}$$

$$= 4,560 \, f_{MHz}^2 \, d_{mi}^2$$

The concepts and relations governing radiation and reception of EMI from directive antennas exhibiting a gain G in a particular direction is also illustrated in Fig. 4.9.

The previous discussion addressed radiation from and reception by antennas associated with communications, navigation and radar systems. The radiated emissions from these systems may also be picked up by other systems, equipments or circuits and can cause EMI. One such pickup mode is illustrated in Figure 4.11 where the interconnecting wires or cables (or the circuit itself) acts as an antenna. In this situation, a voltage will be induced in the loop formed by the interconnecting wires or cables (or the circuit). This situation is often referred to as **field-to-cable differential-mode** coupling because the currents in the two wires forming the loop will be flowing in "different" directions.

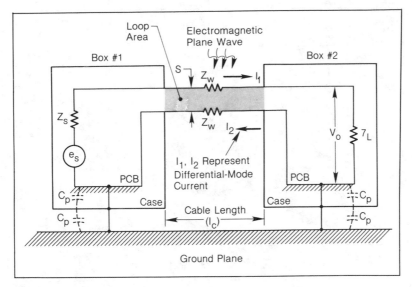

Figure 4.11—Field-to-Cable Differential-Mode Coupling

A second pickup mode for radiated fields is illustrated in Fig. 4.12. In this situation, the loop formed by the interconnecting wires or cables and the ground act as an antenna and pick up the radiated field incident on the equipments or circuits. This situation, which involves a **ground loop**, is often referred to as **field-to-cable common-mode coupling** because the currents in the two interconnecting wires will be flowing in a "common" direction.

The coupling of an electric field into a loop area as indicated in Fig. 4.11 or Fig. 4.12 is a function of the dimensions of the loop (i.e., length of the interconnecting wires and either the spacing between them for differential mode coupling or their height above ground for common mode coupling) and frequency. Figure 4.13 presents curves that establish the relationship between the voltage induced in the loop and the incident field strength for various combinations of loop dimensions and frequencies.

There are several mechanisms by which conducted emissions can be coupled into equipments or systems and produce an EMI problem. First, conducted emissions on interconnecting signal, control or power leads can couple interfering emissions directly into other equipments and cause problems. This is the most obvious mechanism for conducted emissions to produce EMI.

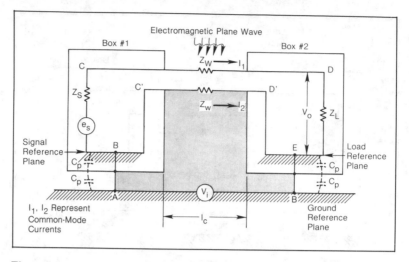

Figure 4.12—Field-to-Cable Common-Mode Coupling

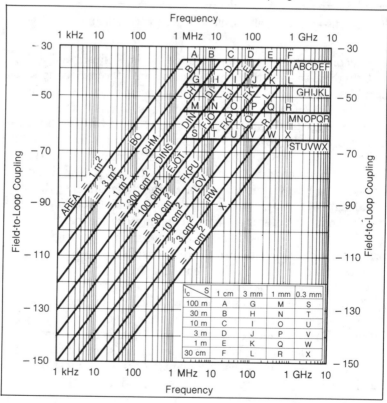

Figure 4.13—Electric Field Strength Coupling into Loop Area

Second, in situations where a number of different equipments or circuits use a common ground, emissions generated by one equipment or circuit can couple into other equipments or circuits if they share a common ground impedance. This coupling mechanism, illustrated in Fig. 4.14, involves a ground loop and is often referred as **common-mode, common ground impedance** coupling. The coupling is "common-mode" because the currents in the two interconnecting wires will be flowing in a "common" direction. The **common ground impedance** term is used because the coupling results from equipments (or circuits) sharing the same ground wire, bus, plane, trace, etc. Examples where this may be a problem include installations where electrical machinery, computers and sensitive instrumentation all use the same ground system or in equipments where analog and digital logic circuits use the same ground.

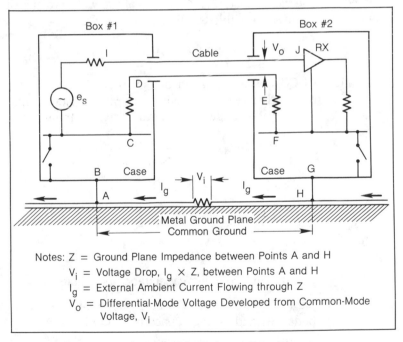

Notes: Z = Ground Plane Impedance between Points A and H

V_i = Voltage Drop, $I_g \times Z$, between Points A and H

I_g = External Ambient Current Flowing through Z

V_o = Differential-Mode Voltage Developed from Common-Mode Voltage, V_i

Figure 4.14—Common Ground Impedance Coupling

The third mechanism by which conducted EMI emissions can couple from a source to a victim involves coupling of EMI (or **crosstalk**) between two pairs of wires (one pair carrying conducted emissions from a source and the other pair connected to a susceptible device). Coupling between two wire pairs, between two coaxial lines or between one wire pair and one coaxial line involves both electric- and magnetic-field coupling. The former is represented by mutual capacitive coupling between the lines, and the latter corresponds to mutual inductive coupling between the EMI source and victim lines.

When the victim circuit impedance is high relative to the characteristic impedance of free space (377 Ω), capacitive coupling predominates. This coupling increases with frequency and with the proximity of the wire pairs. Figure 4.15 shows the network involving capacitive coupling between culprit line and victim circuits. A portion of the available culprit source line voltage (V_c) is coupled into the victim load (Z_v). The ratio of the victim-to-culprit voltages represents the cable-to-cable coupling, CCC:

$$CCC_{dB} = 20 \log(V_v/V_c) \qquad (4.7)$$

The value of CCC_{dB} is often called **crosstalk**.

Based on frequently used math models, the ratio of victim input voltage, V_v, to culprit voltage, V_c, for capacitive coupling is:

$$V_v/V_c = \left(\frac{1}{1 + j/\omega C_{cv} Z_v l_m} \right) \qquad (4.8)$$

$$= \omega C_{cv} Z_z l_m, \text{ for } f \ll 1/2\pi C_{cv} Z_z l_m \quad (4.9)$$

where,

ω = $2\pi f \times$ frequency in Hz

C_{cv} = wire-to-wire coupling capacitance per meter length

Z_v = parallel combination of victim source and load impedances and wiring capacitance (C_v) to ground

 = $1/(1/Z_{v1} + 1/Z_{v2} + j\omega C_v l_m)$

l_m = cable length in meters

C_v = victim wire capacitance to ground return, per meter length

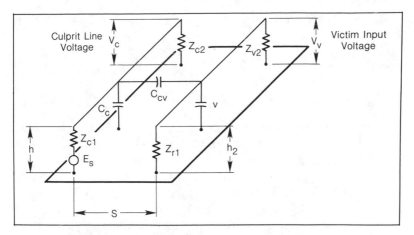

Figure 4.15—Circuit Representation of Capacitive Coupling between Parallel Wires over a Ground Plane

Inductive coupling predominates when the circuit impedances are low relative to 377 Ω (the characteristic impedance of free space). This coupling also increases with frequency and the proximity of the wire pairs.

Figure 4.16 shows a similar cable network involving inductive coupling between culprit and victim line circuits. As before with capacitive coupling, the objective is to determine how much of the available culprit source line voltage, V_c, is coupled into the victim load for varying conditions. This ratio of victim-to-culprit voltages then becomes the cable-to-cable coupling, CCC. Equation (4.7) applies.

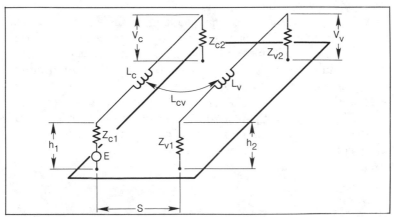

Figure 4.16—Circuit Representation of Inductive Coupling between Parallel Wires over a Ground Plane

Based on frequently used math models, the V_v/V_c ratio for inductive coupling is:

$$\frac{V_v}{V_c} = \left(\frac{Z_{v2}}{Z_{v1} + Z_{v2} + j\omega L_v l_m} \right) \times \omega L_{cv} \times l_m/Z_{c2} \qquad (4.10)$$

where,

ω = 2 f × frequency in Hz
Z_{c2} = culprit load impedance in ohms
L_{cv} = mutual inductance of culprit victim wires (per meter length) in henrys
L_v = self inductance of victim wire in henrys (per meter length)
Z_{v1} = victim source impedance in ohms
Z_{v2} = victim load impedance in ohms
l_m = cable length in meters

4.5 Susceptible Equipments

Any device capable of responding to electrical, electromechanical or electronic emissions or to the fields associated with these emissions is potentially vulnerable to EMI. Susceptibility of all such devices may be divided into two categories:

1. Devices which are susceptible to interfering emissions over a broadband of frequencies
2. Devices that are frequency selective

Typical devices that may be considered vulnerable to interfering emissions over a few or many octaves include remote-control switches, relays, indicator lights, electro-explosive squibs, recording devices, logic circuits and meters. Frequency-selective devices primarily include equipments or systems such as communication, radar and navigation receivers.

Receptors of EMI can be divided into natural and man-made. Figure 4.17 shows such an organization and identifies typical receptors for each category. This section will be concerned with only man-made receptors.

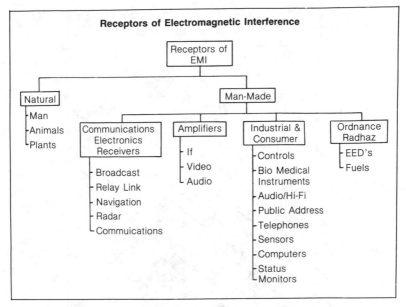

Figure 4.17—Receptors of Electromagnetic Interference

EMI can cause problems in susceptible equipments as a result of either radiated or conducted emissions. Therefore, it is important to consider the susceptibility of electronic equipments and systems to both emission types. Communication receivers are potentially very susceptible to radiated emissions that fall within the receiver passband. The receiver susceptibility to co-channel radiated emissions is determined by the receiver sensitivity (or the receiver input noise power) which may be calculated as follows:

Receiver Input Noise Power, P_{IN} = KTB

where,

K = Boltzmann's constant = 1.38×10^{-23} J/°K
T = absolute temperature (°K) = 273 + °C
B = bandwidth of interest in Hz

Noise Figure, $F = \dfrac{(S/N)_{IN}}{(S/N)_{OUT}}$

Receiver Noise Power, $P_{R(dBm)}$ = $-174 + 10 \log B_{(HZ)} + F_{(dB)}$

4.25

Figure 4.18 provides a plot of the receiver sensitivity versus bandwidth with the noise figure as a parameter.

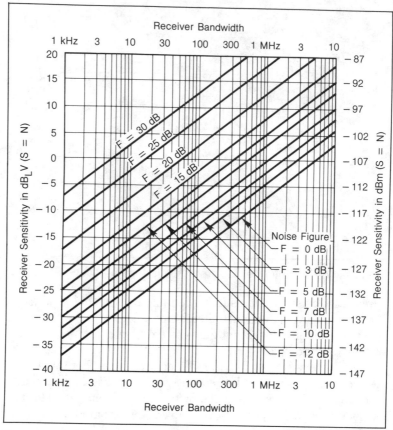

Figure 4.18—Receiver Narrowband Sensitivity vs. Bandwidth & Noise Figure

In addition to the fundamental response, receivers will also respond to radiated emissions at other frequencies. A typical superheterodyne receiver will have a number of spurious responses as illustrated in Fig. 4.19, and these will occur at frequencies, f_{SR}, given by:

$$f_{SR} = \frac{pf_{LO} \pm f_{IF}}{q}$$

where,

p and q = integers corresponding to the harmonics of the local oscillator and incoming signal

f_{LO} = local oscillator frequency

f_{IF} = intermediate frequency

Receivers are typically at least 60 dB less sensitive to spurious responses than they are to the fundamental response.

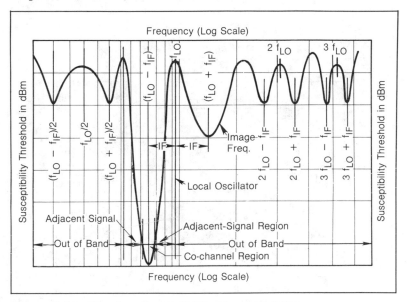

Figure 4.19—Receiver Susceptibility Characteristics

Other electronic equipment may also be susceptible to radiated emissions, and this must be considered by the system designer. Typically, equipments designed for military applications, where MIL-STD-461 is imposed, will be capable of operating in radiated fields of 1 V/m without experiencing EMI problems. Some military equipments are designed for operation in fields in excess of 1 V/m. Commercial equipments typically can operate in fields of up to 0.1 V/m without experiencing problems, and some commercial equipments can operate in even higher radiated fields.

Electronic circuits are susceptible to conducted EMI that is coupled into the circuits through interconnecting wires and cables. The susceptibility of various electronic circuits may vary widely. Sensitive circuits such as analog amplifiers typically will be susceptible to signals in the microvolt to millivolt range, whereas digital logic circuits will typically be susceptible to signals in the volt range.

Electronic components are also susceptible to burnout as a result of exposure to high levels of electromagnetic energy. Figure 4.20 shows typical burnout levels for various solid state components as a result of exposure to a 1 μs pulse.

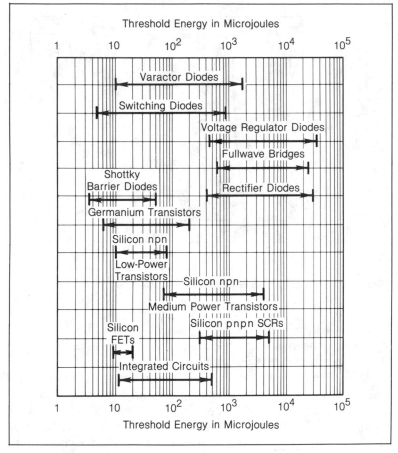

Figure 4.20—Threshold Energy for Damage to Solid-State Components with a 1 μS Pulse

4.6 Design for EMC

EMI design techniques involve both hardware and methods and procedures. They may also be divided into **intrasystem** and **intersystem** EMC design. Engineers and technicians may become knowledgeable and even accomplished in intrasystem EMC design techniques and yet remain relatively naive in the other, or vice versa. This section, however, presents an overview of both techniques.

Figure 4.21 illustrates the basic elements of concern in an intersystem EMC design. This type of EMI distinguishes itself by interference between two or more discrete systems or platforms which are frequently under separate user control. Figure 4.21 presents one organization tree which attempts to group intersystem EMI control techniques by four fundamental categories: frequency management, time management, location management and direction management. System isolation/separation, antenna polarization and other control parameters appear in the figure as subcategories.

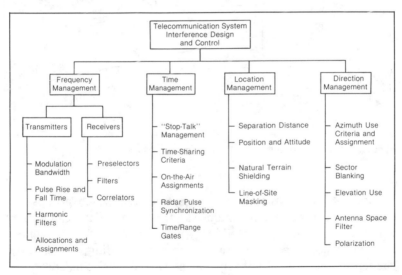

Figure 4.21—Intersystem Interference Design and Control

Figure 4.22 illustrates the basic elements of concern in an intrasystem EMI problem. The test specimen may be a single box, an equipment, subsystem or system (an ensemble of boxes with interconnecting cables). From a strictly intrasystem point of view, the only EMI concern would appear to be degradation of performance due to self-jamming such as suggested at the top of Fig. 4.22. While this is the primary emphasis, latent problems associated with either (a) susceptibility to outside conducted and radiated emissions or (b) the tendency to pollute the outside world from its own undesired emissions, come under the primary classification of intrasystem EMI. Corresponding EMI control techniques address themselves to both self-jamming and emission/susceptibility in accordance with applicable EMI specifications.

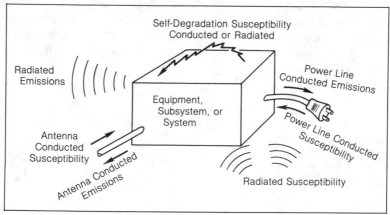

Figure 4.22—Intrasystem EMI Manifestations

Figure 4.23 presents one organization tree which groups intrasystem EMI control techniques by five fundamental categories which often appear in related literature: circuits and components, filtering, shielding, wiring and grounding. Bonding, connectors, gasketing and other topics appear as subcategories as shown in the figure. Specific control techniques for reducing EMI effects resulting from the various modes of coupling are summarized in the following listings.

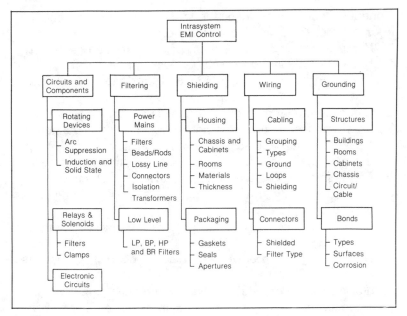

Figure 4.23—Intrasystem EMI Control Organization Tree

EMI effects resulting from emissions that are picked up by the loop formed by interconnecting wires or cables (or the circuit itself) may be reduced by an application of one or more of the following:

1. Minimize the loop area formed by the interconnecting wires or cables (or the circuit).
2. Use twisted-wire pairs for balanced parallel lines.
3. Use shielded wire pairs.
4. Use coaxial or triaxial cables.
5. Use fiber optics to interconnect equipments.

The effects of EMI resulting from emissions that are picked up by a ground loop may be reduced by an application of one or more of the following:

1. Minimize the loop area formed by the circuit and the ground.
2. Float either or both printed circuit boards.
3. Use a balanced circuit or balanced drivers and receivers.
4. Use feedthrough capacitors.
5. Float box shields inside equipment enclosures.
6. Shield entire ground loop area.

Conducted emissions may be reduced or controlled by applying one or more of the following techniques:

1. Filter power leads at the point of entry to the equipment.
2. Use optical isolators or isolation transformers.
3. Use filter pin connectors or feedthrough capacitors to provide a low-pass filter response.

Common-mode common ground impedance problems may be reduced by application of one or more of the following techniques:

1. Do not intermix the ac or dc ground, analog signal ground, digital signal ground, chassis ground or any other ground.
2. Run a single dedicated ground return for each circuit.
3. Do not randomly ground to the chassis — use a single point ground if applicable.
4. Make return conductors as large as possible to minimize impedance.
5. Do not daisy chain power and ground between equipments or circuits.

EMI as a result of crosstalk between interconnecting wires and cables can be minimized by application of one or more of the following:

1. Group like cables into bundles but do not mix cables from different groups (i.e., ac power cables, dc power cables, low-level analog signal cables, digital signal cables, etc.).
2. Route ac power cables along the bottom and sides of the chassis.
3. Treat dc power cables the same as ac power cable but separated as far as possible from them.
4. For analog RF signals (e.g., video), use coaxial cable and route along bottom or side of chassis using the shortest possible route.
5. For digital signal cables, separate the clock and digital signal pairs and route along the bottom or side of the chassis. Maintain maximum possible distance from all other cable runs, especially the ac and dc runs.
6. For low-level analog signals (e.g., microphone preamplifier), use shielded cable and route along bottom or sides of the chassis using the shortest run possible. Maintain maximum possible distance from all other cable runs, especially the ac and digital signal runs.
7. Do not permit a cable bundle to pass across an aperture (chassis opening); this will aggravate or cause a radiation or pickup problem.

8. Do not suspend a cable bundle above the chassis; this will minimize shielding provided by the chassis.
9. When cable bundles must cross, they should do so at right angles; this will minimize mutual coupling.

When designing a metal enclosure there are several techniques one can use to "seal up" the enclosure. Some of the most common are:

1. Avoid metal-to-metal contact of painted surfaces. If paint is necessary for protection against corrosion or oxidation, then use conductive paint.
2. Use overlapping, tight seams. Seams should be tightened using screws and internal tooth lock washers spaced not more than 1 in (25.4 mm) apart (unless RF gasketing is used).
3. When the enclosure uses hinged covers, attach several braided straps at the hinged point between the cover and enclosure using internal tooth lock washers and nuts. Keep the length of the straps as short as possible. In addition, the remaining perimeter of the hinged cover should make electrical contact with the main enclosure through finger stock or an RF gasket.
4. Avoid the use of decorative screws with plastic collars.
5. When the enclosure has removable access panels, use finger stock or RF gasketing around the opening.
6. Where openings for ventilation are necessary, cover with perforated grids or use slots. The size of the grid openings or slots should be as small as possible (a 2 mm maximum dimension is recommended). When using a perforated grid, it should be attached either by a continuous weld or with nuts and internal tooth lock washers spaced not more than 1 in (25.4 mm) apart (greater spacing is acceptable if an RF gasket is used).

When designing enclosures made of plastic, there are several techniques that can be employed to minimize EMI problems. These techniques not only relate to the "outer shell" of the equipment but, also affect the construction of the inner circuitry.

1. Spray the inside of the enclosure with a conductive coating. Ensure that the inside of the enclosure makes a solid electrical connection, at the equipment common point ground. The conductive spray must be applied uniformly. A surface resistance of less than 1 Ω/sq is necessary for the spray to be effective.
2. Use a conductive plastic for the enclosure. Once again, ensure that the inside of the enclosure makes a solid electrical connection at the equipment common point ground.

3. If thermal conditions permit, line the inside of the enclosure with an aluminum or copper foil shield.

4. Use copper or Mumetal® shielding for all high-level circuits such as switching power supplies or video and clock oscillator circuits. In the case of power supplies, where heat dissipation can be a problem, shield with a perforated grid (these techniques are also suggested when using a metal enclosure).

4.7 Summary

EMI is an interdisciplinary problem that can be solved by careful consideration and attention during all phases in the life cycle of a system or equipment. To achieve EMC in an economical and effective manner, it is necessary to use a sound combination of:

1. Interference prediction and analysis techniques to identify and define the problems

2. EMC specifications and standards to ensure comprehensiveness during equipment design and development stages

3. EMI control devices and techniques during equipment or system design, development and production to ensure that specifications and standards are met

4. Measurements to provide prediction inputs and ensure compliance with EMC specifications and standards

5. Suppression techniques during installation and operation to solve specific problems that arise as a result of severe or unusual operating conditions.

During each phase of the equipment life cycle, responsible management and engineering personnel must give appropriate attention to the particular EMC considerations applicable to their areas of responsibility if EMI-free operation is to be assured.

The designer of electronic equipments or systems for use in either military or commercial applications must give careful consideration to EMI. It is particularly important for the designer to define the electromagnetic environment in which his system must operate and the system must be designed so that it can operate in that environment without experiencing operational performance degradation resulting from EMI.

4.8 Bibliography

Capraro, G., "The Intrasystem EMC Problem and Future Directions," *Proceedings of the Fourth Symposium and Technical Exhibition on EMC*, Zurich, Switzerland, 1981.

Clark, O.M., "Capabilities and Limitations of Low Voltage Transient Suppressors," Electromagnetic Compatibility 1977— Second Symposium and Technical Exhibition on EMC, Montreux, Switzerland, June 28-30, 1977.

Jenkins, T.J., "Techniques for Assessing RF Susceptibility of Electro-Explosive Devices in Aircraft Systems," *IEEE International EMC Symposium Record* (New York: IEEE, 1976).

Keenan, R.K., *Digital Design for Interference Specifications* (The Keenan Corp., 1983).

LaMontagne, R., "The Air Force Intrasystem Program (IAP)," *IEEE International EMC Symposium Record* (New York: IEEE, 1976).

McCormick, A.W., "Some Practical Guidelines for Manufacturers Faced with FCC Part 15 Subpart J Compliance," *EMC Expo 86 Symposium Record* (Gainesville, Virginia: Interference Control Technologies, Inc., 1986).

MIL-HDBK-241B, Design Guide for Electromagnetic Interference (EMI) Reduction in Power Supplies, (U.S. Dept. of Defense, 1983).

MIL-HDBK-253, Guidance for the Design and Test of Systems Protected Against the Effects of Electromagnetic Energy (U.S. Dept. of Defense, 1978).

Monroe, L. and Paul, C.R., "Lumped Circuit Modeling of Transmission Lines, *IEEE International EMC Symposium Record* (New York: IEEE, 1985).

Nakauchi, E., "Technique for Controlling Emissions Due to Common Mode," *IEEE International EMC Symposium Record* (New York: IEEE, 1982).

Ott, H.W., *Noise Reduction Techniques in Electronic Systems* (New York: John Wiley & Sons, Inc., 1976).

Paul, C.R., "Effects of Pigtails on Crosstalk to Braided-Shield Cables," *IEEE Transactions on EMC*, Vol. EMC-22, no. 3, August 1980.

Paul, C.R., "Frequency Response of Multiconductor Transmission Lines Illuminated by an Electromagnetic Field," *IEEE International EMC Symposium Record* (New York: IEEE, 1975) and *IEEE Transactions on EMC*, Vol. EMC-18, no. 4, November 1976.

Paul, C.R., "Prediction of Crosstalk in Ribbon Cables," *IEEE International EMC Symposium Record* (New York: IEEE, 1978).

Paul, C.R., "Transmission-Line Modeling of Shielded Wires for Crosstalk Prediction," *IEEE Transactions on EMC*, Vol. EMC-23, no. 4.

Paul, C.R. and McKnight, J.W., "Prediction of Crosstalk Involving Twisted Pairs of Wires," *IEEE International EMC Symposium Record* (New York: IEEE, 1978).

Paul, C.R. and Nasar, S.A., *Introduction to Electromagnetic Fields*, second edition (New York: McGraw-Hill Book Co., 1987).

Rhoades, W.T., "Designing Commercial Equipment for Conducted Susceptibility," *IEEE International EMC Symposium Record* (New York: IEEE, 1979).

Smith, A.A., *Coupling of External Fields to Transmission Lines* (New York: John Wiley & Sons, Inc., 1977).

Vance, E.F., "Shielding Effectiveness of Braided-Wire Shields," *IEEE Transactions on EMC*, Vol. EMC-17, no. 2, May 1975.

Vance, E.F., *Coupling to Shielded Cables* (New York: John Wiley & Sons, Inc., 1978).

White, D.R.J., *EMI Control in the Design of Printed Circuit Boards and Backplanes* (Gainesville, Virginia: Interference Control Technologies, Inc., 1982).

White, D.R.J., Handbook Series on Electromagnetic Interference and Compatibility, Vol. 3, *EMI Control Methods and Techniques* (Gainesville, Virginia: Interference Control Technologies, Inc., 1981).

White, D.R.J. and Mardiguian, M., *EMI Control Methodology and Procedures* (Gainesville, Virginia: Interference Control Technologies, Inc., 1985).

White, D.R.J. and Zorn, J., "EMC Design Synthesis Using Programmable Calculators and Minicomputers," *IEEE International EMC Symposium Record* (New York: IEEE, 1976).

Chapter 5

Grounding and Bonding

The subject of grounding is very important from the standpoint of minimizing and controlling EMI. Grounding is one of the least understood and more significant culprits in many EMI problems. Factors that need to be considered and understood include:

1. Separation of analog and digital grounds
2. Grounding of circuits to equipment cases
3. Safety grounding of equipment cases
4. Grounding of filters and isolation transformers
5. Grounding of cable shields
6. Single-point and multipoint grounding
7. Ground loops, etc.

There are two purposes for grounding devices, cables, equipments, and systems: (1) to prevent a shock hazard in the event that an equipment frame or housing may develop a high voltage due to lightning or an accidental breakdown of wiring or components, and (2) to reduce EMI due to electric-field common-impedance or other forms of interference coupling. Each of these purposes is summarized below, although the EMI part of the problem is emphasized in this chapter.

5.1 Rationale for Grounding

This section presents an overview of the reasons why grounding is important.

5.1.1 Shock and Lightning Hazards

The distribution of ac power in private homes, buildings, hospitals and industrial sites in the U.S. is governed by local and national codes. The National Fire Protection Association (NFPA) has issued NFPA-STD-70-1971, National Electric Code, dealing with standards on wiring and other electrical devices. One requirement is that with each outgoing hot wire (black) and return neutral wire (white) is a reference ground (green) wire. The same applies for three-wire, 115-115-230 Vac systems in which a second hot wire (red) is added as shown in Fig. 5.1.

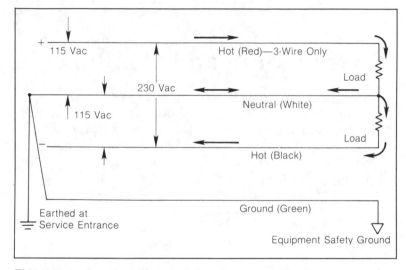

Figure 5.1—Standard 2- and 3-Wire Electrical Wire Coding

Theoretically, no return current passes through the green wire reference ground. If the hot side were accidentally shorted to the equipment frame, the latter would become 115 Vac hot to ground. If someone were touching that frame as shown in Fig. 5.2, a path of current would return through his hand and continue through the body and out either (1) the other hand if it were touching some other reference such as ground, or (2) the soles of the feet to a concrete floor and thence to the building ground. Here, 75 mA of current through the body could be fatal. These **microshock hazards** can be avoided by grounding a third wire (the green wire) to the equipment frame in a modern ac power cord.

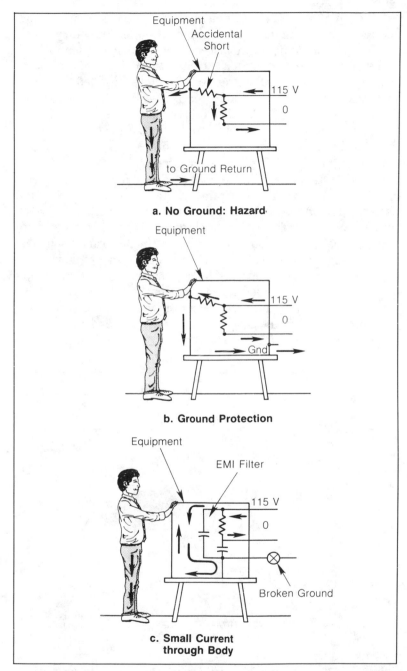

a. No Ground: Hazard

b. Ground Protection

c. Small Current through Body

Figure 5.2—Safety and Shock Hazards with and without Equipment Grounds and EMI Filters

To help reduce EMI in equipment of all types, it is common practice today to use filters in the equipment power line entry. Here, either capacitors or filters are placed from both hot and neutral lines to the ground wire to bypass EMI (the neutral line is also a source of EMI). The National Electric Code previously limited the use of such capacitors to 0.1 μF at 60 Hz, corresponding to a leakage reactive current of 5 mA. Thus, if an individual touched an equipment frame, and the frame was not grounded, the maximum current through the body would be limited to 5 mA.

Another kind of shock hazard exists due to either several devices with EMI filters operating from the same circuit or one device developing a short to the frame. Both situations involve the microshock hazards in hospitals, clinics and medical centers in which catheters are in direct contact with the heart via electrodes from EKG, arterial pressure monitors and similar biomedical instruments. When a high-impedance leakage or direct short develops in an equipment, such as a vacuum cleaner sharing a common ground (green wire) with the medical instruments, a substantial current may flow in the ground wire. This current will partition, with most returning directly to the power distribution panel and some following another path directly through the heart as shown in Fig. 5.3.[1]

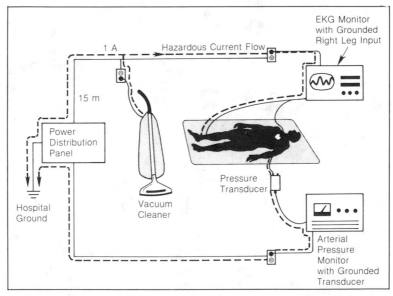

Figure 5.3—Microshock Hazard in Hospitals (continued next page)

5.4

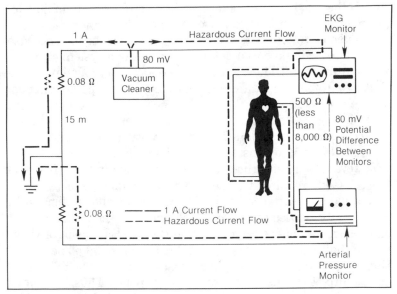

Figure 5.3—(continued)

The other aspect of grounding involves lightning hazards to buildings and their contents. To protect a structure from damage from lightning strokes requires that a lower impedance path be provided from the top of the building to a good building earth ground over that offered by the building, per se. In other words, the lightning stroke would follow the lower potential gradient of the arrestor-grounding system rather than that of the protected building.

5.1.2 EMI Ground References and Impedances

The principal concern about grounding in this chapter is the range of EMI problems that develop as a result of wrong or faulty grounds, how to mathematically model them, and some corrective solutions. Consideration of the grounding of a cable or wire shield serve to illustrate this. There, to effectively perform a Faraday shield between conductors, the shield has to be grounded in two or more places when the cable is longer than 0.1λ at the highest frequency of concern. While this reduces electric-field coupling at high frequencies, it may generate a magnetic-field ground current loop in the process unless certain procedures are followed.

5.5

For other than wire-shield situations, different grounding requirements develop. They all involve bonding equipments to a common potential reference to avoid circulating EMI currents because of a difference in potential between portions of a system or power mains distribution. Thus, a concept develops of a ground plane exhibiting zero potential difference between any two points thereon. It does not matter what the absolute potential of a ground plane to earth may be since aircraft, for example, are isolated; a ship is located in the water; and a building is constructed on earth. The structure of each acts as a ground-plane reference.

However, for land structures, such as a building, the National Electric Code requires that certain specifications be met such as connecting the neutral and ground wire together and earthing them at the utility service entrance. This reduces the shock hazard but may develop an undesirable situation from an EMI point of view.

Note that a low-impedance ground path or ground plane should be the same as that of a source generator return or should be connected directly to the generator reference plane. Thus, aircraft or spacecraft are connected to earth ground when being serviced by ground support equipment powered by ground-based power systems. When disconnected from ground support equipment, the equipment aboard the craft is referenced to the vehicle skin, which serves as the ground plane. During flight, the accumulated excess energy is largely dissipated as an electrostatic discharge in space, and partly by conversion to radiant thermal energy.

5.1.3 Zero-Potential Ground Plane

Any two points on a metallic structure, whether electrically connected or not, may develop a potential difference at some frequency. For structural dimensions, l_s, a potential difference, V, will exist in the presence of a magnetic or electrical field:

$$V = A \sin(2\pi l_s/\lambda) \tag{5.1}$$

$$\approx 2\pi l_s/\lambda, \text{ for } l_s < 0.1 \ \lambda$$

where,

A = amplitude of induced voltage to the ground plane

λ = wavelength corresponding to frequency

Alternatively, the impedance, Z, between two points in a ground plane is:

$$Z = R_{RF} [1 + |\tan(2\pi l_s/\lambda|)] \tag{5.3}$$

$$= kR_{dc} [1 + |\tan(2\pi l_s/\lambda|)]$$

$$\approx kR_{dc}(1 + 2\pi l_s/\lambda) \text{ for } l_s < \lambda/10 \tag{5.4}$$

$$\approx kR_{dc}, \text{ for } l_s < \lambda/20 \tag{5.5}$$

$$\approx 2kR_{dc}, \text{ for } l_s \approx \lambda/8, 3\lambda/8$$

$$= \infty , \text{ for } l_s = \lambda/4, 3\lambda/4$$

where,

R_{dc} = dc surface resistance in ohms per square

k = a number greater than 1, representing the ratio of RF to dc surface resistance, R_{RF}/R_{dc}

and,

$$R_{RF} = 0.26 \times 10^{-6} \times \sqrt{f}, \text{ in ohms per square} \tag{5.6}$$
for copper

$$= 0.26 \times 10^{-6} \times \sqrt{\mu f/\sigma} \text{ ohms per square for} \tag{5.7}$$
any conductor

where,

σ = conductivity of material relative to copper

μ = permeability of material relative to copper

f = frequency

Equation (5.3) indicates that the impedance between two points on a ground plane can become substantial when $l_s > \lambda/8$. Thus, a ground plane offers little equipotential grounding value to two or more equipments which must be grounded thereto at frequencies greater than that corresponding to $\lambda/8$. However, at lower frequencies for which $l_s < \lambda/20$, the impedance between two points in a ground plane is proportional to the RF impedance in ohms per square as indicated in Eqs. (5.5) and (5.6).

Illustrative Example 5.1

Determine the impedance between two end points in a galvanized steel cable-tray ground plane measuring 6" x 20' (0.15 x 6.1 m) at 100 kHz and 10 MHz.

The wavelength λ at 10 MHz is 30 m, or approximately 100 ft. For a 20' (6.1 m) separation, this corresponds to $\lambda/5$. Thus, Eq. (5.3) (in modified form) and Eq. (5.7) are:

$$Z = R_{RF}[1 + |\tan(2\pi l_s/\lambda|)]1_s/w_s \qquad (5.8)$$

$$= 6.1/0.26 \times R_{RF}(1 + |\tan 2\pi/5|)$$

$$= 40 \, R_{RF}(1 + 3.73) = 189 \, R_{RF}$$

where,

w_s = width of cable-tray

$$R_{RF} = 0.26 \times 10^{-6} \sqrt{1,000 \times 10^7/0.1} \quad = 0.08 \, \Omega/\text{sq}$$

Thus,

$$Z = 189 \times 0.08 = 15 \, \Omega$$

The wavelength at 100 kHz is 3 km, or approximately 10^4 ft. Since the 20 ft separation corresponds to $l_s = 0.002\lambda$, Eqs. (5.5) and (5.7) apply:

$$Z = 40 \times 0.26 \times 10^{-6}\sqrt{1,000 \times 10^5/0.1} = 0.32 \, \Omega$$

Had the cable tray been made of copper, the impedances end-to-end would have been 150 mΩ at 10 MHz and 3.2 mΩ at 100 kHz.

The RF impedance between two points in a ground plane has significance only if equipments tied thereto have a potential difference and common circulation currents can flow between them. As explained in the next section, this can cross couple a source EMI voltage to a victim network.

5.2 Common-Mode Impedance Coupling

EMI problems sometimes result from using a ground plane as a return path instead of using a dedicated return wire (or PCB trace) with each signal wire in a circuit or equipment.

Figure 5.4 illustrates a risky, but frequently encountered practice in which two different circuits share the same ground plane for their return paths. The voltage, V_c, developed across Z, the equivalent impedance of the ground plane, from the potential culprit EMI source, is:

$$V_c = \frac{ZV_1}{R_{g1} + R_{L1} + Z} \approx \frac{ZV_1}{R_{g1} + R_{L1}}, \qquad (5.9)$$

for $Z \ll R_{g1} + R_{L1}$

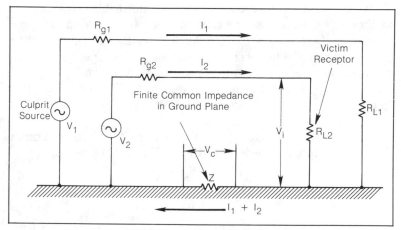

Figure 5.4—Common-Mode Impedance Coupling Between Circuits

The resulting voltage, V_i, developed across the potential victim lead in circuit #2 is:

$$V_i = \frac{R_{L2}V_c}{R_{g2} + R_{L2}}, \text{ for } Z \ll R_{g2} + R_{L2} \qquad (5.10)$$

Substituting Eq. (5.9) into Eq. (5.10) yields:

$$V_i = \frac{ZR_{L2}V_1}{(R_{g1} + R_{L1})(R_{g2} + R_{L2})} \qquad (5.11)$$

The crosstalk, CT, in dB between the two circuits due to common-mode impedance coupling, then, may be expressed as a math model:

$$CT_{dB} = 20 \log \frac{ZR_{L2}}{(R_{g1} + R_{L1})(R_{g2} + R_{L2})} \tag{5.12}$$

where,

Z = common impedance appearing in Eq. (5.3)

Illustrative Example 5.2

Two wire conductors are run down the same cable tray described in Example 5.1 and use the tray as a ground return (a bad practice). The first circuit is carrying 100 kHz clock pulses at an amplitude of 5 V. The second circuit is an oscilloscope monitor with a sensor at one end; the scope has a sensitivity of 1 mV. The source and load impedances of circuit #1 are 100 Ω. The source and load impedances of circuit #2 are 100 Ω and 10 MΩ, respectively. Determine if an EMI problem will exist.

From the previous example, at 100 kHz, Z = 0.32 Ω. The interference voltage is determined from Eq. (5.11).

$$V_i = \frac{0.32 \times 10^7 \times 5 \text{ V}}{200 \times 10^7} = 8 \text{ mV}$$

Thus, since V_i = 8 mV, which is greater than the scope's 1 mV sensitivity, EMI due to common-mode impedance coupling will exist.

5.3 Single-Point vs. Multipoint Grounding

This section reviews the often controversial topic regarding whether equipments and subsystems should be grounded to a reference at a single point or if multipoint grounding should be used. The matter of hybrid grounds is also reviewed. It will be shown that all systems are a continuation of each other at higher frequencies, but that certain correct practices should be followed. Conversely, the grounding scheme at lower frequencies is more clearly defined regarding correct and incorrect techniques.

5.3.1 Single-Point Grounding

Modern electronic systems seldom have only one ground plane. To mitigate interference such as that which results from common-mode impedance coupling, as many separate ground planes as possible are used. Separate ground planes in each subsystem for structural grounds, signal grounds, shield grounds, and ac prime and secondary power grounds are desirable if economically and logistically practical. These individual ground planes from each subsystem are finally connected by the shortest route back to the system ground point where they form an overall system potential reference. This method is known as a **single-point ground** and is illustrated in Fig. 5.5.

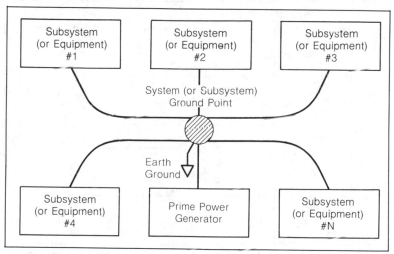

Figure 5.5—Single-Point or Star Grounding Arrangement

The single-point or **star** type of grounding scheme shown in the figure avoids the problems of common-mode impedance coupling which were discussed in the previous section. The only common path is in the earth ground (for earth-based structures), but this usually consists of a substantial conductor of very low impedance. Thus, as long as zero or low ground currents flow in any low-impedance common paths, all subsystems or equipments are maintained at essentially the same reference potential.

The problem of implementing the single-point grounding scheme comes about when: (1) interconnecting cables are used, especially ones having cable shields which have sources and receptors operating over cable lengths, l_c, above about $\lambda/20$, and (2) parasitic capacitance exists between subsystem or equipment housings or between subsystems and the grounds of other subsystems.

This situation is illustrated in Fig. 5.6. Here, cable shields connect some of the subsystems together so that more than one grounding path from a particular subsystem to the ground point exists. Unless certain precautions are taken, common-impedance ground currents could flow. At high frequencies, the parasitic capacitive reactance represents low-impedance paths and the bond inductance of a subsystem-to-ground point results in higher impedances. Thus, again common-mode currents may flow or unequal potentials may develop between subsystems.

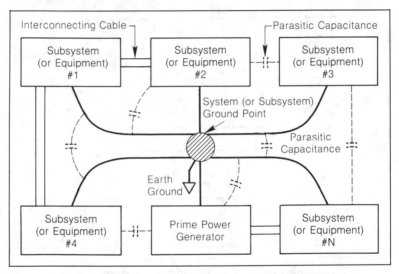

Figure 5.6—Degeneration of Single-Point Ground of Fig. 5.5 by Interconnecting Cables and Parasitic Capacitance

5.3.2 Multipoint Grounding

Supporters of the multipoint grounding concept argue that, pragmatically, the situation shown in Fig. 5.6 exists anyway and not that of the ideal single-point ground shown in Fig. 5.5. Thus, rather than having an uncontrolled situation as shown in Fig. 5.6, if everything were heavily bonded to a solid ground conducting plane to form a homogeneous, low-impedance path, common-mode currents and other EMI problems would be minimized.

An example of such a situation is shown in Fig 5.7, where each subsystem or equipment is bonded as directly as possible to a common low-impedance equipotential ground plane. The ground plane then is earthed for safety purposes.

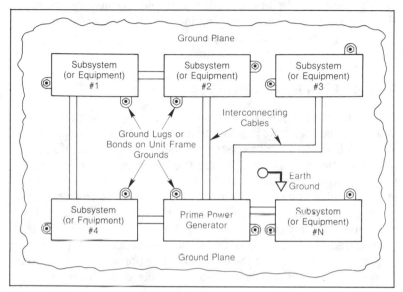

Figure 5.7—Multipoint Grounding System

In fact, a single-point grounding scheme operates better at low frequencies and a multipoint ground behaves best at high frequencies. If the overall system, for example, is a network of audio equipment, with many low-level sensors and control circuits behaving as broadband transient noise sources, then the high-frequency performance is irrelevant since no receptor responds above audio frequencies (assuming no HF spurious or parasitic responses, which is not always the case). Conversely, if the overall system were a receiving complex of 30 MHz to 1,000 MHz tuners, amplifiers and displays, then low-level, low-frequency performance would be irrelevant. Here, multipoint grounding applies, and interconnecting, unbalanced coaxial lines are used.

The above dichotomy of audio versus VHF/UHF systems makes clear the selection of the correct approach. The problem then narrows down to defining where low- and high-frequency crossover exists for any given subsystem or equipment. The answer in part

5.13

involves the highest significant operating frequency of low-level circuits relative to the physical distance between the furthest located equipments. In other words, this twilight crossover frequency region involves: (1) the magnetic versus electric field coupling problems and (2) the ground-plane impedance problems due to separation. Hybrid single and multipoint grounding systems are often the best approach for twilight-region applications.

5.3.3 Hybrid Grounding

The matter of single-point versus multipoint grounding discussed in the previous sections is summarized as a general guideline model in Fig. 5.8. This model is based on the relations of Eq. (5.3) and the separation criteria of $l_s = \lambda/20$ presented in Eq. (5.5). For low-frequency operation and small dimensions, use single-point grounding. For high-frequency operation and large dimensions, use multipoint grounding. For transitional situations, one or the other may perform better as shown in the figure. Hybrid grounds perform best in situations in which portions of the low-frequency systems use single-point grounding while high-frequency portions use multipoint grounding, and all are connected in a ground-tree fashion.

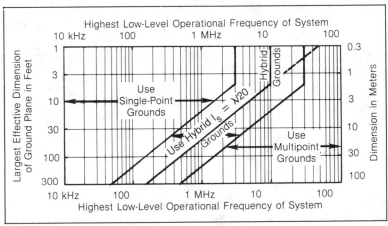

Figure 5.8—Crossover Regions of Single-Point vs. Multipoint Grounding

The term **hybrid grounds** is sometimes used in two somewhat different senses: (1) when a grounding scheme either appears as a single-point ground at low frequencies and a multipoint ground at high frequencies, or appears different at both frequencies, and (2) when a system grounding configuration employs both single-point and multipoint grounds. Each of these is discussed in the following text.

Figure 5.9 shows a low-level video circuit in which both the sensor and driven circuit chassis must be grounded to the skin of a vehicle (not by choice) and the coaxial cable shield is grounded to the chassis at both ends through its mating connectors. A low-frequency ground current loop would be generated were it not for the capacitor. At high frequencies, the capacitor assures that the cable shield is grounded to protect the Faraday-shield effect. Thus, this circuit simultaneously behaves as a single-point ground at low frequencies and a multipoint ground at high frequencies.

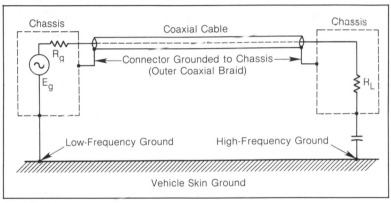

Figure 5.9—Low-Frequency Ground Current Loop Avoidance with High-Frequency Ground

A different kind of an example is shown in Fig. 5.10 in which all the computer and peripheral frames must be grounded to the power system green wire for safety purposes (shock-hazard protection) pursuant to the National Electrical Code. Since it is recognized that the green wire generally contains significant electrical noise trash, this code conflicts with the desire to float the computer system ground from the noisy green wire ground. Thus, one or more isolation coils of about 1 mH value are used to provide a low-impedance (less than 0.4 Ω) safety ground at ac power line frequencies and RF isolation (of the order of 1,000 Ω) in the 50 kHz to 1 MHz spectrum containing the principle energy of computer pulses. This inductor helps keep induced transient and EMI noise in the green wire off the computer supply voltage logic buses.

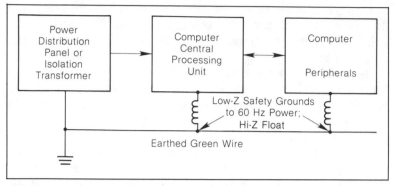

Figure 5.10—Safety Ground with High Frequency Isolation

To illustrate the second form of hybrid-ground systems, Fig. 5.11 shows a 19-inch cabinet rack containing five separate sliding drawers. Each drawer contains a portion of the system (top to bottom):

1. RF and IF preamp circuitry for intercept of microwave signals
2. IF and video signal amplifiers
3. Display drivers, displays and control circuits
4. Low-level audio circuits and recorders for documenting sensitive multichannel, hard-line telemetry sensor outputs
5. Secondary and regulated power supplies

The hybrid aspect results from:

1. The RF and IF video drawers are similar. Here, unit-level boxes or stages (interconnecting coaxial cables are grounded at both ends) are multipoint grounded to the drawer-chassis ground plane. The chassis is then grounded to the dagger-pin, chassis-ground bus as suggested in Fig 5.12. The power ground to these drawers, on the other hand, is using a single-point ground from its bus in a manner identical to the audio drawer.

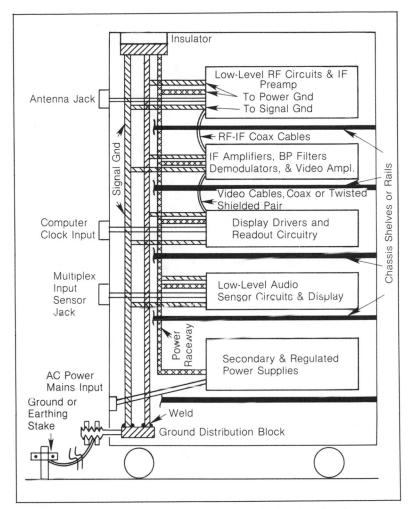

Figure 5.11—Grounding Arrangement Used in Cabinet Racks

2. Each chassis or signal ground and power ground buses constitutes a multipoint grounding scheme to the drawer level. The individual ground buses are single-point grounded at the bottom ground distribution block. This avoids circulating common-mode current between chassis or signal ground and power grounds since power-ground current can vary due to transient surges in certain modes of equipment operation.

3. Interconnecting cables between different drawer levels are run separate and their shields, when used, are treated in the same grounding manner as at the drawer level.

4. The audio and display drawers shown in Fig. 5.12 use single-point grounding throughout for both their unit-level boxes (interconnecting twisted cable is grounded at one end to its unit) and power leads. Cable and unit shield strike-plate holes are all grounded together at the common dagger-pin bus. Similarly, the outgoing power leads and twisted returns are separately bonded on their dagger-pin buses.

To test the above scheme with Fig. 5.8, the following is observed:

1. The audio and display drawers have ground runs of about 2 ft (0.61 m) and an upper frequency of operation of about 1 MHz (driver and sweep circuits). Thus, single-point grounding to the strike pins is indicated.

2. The RF and IF drawers process UHF and 30 MHz signals over a distance of a few feet so that multipoint grounding is indicated.

3. The regulated power supplies furnish equipment units having transient surge demands. The greatest length is about 5 ft (1.53 m), and significant transient-frequency components

may extend up into the HF region. Here, hybrid grounding is indicated: single-point within a drawer, and multipoint from the power bus to all drawers.

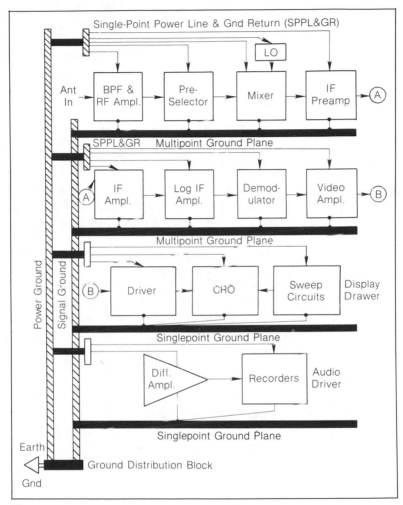

Figure 5.12—Block Diagram Detail of Fig. 5.11

5.19

When miniature and printed circuits and ICs are used, network proximity is considerably closer. Thus, multipoint grounding is more economical and practical to produce per card, wafer or chip. Interconnection of these components through wafer risers, mother boards, etc., should use a grounding scheme following the illustrations of previous paragraphs and the general criteria of Fig. 5.8. This will likely still represent a multipoint or hybrid grounding approach in which any single-point grounding (for hybrid grounds), if used, would be to avoid low-frequency ground current loops and common-mode impedance coupling.

5.4 Electrical Bonding

Electrical bonding refers to the process in which components or modules of an assembly, equipment or subsystem are electrically connected by means of a low-impedance conductor. The purpose is to make the structure homogenous with respect to the flow of RF currents. This mitigates electrical potential differences which can produce EMI among metallic parts.

An example of the importance of bonding to reduce EMI is shown in Fig. 5.13a in which the effectiveness of a filter can be nullified by improper bonding. In this example, the contact resistance of a poor bond does not provide the low-impedance path necessary for shunting interference currents coming from the power mains. The current now flows through the filter capacitors and on to other equipment which was to have been protected.

In Fig. 5.13b, the receiver is not well bonded to a common ground plane reference for both the antenna and the power mains return. Thus, RF currents appearing on the power mains share a common impedance path at the bond with RF signals picked up by the antenna.

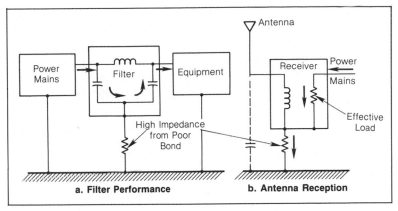

Figure 5.13—Two Effects of Poor Bonding

5.4.1 Equivalent Circuits of Bonds

A low-impedance path is possible only when the separation of the bonded members is small compared to a wavelength of the EMI being considered, and the bond is a good conductor. This was discussed in Section 5.1.3. At high frequencies, structural members behave as transmission lines whose impedance can be inductive or capacitive (in varying magnitudes, depending upon geometrical shape and frequency) in a manner similar to that explained in connection with Eq. (5.3).

Figure 5.14 is the equivalent electrical circuit of a bond strap. The circuit contains resistance due to the finite conductance of the strap in series with the self-inductance of the bond. Shunt capacitance exists due to the residual capacity of the strap and its mounting. This capacitance and self-inductance form a parallel antiresonant circuit, resulting in the adverse impedance response shown in the figure.

There is little correlation between the dc resistance of a bond and its RF impedance. The measured RF impedance of artificial bonds, per se, such as jumpers, straps, rivets, etc., is not a reliable indication of the bonding effectiveness in an actual installation. Here, the artificial bond is in parallel with the members to be bonded, and the total impedance includes various parallel paths over which RF conductive or displacement currents may flow. Thus, a bond strap of low inductance combines with the capacitance of the installation as shown in Figs. 5.14 and 5.15 to form a high impedance antiresonant circuit at some frequency. The bibliography contains a number of sources presenting math models of various bond configurations.

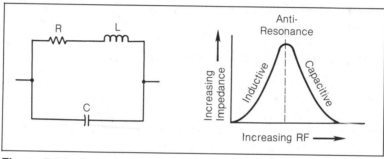

Figure 5.14—Equivalent Circuit of Bond Strap and Its Impedance

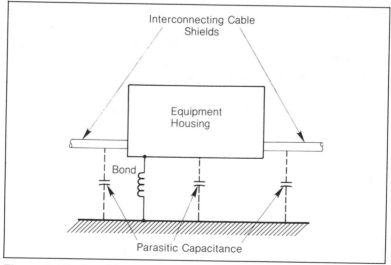

Figure 5.15—Bond Impedance and Installation Parasitics

5.4.2 Types of Bonds

The best electrical bond consists of a permanent, direct, metal-to-metal contact such as provided by welding, brazing, sweating or swaging. Though adequate for most purposes, the best soldered joints have appreciable contact resistance and cannot be depended upon for the most satisfactory type of bonding. Semipermanent joints such as provided by bolts or rivets can provide effective bonding. However, relative motion of the joined members will likely reduce the bonding effectiveness by introducing impedance variations.

5.4.3 Bonding Hardware

Star or lock washers should be used with bolt or lock-thread bonding nuts to ensure the continuing tightness of a semipermanent bonded joint. Figure 5.16a shows one recommended arrangement. Star washers are especially effective in cutting through protective and insulating coatings on metal (e.g., anodized aluminum) as well as unintentional oxides and grease films which develop between maintenance procedures.

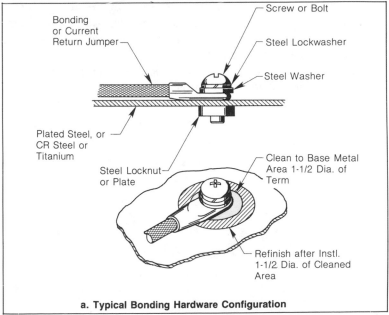

a. Typical Bonding Hardware Configuration

Figure 5.16—Bonding Connections (Courtesy AFSC Design Handbook DH 1-4) (continued next page)

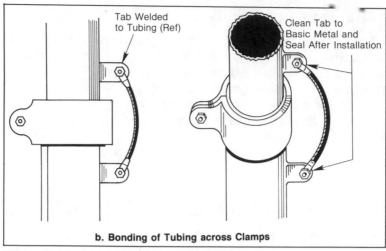

b. Bonding of Tubing across Clamps

Figure 5.16—(continued)

Joints that are press-fitted or joined by self-tapping or sheet-metal screws cannot be relied upon to provide low-impedance RF paths. Among other considerations, these screws are made on screw machines which use a jet of coolant oil. Thus, the threads may contain some residual oil in spite of a degreasing bath, and this oil tends to inhibit good electrical contact.

Often there is a need for relative motion between members that should be bonded, as in the case of shock mounts. A flexible metal strap can be used as a bonding agent as shown in Fig. 5.17.

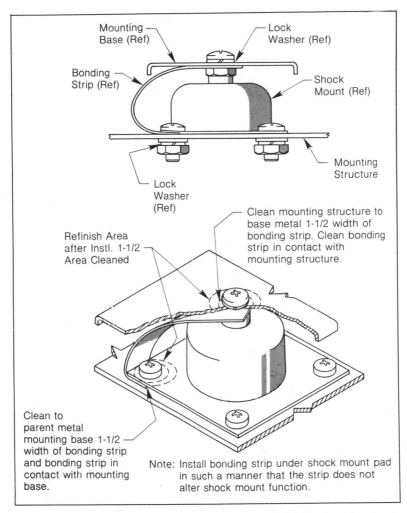

Mounting Base (Ref)

Lock Washer (Ref)

Bonding Strip (Ref)

Shock Mount (Ref)

Mounting Structure

Lock Washer (Ref)

Refinish Area after Instl. 1-1/2 Area Cleaned

Clean mounting structure to base metal 1-1/2 width of bonding strip. Clean bonding strip in contact with mounting structure.

Clean to parent metal mounting base 1-1/2 width of bonding strip and bonding strip in contact with mounting base.

Note: Install bonding strip under shock mount pad in such a manner that the strip does not alter shock mount function.

Figure 5.17—Bonding Shock Mounts (Courtesy AFSC Design Handbook DH 1-4)

5.4.4 Bonding Jumpers and Bond Straps

Bonding jumpers are conductors which are short, round and either braided or stranded. Intended for application where interference frequencies to be grounded are below about 10 MHz, they often are used in low-frequency devices where the development of static charges must be prevented. They are also used to provide good electrical continuity across tubing members and associated clamps such as shown in Fig. 5.16b. The clamps should not be relied upon for continuity because their electrical bonding performance is degraded by tubing finishes, grease films and oxides.

To provide a low-impedance path at RF, it is necessary to minimize both the self-inductance and residual capacitance of a bond to maximize the parasitic resonant frequency. Since it is difficult to change the residual capacitance of the strap and mounting, self-inductance becomes the main controllable variable. Thus, bond straps are preferable to round wires of equivalent cross-sectional areas.

Bond straps are either solid, flat, metallic conductors or made in a woven braid configuration where many conductors are effectively in parallel. Solid metal straps generally are preferred for most applications. Braided or stranded bond straps generally are not recommended because of several undesirable characteristics:

1. Oxides may form on each strand of unprotected wire and cause corrosion. Because such corrosion is not uniform, the cross-sectional area of each strand of wire will vary throughout its length.
2. The nonuniform cross-sectional areas (and possible broken strands of wire) may lead to generation of EMI within the cable or strap.
3. Broken strands may act as efficient antennas at high frequencies, and interference may be generated by intermittent contact between strands.

Solid bond straps are also preferable over stranded types because of lower self-inductance. The direct influence of bond-strap construction on RF impedance is shown in Fig. 5.18, where the impedances of two bonding straps and of no. 12 wire are compared as a function of frequency. The relatively high impedance at high frequencies illustrates that there is no adequate substitute for direct metal-to-metal contact. A rule of thumb for achieving minimum bond strap inductance is that the length-to-width ratio of the strap should be a low value, such as 5:1 or less. This ratio determines the inductance, the major factor in the high-frequency impedance of the strap.

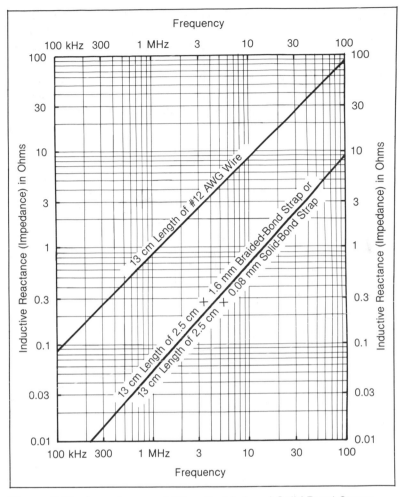

Figure 5.18—Impedances of Wire, Braided and Solid-Bond Straps

5.4.5 Rack Bonding

Equipment racks (19" or other sizes) provide a convenient means of maintaining electrical continuity between such items as rack-mounted chassis, panels and ground planes. They also act as electrical inter-ties for cable trays. A typical equipment cabinet, with the necessary modifications to provide such bonding, is shown in Fig. 5.19. Bonding between equipment chassis and rack is achieved

5.27

through equipment front-panel and rack right-angle brackets. These brackets are grounded to the unistrut horizontal slide, which is welded to the rack frame. The lower surfaces of the rack are treated with a conductive protective finish to facilitate bonding to a ground-plane mat. The ground stud at the top of the rack is used to bond a cable tray, if used, to the rack structure, which is of welded construction. Figure 5.20 illustrates a typical bonding installation.

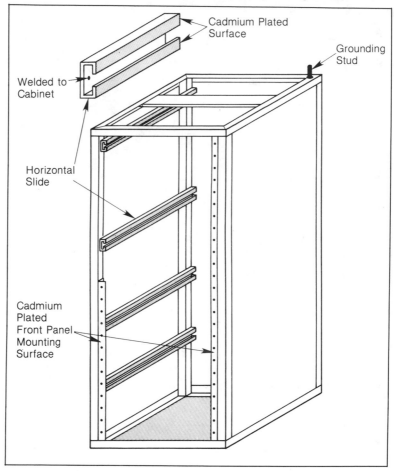

Figure 5.19—Cabinet Bonding Modifications

Cable trays are bonded together and the cable tray is bonded to the cable chute. The cable chute is bonded to the top of the cabinet, the cabinet is bonded to the flush-mounted grounding insert (which

is welded to the ground grid), and the front panel of the equipment is bonded to the rack or cabinet front-panel mounting surface. Non-conductive finishes are removed from the equipment front panel before bonding. The joint between equipment and cabinet may serve a dual purpose: that of achieving a bond and that of preventing interference leakage from the cabinet if the joint is designed to provide shielding. If such shielding is a requirement, conductive gaskets should be used around the joint to ensure that the required metal-to-metal contact is obtained. If equipment is located in a shock-mounted tray, the tray should be bonded across its shock mounts to the rack structure.

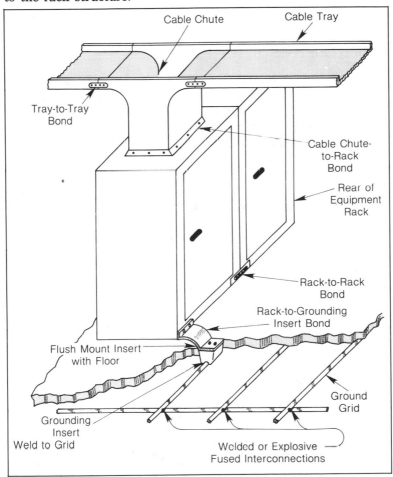

Figure 5.20—Typical Cabinet Bonding Arrangements

Connector mounting plates should use conductive gasketing to improve chassis bonding. If chassis removal from the rack structure is required, a 1" (25.4 mm) wide braid with a vinyl sleeving should be used to bond the back of the chassis to the rack. The braid should be long enough to permit withdrawal of the chassis from the rack.

5.5 Corrosion and Control

This section discusses aspects of bonding dealing with the side-effect problem of corrosion and its control.

5.5.1 Corrosion

When two metals are in contact (bonded) in the presence of moisture, corrosion may take place through either of two chemical processes. The first process is termed **galvanic corrosion**, and it develops from the formation of a voltaic cell between the metals with moisture acting as an electrolyte. The degree of resultant corrosion depends on the relative positions of the metals in the electrochemical (sometimes called electromotive) series. This series is shown in Table 5.1, with the metals listed at the top of the table corroding more rapidly than those at the bottom.

If the metals differ appreciably in this series, such as aluminum and copper (2.00 V difference) the resulting electromotive force will cause a continuous ion stream with a significant accompanying decomposition of the more active metal (higher in the series or less noble) as it gradually goes into solution.

Table 5.1—Electrochemical Series

Metal	EMF (Volts)	Metal	EMF (Volts)
Magnesium	+ 2.37	Lead	+ 0.13
Magnesium Alloys		Brass	
Beryllium	+ 1.85	Copper	− 0.34
Aluminum	+ 1.66	Bronze	
Zinc	+ 0.76	Copper-Nickel Alloys	
Chromium	+ 0.74	Monel	
Iron or Steel	+ 0.44	Stainless Steel	
Cast Iron		Silver Solder	
Cadmium	+ 0.40	Silver	− 0.80
Nickel	+ 0.25	Graphite	
Tin	+ 0.14	Platinum	− 1.20
Lead-Tin Solders		Gold	− 1.50

The second chemical corrosion process is termed **electrolytic corrosion**. While this process also requires two metals in contact through an electrolyte, the metals need not have different electrochemical activity, i.e., they can be the same material. In this case, decomposition is attributed to the presence of local electrical currents which may be flowing as a result of using a structure as a power system ground return.

Since mating bare metal to bare metal is essential for a satisfactory bond, a frequent conflict arises between bonding and finishing specifications. For EMI control, it is preferable to remove the finish where a compromise in bonding effectiveness would occur. Generally, one need not remove conductive coatings such as alodine, iridite, and Dow #1, and protective metal platings such as cadmium, tin and silver. Most other coatings, however, are nonconductive and destroy the concept of a bond offering a low-impedance RF path. For example, anodized aluminum appears to the eye to be a good conductive surface for bonding, but in reality it is an insulated coating.

Figure 5.21 shows the effect of various protective coatings on the electric-field shielding effectiveness of aluminum and magnesium. The shielding effectiveness is a function of the coating conductivity. The superiority of bare metal over a 12 octave frequency range is evident.

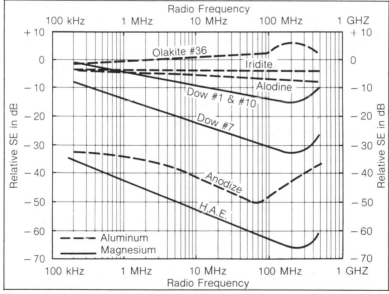

Figure 5.21—Effect of Various Finishes on Shielding Effectiveness of Aluminum and Magnesium

5.5.2 Corrosion Protection

The most effective way to avoid the adverse effects of corrosion is to use metals low in the electrochemical activity table such as tin, lead or copper. This is impractical in the design of many structures (e.g., aircraft) due to weight considerations. Consequently, the more active, lighter metals, such as magnesium and aluminum, are employed, although stainless steel has been used in many missile programs.

Joined metals should be close together in the activity series if excessive corrosion is to be avoided. Magnesium and stainless steel form a galvanic couple of high potential (about 3 V), which tends to a rapid corrosion of the magnesium. Where dissimilar metals must be used, select replaceable components for the object of corrosion (e.g., grounding jumpers, washers, bolts or clamps) rather than structural members. Thus, the smaller mass should be of the higher potential, such as steel washers for use with brass structures.

When members of the electrolytic couple are widely separated in the activity table, it is often practical to use a plating, such as cadmium or tin, to help reduce the dissimilarity. Sometimes, it is possible to electrically insulate metals with organic and electrolytic finishes and seal the joint against moisture to avoid corrosion. However, this is an unacceptable practice for EMI control. One solution to electrolytic corrosion is to avoid the use of the structure or housing for power-ground return. Any anticipated corrosion should be designed to occur in easily replaceable items, as previously mentioned. Joints should also be kept tight and well coated after bonding to prevent the entrance of liquids or gases, since a galvanic cell cannot function without moisture.

5.6 References

1. Friedlander, G.D., "Electricity in Hospitals: Elimination of Lethal Hazards," *IEEE Spectrum*, Sept. 1971; pp. 40-51.

5.7 Bibliography

Dalziel, C.F., "Electric Shock Hazard," *IEEE Spectrum,* Vol. 9, no. 2, February 1972, pp. 41-50.

Denny, H.W., *Grounding for the Control of EMI* (Gainesville, Virginia: Interference Control Technologies, Inc., 1983).

Denny, H.W., et. al., *Electronic Facility Bonding, Grounding and Shielding Review,* Report no. FAA-RD-73-51 (Washington, DC: U.S. Dept. of Transportation, November 1972).

Denny, H.W., et. al., *Grounding, Bonding and Shielding Practices and Procedures for Electronic Equipments and Facilities* (3 volumes), Report no. FAA-RD-75-215, Contract DT-FA72WA-2850, AD A022 332, AD A022 608 and Ad A022-871 (Atlanta, Georgia: Engineering Experiment Station, Georgia Institute of Technology, 1975).

Herring, T.H., *Large System Grounding,* Report no. FAA-RD-74-174, FAA/GIT Workshop on the Grounding of Electronic Systems, Atlanta, Georgia, 1974.

MIL-B-5087B, "Bonding, Electrical and Lightning Protection, for Aerospace Systems," October 1964.

MIL-STD-124-188, "Grounding, Bonding and Shielding for Common Long Haul/Tactical Communication Systems," June 1978.

MIL-STD-1310(E), "Shipboard Bonding, Grounding and Other Techniques for EMC and Safety."

MIL-STD-1542 (USAF), "Electromagnetic Compatibility (EMC) and Grounding Requirements for Space System Facilities," (U.S. Dept. of Defense, April 1974).

Morrison, R., *Grounding and Shielding Techniques in Instrumentation* (New York: John Wiley & Sons, Inc., 1967).

Osburn, J.D.M., "Integration of Facilities Ground Systems with User Electronic Systems," *EMC Technology,* Vol. 5, no. 1, September 1986, p. 29.

Vance, E.F., "Cable Grounding for the Control of EMI," *EMC Technology,* January 1983.

Chapter 6

Shielding Theory, Materials and Protection Techniques

Shielding is a major means of EMI control at all levels of EMC, viz.: component; chassis or black box; equipment; subsystem; system; and entire vehicular or housing structures such as ships, aircraft and buildings. This section presents shielding theory, shielding materials and some mathematical models of shielding effectiveness (SE).

The performance of shields is a function of whether the source appears as an electric or magnetic field in the near-in induction region or an electromagnetic field in the far-field region. These considerations are a function of both the source and receptor geometry separation and frequency of operation. Consequently, it is pertinent to first establish criteria for far-fields and near-fields as a function of these parameters.

6.1 Field Theory

The purpose of this section is to present some pragmatic relations about magnetic, electric and electromagnetic fields as pertinent background to understanding and applying shielding criteria. Since EMC literature is replete with excellent discussions of Maxwell's equations and field theory, only a few aspects are presented here.

The electric (E_θ, E_r) and magnetic (H_ϕ) fields existing about an oscillating doublet (or circuit) which exhibits high impedance and is oriented as shown in Fig. 6.1 are obtained from applying Maxwell's equations:

$$E\theta = \frac{Z_0 ID\pi \sin \theta}{\lambda^2} \left[\left(\frac{\lambda}{} \right)^3 \cos \psi \right.$$

$$- \left(\frac{\lambda}{2\pi r} \right)^2 \sin \psi$$

$$\left. + \left(\frac{\lambda}{2\pi r} \right) \cos \psi \right]$$
(6.1)

$$E_R = \frac{2Z_0 ID\pi \cos \theta}{\lambda^2} \left[\left(\frac{\lambda}{2\pi r} \right)^3 \cos \psi \right.$$
(6.2)

$$\left. + \left(\frac{\lambda}{2\pi r} \right)^2 \sin \psi \right]$$

$$H_\phi = \frac{ID\pi \cos \theta}{\lambda^2} \left[\left(\frac{\lambda}{2\pi r} \right)^2 \sin \psi \right.$$
(6.3)

$$\left. + \frac{\lambda}{2\pi r} \cos \psi \right]$$

where,

Z_0 = free-space impedance (for $r \gg \lambda/2\pi$

  I = current in short wire (doublet)

  D = length of short wire (doublet) in which $D \ll \lambda$

  Θ = zenith angle to radial distance r

  λ = wavelength corresponding to frequency ($f = c/\lambda$)

  r = distance from short wire doublet to measuring or observation point

  ω = radial frequency = $2\pi f$

  ψ = $2\pi r/\lambda - \omega t$

  t = time = $1/f$

  c = $\sqrt{\mu\epsilon}$ = 3×10^8 meters per second

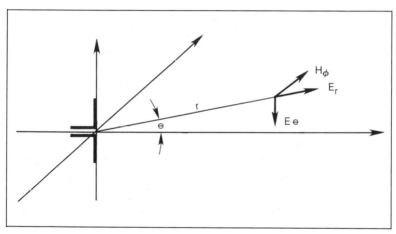

Figure 6.1—Fields From A Vertical Doublet

1. The electric and magnetic-field components contain terms that involve $\lambda/2\pi r$. For most conditions, the E_r term will be small relative to the E_θ term and is usually considered to be insignificant. Thus, E_r will not be considered further.

2. When the multiplier, $\lambda/2\pi r$, equals 1 in the electric-field and magnetic-field terms, all coefficients of either the sin or cos are unity and equal. Thus, $r = \lambda/2\pi$ (about one-sixth wavelength), corresponds to the transition-field condition or boundary between the near-field (first term of both equations) and far-field (last term).

3. When $r \gg \lambda/2\pi$ (far-field conditions), only the last term of each equation is significant. For this condition the wave impedance $Z_0 = E_\theta/H_\phi = 377\ \Omega$. This is called the **radiation field** (plane waves), and both E_θ and H_ϕ are in time phase, although in directional quadrature.

4. When $r \ll \lambda/2\pi$ (near-field conditions), only the first term of each equation is significant. For this condition, the wave impedance, $E_\theta/H_\phi = Z_0 \times \lambda/2\pi r$. Note that the wave impedance is now $\gg Z_0$. This is sometimes called simply an **electric field** or a **high-impedance** field, (i.e., high relative to a plane-wave impedance). It is also the induction field, and E_θ and H_ϕ are in both time phase and directional quadrature.

5. If the oscillating source had been low impedance, the electric-field and magnetic-field equations would be similar to the ones given previously, except that the first term in Eq. (6.1) would vanish and a similar first term would have to be added to Eq. (6.3). For this condition, the wave impedance in the near field, $E_\theta/H_\phi = Z_0\, 2\pi r/\lambda$. This is sometimes called a **magnetic field** or a **low-impedance field** (i.e., low relative to Z_0, the plane-wave radiation impedance).

Figure 6.2 illustrates conceptually the fourth and fifth conditions in the near or induction field. The situation shown in 6.2a is a monopole, straight wire or circuit in which the RF current is low. Consequently, the source impedance = V/I is a high impedance. The wave impedance near-in is also high, being made up predominantly of the electric field. The electric field attenuates more rapidly ($1/r^3$) with an increase in distance than the magnetic field ($1/r^2$) in the induction region [cf. Eqs. (6.1) and (6.2)]. Thus, the wave impedance decreases with distance where it asymptotically approaches $Z_0 = 377\ \Omega$ in the far or radiation field.

The converse applies for the situation in Fig. 6.2b, wherein a low-impedance source creates a low-impedance wave predominantly of the magnetic-field component. This impedance increases with distance where it asymptotically approaches 377 Ω in the far field. Figure 6.3 illustrates these impedances of both fields as a function of distance, r.

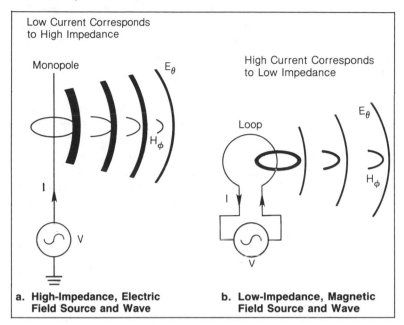

a. High-Impedance, Electric Field Source and Wave

b. Low-Impedance, Magnetic Field Source and Wave

Figure 6.2—Conceptual Illustration of Field Intensities vs. Source Type and Distance

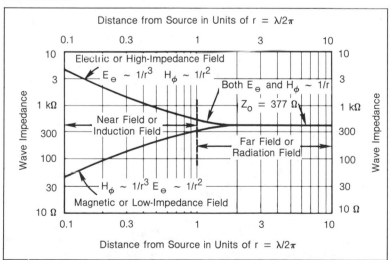

Figure 6.3—Wave Impedance as a Function of Source Distance

6.2 Shielding Theory

Shielding provided by a metallic barrier can be analyzed from either of two viewpoints: (a) that of field or wave theory, or (b) that of circuit theory. In the circuit-theory approach, currents from the interference source induce currents in the shield such that the associated external fields due to both currents are out of phase and tend to cancel. Since the field-theory approach is more widely adopted in EMC literature, however, it will be used in the remainder of this discussion.

Figure 6.4 depicts the phenomena of both reflection and transmission that are employed in removing energy from an incident wave (plane-wave example shown). If an incident plane wave is intercepted by a barrier to its passage at the region A of the interface, both reflection and transmission occur. The amplitudes of these two portions of the original wave depend on the surface impedance of the barrier material with respect to the impedance of the wave. Since the reflected wave is not proceeding in a direction that contributes to the surviving wave on the far side of the barrier, this is considered a loss mechanism.

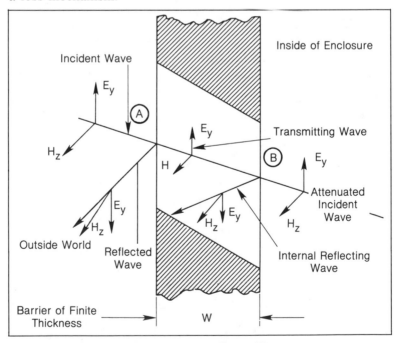

Figure 6.4—Shielding Phenomena for Plane Waves

The transmitted portion of the incident wave, continuing in approximately the same direction after penetrating the interface, experiences absorption while traversing the finite thickness of the barrier. At the second barrier (interface B of Fig. 6.4), reflection and transmission phenomena again occur. The transmitted portion is the amount of energy that traversed the first interface, less the energy absorbed in traversing the barrier and that reflected at B. The second reflection contributes an insignificant amount in the removal of energy and is usually neglected.

At plane-wave (far-field) frequencies, the SE of a barrier in reducing the energy of an electromagnetic field can be readily computed. Each of the contributing factors discussed above is computed separately, and then their total contribution is summarized. This is accomplished in the following manner for expressing shielding effectiveness in dB (SE_{dB}):

$$SE_{dB} = R_{dB} + A_{dB} + B_{dB} \qquad (6.4)$$

where,

R_{dB} = reflection loss in dB

A_{dB} = transmission or absorption loss in dB

B_{dB} = internal reflection loss at exiting interface in dB (usually neglected)

The SE to electric or electromagnetic fields may also be measured in terms of the fraction of the impinging field which exists at the other side of the barrier:

$$SE_{dB} = 20 \log \left(\frac{E_1}{E_2} \right) \qquad (6.5)$$

where,

E_1 = impinging field intensity in volts per meter

E_2 = exiting field intensity in volts per meter

The individual contributing factors to the SE in Eq. (6.4) are separately computed in the next sections.

6.2.1 Absorption Loss

The absorption loss, A_{dB}, is independent of the type of wave impinging on the shield and is expressed as follows:

$$A_{dB} = 3.34 \times 10^{-3} t\sqrt{fG\mu} \qquad (6.6)$$

$$= 3.34\, t\sqrt{f_{MHz}G\mu}\ dB$$

where,

    A = attenuation in dB

    t = thickness of barrier in mils (unit of 0.001", or 0.0254 mm)

    f = frequency in Hz

    G = conductivity relative to copper (G = 1)

    μ = magnetic permeability of material relative to vacuum or copper (μ = 1)

  f_{MHz} = frequency in MHz

Equation (6.6) is plotted in Fig. 6.5 for the parameters copper (G = 1, μ = 1), iron (G = 0.17, μ = 1,000) and Hypernick (G = 0.06, μ = 80,000). Absorption loss is the dependent variable, and frequency is the independent variable with thickness in mils as a second parameter. It is noted that the brute-force approach of using a thick sheet (1/8", or 3.175 mm) of iron at low frequencies (e.g., at 60 Hz) results in a significant absorption loss (approx. 45 dB). On the other hand, a thin sheet (e.g., 1 mil) of copper at 1 GHz yields significant absorption loss (> 100 dB). This illustrates the difficulty of achieving a significant absorption loss at ELF in contrast to UHF.

The internal reflection loss, B, in Eq. (6.4) is negligible when A_{dB} is greater than about 4 dB. When A_{dB} is not greater than 4 dB, B_{dB} is negative since it is a coherent term which would have made E_2 in Eq. (6.5) larger. The value of B_{dB} is shown in the lower right corner of Fig. 6.5.

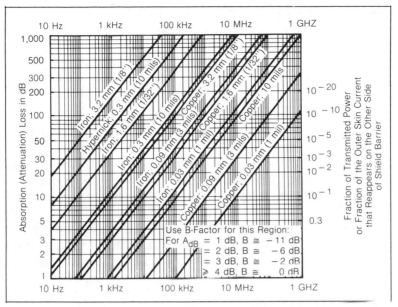

Figure 6.5—Shielding Absorption (Penetration/Attenuation) Loss vs. Frequency, Material and Thickness (Independent of Wave Impedance)

6.2.2 Reflection Loss

Reflection loss, R_d, is represented by forming the ratio of the wave impedance, Z_w, to the surface impedance of the barrier material, Z_b.

$$R_{dB} = 20 \log \frac{(K + 1)^2}{4K} \approx 20 \log \left(\frac{Z_w}{4Z_b} \right), \text{ for } K > 10 \quad (6.7)$$

Equation (6.7) indicates that if either the wave impedance is high (e.g., electric field), the barrier surface impedance is low (e.g., copper), or both, the loss will be substantial. Conversely, if the wave impedance is low (e.g., magnetic field), the barrier impedance is relatively high (e.g., iron), or both, the reflection loss will be significantly less. Each of these situations is now discussed in further detail.

6.2.3 Reflection Loss to Plane Waves

The reflection loss of a plane wave, R_{dB}, may also be calculated from:

$$R_{dB} = 108 + 10 \log (G/\mu f_{MHz}) \text{ dB} \qquad (6.8)$$

Equation (6.8) is plotted in Fig. 6.6 for copper, iron and hypernick. Compared with absorption loss, the figure indicates that the reflection loss of plane waves at low frequencies is the major attenuation mechanism. High-conductivity, low-permeability material is more effective in establishing reflection loss, since the barrier surface impedance is lower with regard to that of a plane wave where $Z_w = 377 \ \Omega$, and the ratio of the latter to the former (the loss mechanism) is greater [cf. Eq. (6.7)]. At UHF, the reflection loss becomes less effective since the barrier skin depth decreases (surface resistivity increases) and the barrier impedance increases. This results in a smaller ratio of plane-wave to barrier impedance. In comparing Figs. 6.5 and 6.6, note that the absorption loss becomes the more significant loss mechanism at UHF.

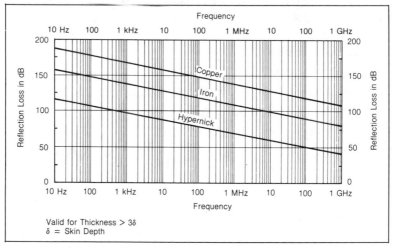

Figure 6.6—Reflection Loss of Plane Waves vs. Frequency

6.2.4 Reflection Loss to Electric and Magnetic Fields

When there is a substantial difference in the impedance of the incident wave and the shielding barrier, reflection at the boundary is significant, and good shielding is obtained. The high-impedance wave in the near field is known as an **electric-field wave**, and its reflection loss is:

$$R_{dB} = 354 + 10 \log \left(\frac{G}{f^3 \mu r^2} \right) \text{ dB} \qquad (6.9)$$

where,

r = distance from source to barrier in inches

The other terms are as defined under Eq. (6.6)

Equation (6.9) is plotted in Fig. 6.7 for the parameters of separation distances, r, of 25 mm (1"), 1m (3.3 ft.) and 30 m (100') for copper and iron. As before, frequency is the independent variable, and reflection loss (R_{fB}) is the dependent variable. The above distance parameter covers a range of 1,200, or about 62 dB difference in reflection loss, whereas the G/μ range for copper to iron is about −38 dB.

Figure 6.7 shows that the reflection loss of an electric field decreases with frequency until the separation distance becomes $\lambda/2\pi$, where far-field conditions prevail. Thus, Eq. (6.9) applies until the losses meet that of Eq. (6.8), the plane-wave losses. Thereafter, the two merge. For this reason, the plane-wave reflection losses are also shown as a reference in Fig. 6.7 and are identical to those previously shown in Fig. 6.5.

For low-impedance or magnetic-field waves, the reflection loss is:

$$R_{dB} = 20 \log[(0.462/r)\sqrt{\mu/fG} + (0.136r)\sqrt{Gf/\mu} + \qquad (6.10)$$

$$0.354] \text{ dB}$$

6.11

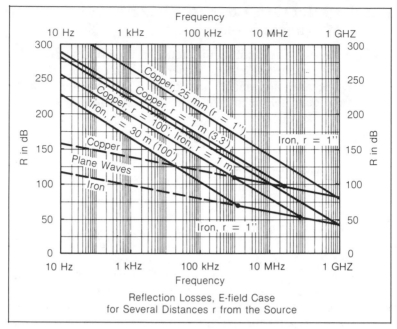

Figure 6.7—Reflection Loss of Electric Fields vs. Frequency

Equation (6.10) is plotted in Fig. 6.8 for the parameters of separation distance, r, of 25 mm (1"), 1 m (3.3 ft) and 100 ft (30 m), for copper and iron. The reflection loss to iron (25 mm (1") separation) approaches 0 dB at about 30 kHz when the magnetic-field wave impedance approximates that of the barrier impedance [loss = 0 dB from Eq. (6.7)]. Below 30 kHz, the wave impedance is less than the barrier impedance, and the loss again increases. The reflection loss of a magnetic field shown in the figure increases with frequency until the source-to-barrier separation distance is about $\lambda/2\pi$, where the plane-wave losses of Fig. 6.6 again prevail.

In comparing Figs. 6.7 and 6.8, it is noted that reflection-loss shielding for providing a reduction in absolute field intensity to magnetic fields at low frequencies is distinctly different from that for electric fields. Magnetic fields are shielded at dc and ELF only by providing a low-reluctance path as an alternative for the incident magnetic field.

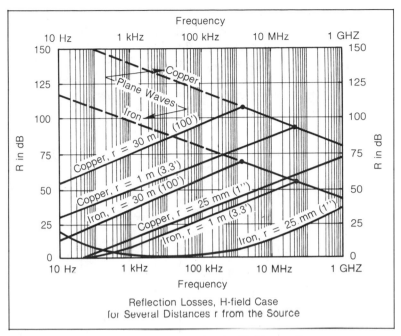

Frequency

Reflection Losses, H-field Case
for Several Distances r from the Source

Figure 6.8—Reflection Loss of Magnetic Fields vs. Frequency

Figure 6.9 depicts a simple representation of a uniform magnetic field existing in free space. The vertical lines show the direction of the orientation of the magnetic-field vector throughout the two dimensions. Figure 6.10 shows the effect on the field lines by including a hollow permeable object in this uniform magnetic field. The field-intensity lines enter the object at an angle of 90° to its surface. In the interior of this hollow object, the field intensity lines are less intense than in the surrounding free-space medium. (The magnetic field in the inside is about $\mu t/s$ of the value on the outside, where μ is the relative permeability, t is the thickness and s is the dimension of one side.) However, these magnetic-field lines in the solid barrier are much more intense than in either the hollow center or the exterior of the barrier. This effect is due to the relatively higher reluctance of free space both surrounding the barrier and in the interior versus that of the barrier itself.

The lower reluctance of this barrier divides the field-intensity lines, thus reducing the intensity of the absolute magnetic field in the interior of the enclosure to yield a shielding effect. This effect is quite pronounced at dc, where SE values in excess of 50 dB have been achieved through the utilization of extremely high-permeability materials configured on a double-barrier enclosure.

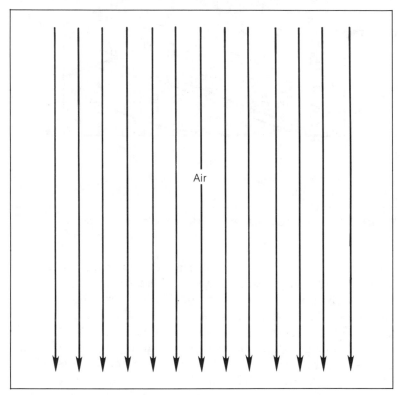

Figure 6.9—Uniform Magnetic Field

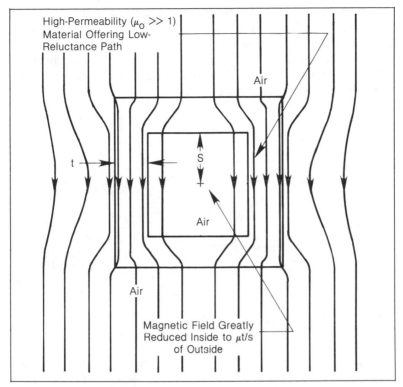

High-Permeability ($\mu_o \gg 1$)
Material Offering Low-
Reluctance Path

Air

t

S

Air

Air

Magnetic Field Greatly
Reduced Inside to $\mu t/s$
of Outside

Figure 6.10—Cross Section of a Hollow, Rectangular Solid of High Permeability in Uniform Field

6.2.5 Composite Absorption and Reflection Loss

When either Eqs. (6.6) through (6.10) or Figs. 6.5 through 6.8 are combined, the overall attenuation or SE given in Eq. (6.4) results. These relationships are plotted in Fig. 6.11. Since there are many variables, the composite curves represent the parameters of copper and iron materials having a thickness of one mil and 0.8 mm (1/32"); electric and magnetic fields and plane-wave sources; and a source-to-barrier distance of 25 mm (1") and 1 m (3.3 ft).

Except for LF magnetic fields, the figure shows that reflection loss is the principal attenuation mechanism at low frequencies, whereas absorption loss is the main mechanism at HF. Figure 6.11 is but one of a family of mathematical models which define shielding attenuation. Other models would reflect different materials, thickness and emission source distances.

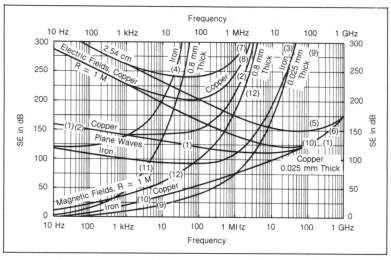

Figure 6.11—Total Shielding Effectiveness vs. Frequency for Electric and Magnetic Fields and Plane Waves

6.3 Shielding Materials

Good shielding efficiency for electric (high-impedance) fields is obtained by the use of high-conductivity materials such as copper and aluminum. As shown in Eq. (6.9) and Fig. 6.7, the SE for electric fields is infinite at dc and decreases with an increase in frequency. However, magnetic fields [Eq. (6.10)] are more difficult to shield because the reflection loss may approach zero for certain combinations of material and frequency. With decreasing frequency, the magnetic-field reflection and absorption losses decrease for nonmagnetic materials such as aluminum. Consequently, it is difficult to shield against magnetic fields using nonmagnetic materials. At high frequencies, the SE is good due to both reflection and absorption losses, so that the choice of materials becomes less important.

Regarding plane waves, magnetic materials provide better absorption loss (Fig. 6.5), whereas good conductors provide better reflection loss (Fig. 6.6). These and the above relations are summarized qualitatively in Table 6.1. Table 6.2 summarizes the absorption loss of a number of different materials which, in one form or another, may be used for shielding. The loss is given in dB per mil thickness of the metal. The high-permeability ($\mu > 80,000$) materials shown are especially interesting for their low-frequency, magnetic-field shielding properties. However, they are prone to saturation at lower field densities, and they require careful handling procedures.

It is often assumed that most materials which have adequate structural rigidity will also possess sufficient thickness to provide satisfactory shielding efficiency. This is not generally true for equipments operated in the audio-frequency region. At these low frequencies it is necessary to use a high-permeability material such as Hypernom, Mumetall® or Netic® or Co-Netic® foil to provide satisfactory shielding efficiency to magnetic fields.

Table 6.1—Summary of Shielding Effectiveness of Permeable and Nonpermeable Materials

Permeable Materials	Frequency	Absorption Loss A_{dB} All Fields	Reflection Loss, R_{dB}		
			Electric Fields	Magnetic Fields	Plane Waves
Magnetic ($\mu \geqslant 1,000$)	Low < 1 kHz	Bad	Excel.	Fail	Good
	Medium 1 - 100 kHz	Good	Good	Bad	Fair
	High > 100 kHz	Excel.	Fair	Poor	Fair
Non-Magnetic ($\mu = 1$)	Low < 1 kHz	Fail	Excel.	Bad	Good
	Medium 1 - 100 kHz	Bad	Excel.	Poor	Good
	High > 100 kHz	Good	Good	Fair	Fair

Assumptions:
  Material Thickness: 1/32"
  Source Distance: 10 feet (3 m)
  Radio Frequency: as shown

Attenuation Scores:
  Excellent: >150 dB   Poor: 30 - 50 dB
  Good: 100-150 dB   Bad: 10-30 dB
  Fair: 50-100 dB   < 10 dB

Table 6.2—Characteristics of Metals Used for Shielding

Metal	Conductivity Relative to Copper	Relative Permeability (100 kHz)	Absorption Loss in dB per mil (0.0001")		
			100 Hz	10 kHz	1 MHz
Silver	1.05	1	0.03	0.34	3.40
Copper-Annealed	1.00	1	0.03	0.33	3.33
Copper-Hard Drawn	0.97	1	0.03	0.32	3.25
Gold	0.70	1	0.03	0.28	2.78
Aluminum	0.61	1	0.03	0.26	2.60
Magnesium	0.38	1	0.02	0.20	2.04
Zinc	0.29	1	0.02	0.17	1.70
Brass	0.26	1	0.02	0.17	1.70
Cadmium	0.23	1	0.02	0.16	1.60
Nickel	0.20	1	0.01	0.15	1.49
Bronze	0.18	1	0.01	0.14	1.42
Iron	0.17	1,000	0.44	4.36	43.60
Tin	0.15	1	0.01	0.13	1.29
Steel (SAE 1045)	0.10	1,000	0.33	3.32	33.20
Beryllium	0.10	1	0.01	0.11	1.06
Lead	0.08	1	0.01	0.09	0.93
Hypernom®	0.06	80,000	2.28	22.8	228.00
Monel	0.04	1	0.01	0.07	0.67
Mumetall®	0.03	80,000	1.63	16.3	163.00
Permalloy	0.03	80,000	1.63	16.3	163.00
Stainless Steel	0.02	≈ 1	0.15	1.47	14.70

While the above equations and figures show a high theoretical value of shielding efficiency from magnetic materials, in practice such levels are seldom achieved, particularly at low frequencies where the required thickness is substantial. Some of the best results have been obtained by the use of multiple Permalloy sheets or the Netic and Co-Netic sandwich foils. These latter products are available in a variety of ready-made forms and sizes to fit diverse applications.

Illustrative Example 6.1

A sensitive parallel-T amplifier tuned to 120 Hz is to be located about 1 m away from a 60 Hz amplidyne. By measurement, the magnetic flux density, B, from the amplidyne at a 1 m distance at its second harmonic is 180 dBpT or 10 gauss (10^{-3} weber/m^2). The cable feeding the tuned amplifier is 0.4 m (16") long and is equivalent to a conductor separation of 2.54 mm (0.1"). Determine the induced voltage and specify the magnetic shield required to protect the 1 V amplifier sensitivity, if necessary.

The cable loop area is, $A = lw = 0.4\ m \times 0.0025\ m = 10^{-3}\ m^2$. The magnetic flux, ϕ, crossing the cable loop is $BA = 10^{-3}$ weber/m^2 $\times\ 10^{-3}\ m^2 = 10^{-6}$ weber. The induced voltage, V, is:

$$V = d\phi/dt = -d/dt\ (10^{-6}\ \text{webers} \times \cos \omega t)$$

$$= |\omega 10^{-6} \sin \omega t|\ \text{volts}$$

$$= 2\pi \times 120\ \text{Hz} \times 10^{-6}$$

$$= 750\ \mu V\ (58\ dB\mu V)$$

Since the induced voltage is 58 dB above the 1 μV amplifier sensitivity, about 60 dB of magnetic shielding of the cable is required at 120 Hz. At this frequency, from Fig. 6.11, a 0.8 mm (1/32") iron sheet offers about 15 dB attenuation, and copper of any thickness offers about 40 dB. Neither will provide the shielding required.

Table 6.2 indicates that Hypernom offers 2.3 dB per mil thickness at 100 Hz. Thus, about 26 mils of Hypernom (60 dB attenuation) should adequately shield the twin-T amplifier cable.

The attenuation offered by materials to electric, magnetic and electromagnetic waves described in the previous sections is theoretically achievable. In practice, however, this attenuation is not often realized because a shielded enclosure or housing is not completely sealed. In other words, nearly any practical application of shielding will require penetrations which compromise SE.

6.4 EMI Shielding Components and Equipments

The preceding sections covered the subject of shielding theory and materials. It was shown that for other than low-frequency magnetic fields, it is easy to obtain more than 100 dB SE across the spectrum for nearly any metal. The shielding problem then develops from the fact that practical enclosures have apertures and penetrations which compromise the effectiveness of the basic shield material. Thus, SE of a housing could be reduced to 60 dB or less through loss of enclosure integrity.

It now remains to bring the foregoing material together in the form of practical shielded-housing applications. Consequently, this section reviews the subjects of shielded compartments, chassis and equipments and cabinets. Typical examples of equipment-level shielded housing include cabinets for electronic test instruments, biomedical equipment, mobile transceivers, hi-fi amplifiers and minicomputers.

Figure 6.12 illustrates a typical equipment case with a number of representative shielding compromises including:

1. Cover plate for access
2. Holes for cooling
3. Power and signal cable entry holes
4. Displays, instruments and switches

The designer of an equipment case must give careful consideration to these shielding compromises and should incorporate various protective measures to minimize the compromise in shielding integrity.

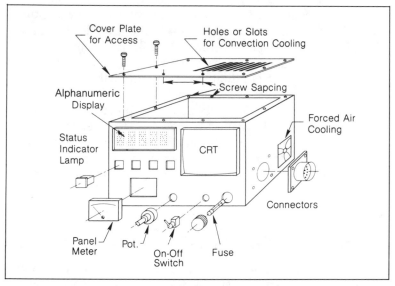

Figure 6.12—Some Principal Box Shielding Compromises

Many of the shielding integrity compromises in an equipment case (such as openings or seams) can be regarded as apertures, and the leakage will be a function of the aperture size relative to wavelength. Figure 6.13 illustrates the principle of leakage through an aperture. Referring to Fig. 6.13, it can be observed that as the aperture size approaches λ/2, the leakage increases. At λ/2, the aperture provides no shielding at all. Therefore, in designing equipment cases, it is particularly important to keep the size of any aperture much less than λ/2 at the highest frequency for which shielding is required. Shielding integrity protection techniques are described in the following sections.

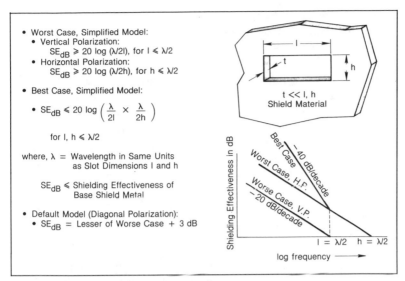

Figure 6.13—Slot and Aperture Leakage

6.5 Shielding Integrity Protection

The previous sections discussed the subjects of shielding theory and materials. With the exception of low-frequency, magnetic-field shielding, it was shown that it is quite simple to obtain more than 100 dB of SE across the entire spectrum from dc to daylight for electric and electromagnetic waves. However, because the introduction of apertures creates a loss of shielding integrity, the theoretical SE is never obtained.

6.5.1 Integrity of Shielding Configurations

It is not uncommon to find the plane-wave attenuation of a basic shield material to be 120 dB, for example, while the actual enclosure will exhibit 50 dB in the VHF/UHF portion of the spectrum. Here, leakage compromises the integrity of the basic shielding material. Protective measures that may be used to reduce leakage are described in the following paragraphs.

6.5.1.1 Bonding Seams and Joints

Loss of RF shielding integrity across the interface of clean mating material members is a main reason why SE is compromised. Depending on the nature of the interface bond, the conductivity of the interface may be much higher, the permeability may be much lower, or both. Thus, resulting material interfaces may be classified into two types: **physically inhomogeneous** and **physically homogenous**.

A physical inhomogeneous interface bond results when shielding members are directly connected by screws, rivets, spot welds and the like. The interface connection is not continuous, and there results a bowing or waviness effect between connected members. This creates slits or gaps which allow radiation or penetration at frequencies approaching 0.01λ. The attenuation, A, in dB at such a gap follows the waveguide-beyond-cutoff (WBCO) criterion:

$$A_{dB} = 0.0018 \times l_d \times f_{MHz} \times \sqrt{(f_c/f_{MHz})^2 - 1} \quad dB \quad (6.11)$$

where,

$\quad\quad l_d$ = gap depth in centimeters for overlapping members or
$\quad\quad\quad\quad$ the thickness of the material for butting members
$\quad f_{MHz}$ = operating frequency in MHz
$\quad\quad f_c$ = cutoff frequency of gap in MHz
$\quad\quad\quad$ = 14,986/g for a rectangular gap
$\quad\quad\quad$ = 17,577/g for circular gap

$\quad\quad g$ = largest gap transverse dimension in centimeters

When $f_c \gg f_{MHz}$, Eq. (6.11) becomes:

$$A_{dB} = 0.0046 \times l_d \times f_c \quad\quad\quad\quad (6.12)$$
$$= 27 \times l_d/g \quad dB, \text{ for a rectangular gap}$$
$$= 32 \times l_d/g \quad dB, \text{ for a circular gap}$$

Figure 6.14 is a plot of Eq. (6.11), representing attenuation through a rectangular gap versus frequency as a function of gap dimensions. The figure shows that more than 100 dB attenuation exists over the dc to 10 GHz spectrum for both g/l_d ratios greater than about 4 and the largest gap dimension less than 5 mm (cutoff frequency of about 30 GHz).

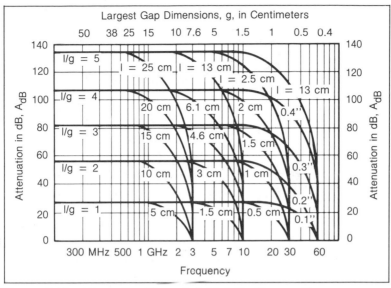

Figure 6.14—Attenuation Through A Metallic Gap vs. Frequency

There are a number of techniques available for reducing electromagnetic emission leakage and receptor penetration of a shielded specimen. If members are joined by screws or rivets, Eq. (6.12) shows that A_{dB} may be significantly increased by using more screws or rivets per linear dimension of the interface due to the reduction in the gap, g. Figure 6.15 shows a joint SE, as a function of screw spacing, for the indicated parameters. Also note the improvement due to the application of a typical EMI mesh gasket.

Other techniques available for reducing the leakage in a physical inhomogeneous mating member bond involve eliminating or reducing the inhomogeneity. Figure 6.16 illustrates some of these approaches. Where members do not have to be disengaged or separated, a continuous seam weld around the periphery of the mating surfaces is preferred. This type of weld is not critical, provided it is continuous and has no weld pinholes. One exception involves the departure of the weld filler material from the basic shield member material. Hence, either the conductivity or permeability of the weld filler may be much lower, resulting in degradation of SE.

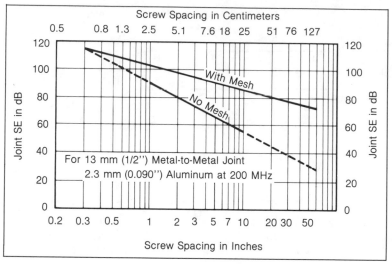

Figure 6.15—Shielding Effectiveness for Screw-Secured Joints

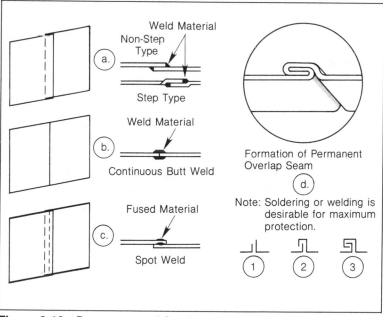

Figure 6.16—Permanent and Semipermanent Shield Seam Configurations (Courtesy of USAFSC DH 1-4)

6.24

The seam weld technique is of questionable value when used with the more exotic magnetic materials ($\mu > 1,000$; see Table 6.1) which must be annealed before assembly. Here, welding will destroy the specific properties that the annealing produced.

An alternative technique shown in Fig. 6.16 is the overlap seam. All nonconductive material (e.g., paint, rust, coatings, etc.) must be removed from the mating surfaces before they are crimped. Crimping must be performed under sufficient pressure to ensure positive contact between all mating surfaces.

Shield members such as cover and access plates may have to be separated from time to time for equipment alignment or maintenance. Therefore, none of the above techniques is acceptable. A temporary but effective RF gasketing material is required, such as finger stock or resilient mesh. The subject of gaskets is discussed in a later section.

6.5.1.2 Ventilation Openings

Most shielded enclosures require either convection or forced-air cooling. Since associated openings will compromise the integrity of the basic shield material, a suitable electromagnetic mask must be sought which will provide substantial attenuation at RF while not significantly impeding the mechanical flow of air. Two approaches are possible: screened covers and honeycomb aperture covers. As explained in the next section, screens are inexpensive approaches to this problem but are limited in SE and tend to block the flow of air due to turbulence. Thus, a honeycomb material is generally used because it provides higher SE and maintains a streamlined flow of air.

In typical honeycomb construction, illustrated in Fig. 6.17, the hexagonal elements use the WBCO technique to accomplish the desired SE. A representative honeycomb configuration is shown in Fig. 6.18. Equation (6.11) previously indicated the expected attenuation. However, for honeycomb, the SE at frequencies well below cutoff is reduced by the number of waveguide elements, N, in the panel since the emerging field from each hex cell coherently combines with its neighbor. Thus, the results for honeycomb ventilation covers are:

$$A_{dB} \approx 27\ l_c/g - 20 \log N \qquad (6.13)$$

where,

l_c = thickness of cover panel

g = largest dimension of hex cell

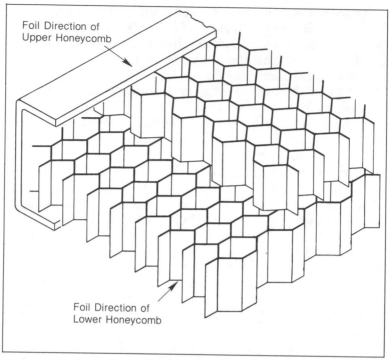

Figure 6.17—Typical Honeycomb Construction (Courtesy of Metex Corp.)

Figure 6.18—Representative Honeycomb Configurations

Figure 6.19 illustrates typical performance of different honeycomb configurations. The LF magnetic field performance, however, does not follow Eq. (6.16). Rather, the applicable relation is Eq. (6.6).

Sometimes it is necessary to provide reduction or removal of dust in the ventilation process. Honeycomb construction will not remove dust. Thus, a shield screen is fabricated of a woven wire mesh. The shielding mesh medium can be either dry (see Fig. 6.20) or wet (to accommodate an oil coating for more dust removal; see Fig. 6.21). Figure 6.22 shows typical attenuation of shielding mesh covers versus frequency.

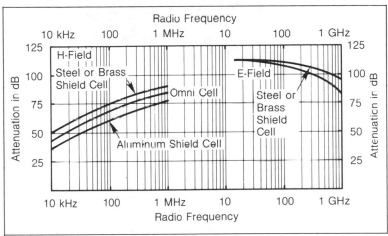

Figure 6.19—Typical Shielding Effectiveness of Honeycomb Vent Covers

Figure 6.20—Representative Shield Screen Mesh Ventilation Covers for Air Filtering

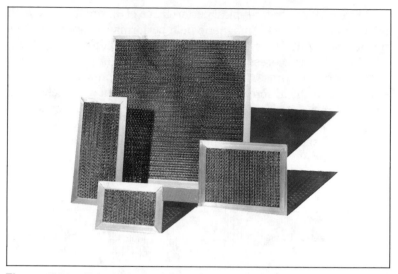

Figure 6.21—Shield Screen Mesh Ventilation Permitting Dust Removal by Oil Impregnation

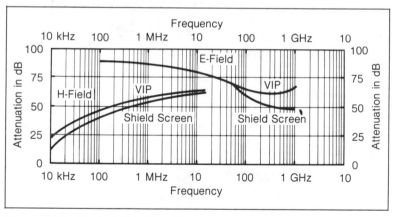

Figure 6.22—Typical Shielding Effectiveness of Shield Screen Mesh Vent Covers

6.28

When ventilation cover panels are used for convection cooling, it is common practice to employ a number of perforations in the panel rather than to use honeycomb or screen. The same die that cuts the cover panel also punches the holes. For this situation, the SE, A_{dB}, is:

$$A_{dB} = (kl_c/g) + 20 \log (C/D)^2 \qquad (6.14)$$

where,

    k = 27 for square perforations (opening holes)

        = 32 for circular perforations

    l_c = thickness of cover panel

    g = width of square perforations or diameter of circular perforations

    C = center-to-center spacing of perforations

    D = length of aperture for squares or diameter for circular apertures

The above measurement variables are valid in inches or centimeters.

If the cover plate perforations are not equally spaced, then C^2 in Eq. (6.14) may be replaced by $C^2 = A/N$, where A = area of aperture = D^2, and N = number of perforations or holes. For this situation, Eq. (6.14) becomes:

$$A_{dB} = (kl_c/g) - 20 \log(D^2 N/A) \qquad (6.15)$$

$$= (kl_c/g) - 10 \log N$$

Both the honeycomb and mesh covers are mounted over the ventilation opening with gasketing material.

6.5.1.3 Viewing Apertures

Another requirement which compromises the integrity of the basic shield material is the provision for panel meters, digital displays, scopes and other types of status monitors and readout presentations in the shielded housing or enclosure. (Such viewing apertures can also be windows in buildings or hospital shielded enclosures, canopies in aircraft and the like.) This is accomplished by either a laminated screen window or a conductive optical substrate.

6.5.1.3.1 Screen Windows

A shield screen window in which fine knitted wire is laminated between two layers of acrylic or glass may be used to block RF penetrations. Figure 6.23 illustrates this. The wire may be monel with typical aperture diameters of 0.051 mm (0.002", or 20 to 25 openings per square inch) or 0.114 mm (0.0045", or 10 to 13 openings per square inch). This corresponds to a low shadow area (15 to 20 percent blockage, giving good visibility). Typical SE is shown in Fig. 6.24. This approach is becoming less popular than that of the conductive optical substrate described below because of the less aesthetic aspects of the former. Furthermore, the screen window exhibits undesired diffraction-grating viewing problems under some conditions.

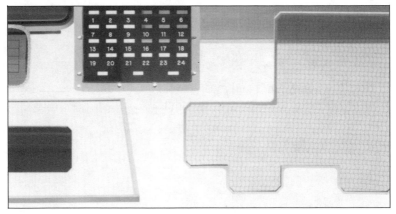

Figure 6.23—Representative Shield Screen Windows for Viewing

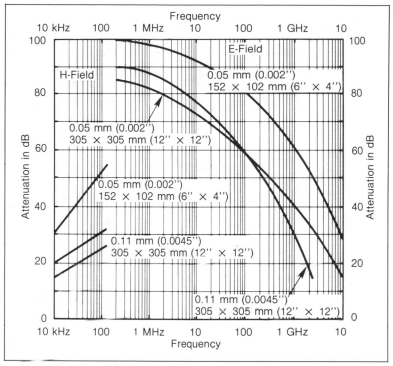

Figure 6.24—Shielding Effectiveness of Shield Screen Windows

6.5.1.3.2 Conductive Optical Substrate Windows

Another approach is available for providing shielding across apertures through which either optical viewing or the transmission of light is necessary. This approach involves the use of a conductive window, a technique in which a thin film of metal is vacuum deposited on an optical substrate. These conductive window designs such as shown in Fig. 6.25 are derived by establishing some or all six basic design parameters, as applicable:

1. Window material
2. Reticle requirements
3. Conductive coating
4. EMI gasketing
5. Optical coating and finishes
6. Framing and mounting

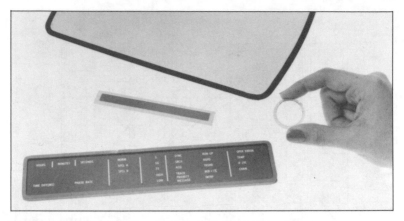

Figure 6.25—Typical Conductive Optical Viewing Panels

Most plastic and glass panel materials are suitable as substrates for the application of a conductive coating. In fact, it can be applied to almost any solid substrate, making it conductive for use as an EMI shield, switch element, filter or other active low-current-carrying device. Acceptable substrates are those which will not outgas in a high vacuum. A quick test may be made by checking the substrate for odor. If there is none, it is not likely to outgas.

The most common substrate materials are glass, acrylic, polycarbonate and fluorocarbon plastics. The substrates may be clear or colored as required by the application. There are no restrictions on substrate thickness. Curved or three-dimensional parts generally can be coated.

Most thermosetting and thermoplastic substrates have minute surface scratches produced in their normal manufacture. The application of the coating will make these more apparent, although actual user experience indicates that no functional problems will arise. Table 6.3 lists a sample of the large selection of substrate materials suitable for conductive coating.

Table 6.3—Substrate Materials Suitable for Conductive Coating

1. Glass, Plate
2. Plexiglass$_3$, thermoplastic acrylic
3. Glass, single-strength
4. Plexiglass, transparent, colorless
5. Glass, float
6. Plexiglass, frosted, colorless
7. Glass, tempered
8. Plexiglass, colored: yellow, amber, grey, bronze, green, red, blue
9. Glass, laminated, PVB film, safety
10. Homalite$_4$ thermosetting plastic
11. Glass, quartz
12. Kapton$_5$
13. Crystals, ruby
14. Mylar$_5$
15. Crystals, quartz
16. Abcite$_5$, coated acrylic
17. Vycor$_1$
18. Polycarbonate
19. Pyrex$_1$
20. Self-extinguishing Plexiglass
21. Lexan$_2$
22. Fluorocarbons

Trademarks of: 1. Corning, 2. General Electric, 3. Rohm & Hass, Homalite and 5. DuPont.

In the plastic substrate group, the most scratch-resistant materials are Abcite followed by Homalite.

Polarized filter laminate finishes are available for contract improvement. Coatings are unaffected by application of laminated circular polarizers. Translucent or frosted finishes, rough in surface nature, are available. They are best employed on the side opposite the conductive face. They can be used only for display of rear projections or where the object is extremely close to the window surface. Antireflective, vacuum-deposited coatings may be applied to windows before coating.

Figure 6.26[1] illustrates typical SE versus frequency for different film coating thicknesses on glass measured in surface resistance units of ohms per square (Ω/sq). Since the film thickness is deposited in microns, little contribution to attenuation comes from absorption loss. Accordingly, reflection loss, as previously shown in Figs. 6.6 and 6.7, is the media of attenuation. Above about the 1 MHz, the loss decreases with an increase in frequency at the rate of approximately 20 dB per decade and becomes negligible above about 1 GHz.

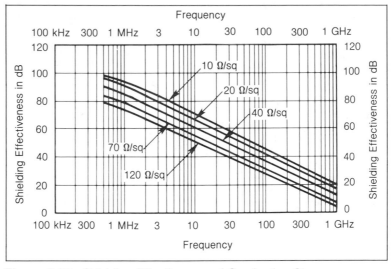

Figure 6.26—Shielding Effectiveness of Conductive Glass

Light transmission versus surface resistance for the above conductive glass is shown in Fig. 6.27. Transmission values of 60 to 80 percent correspond to resistances of about 10 to 100 Ω/sq. Thus, the values shown in Fig. 6.26 may now be compared with the attenuation data of the shield screen depicted in Fig. 6.24 specimens of comparable area. The shield screen is seen to be everywhere superior in SE, as shown in Table 6.4, in which the difference becomes greater with increasing frequency.* Thus, it is concluded that if significant VHF and UHF attenuation is required for viewing apertures, shield screen windows should be used. If the esthetics or other considerations do not permit this, conductive glass cannot be relied upon to provide significant RF attenuation to E-Fields much above 30 MHz.

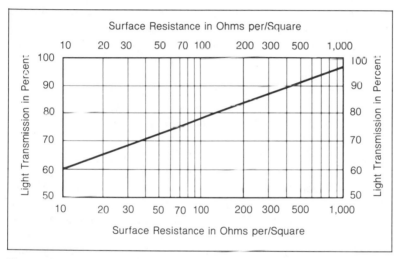

Figure 6.27—Light Transmission of Conductive Glass

---

*In reviewing the sales literature of Technical Wire Products, Inc. and other manufacturers, it is noted that the performance of conductive optical substrates for surface resistivities of the order of 10 Ω/sq more nearly approximates that of the screen. Because measurements were made by different observers, using different test setups on different specimens, variations are expected.

Table 6.4—Comparison of Shielding Effectiveness of Screen and Conductive Glass Windows

Frequency	Shield Screen	Conductive Glass	Superiority of Shield Screen
1 MHz	98 dB	74 - 95 dB	3 - 24 dB
10 MHz	93 dB	52 - 72 dB	21 - 41 dB
100 MHz	82 dB	28 - 46 dB	36 - 54 dB
1 GHz	60 dB	4 - 21 dB	39 - 56 dB

6.5.1.4 Control Shaft Apertures

Another aperture class which compromises the shielding integrity of an equipment housing or instrument panel is that resulting from shafts of potentiometers, tuning dials and control devices. Generally, an external metallic front panel or housing is either drilled or punched with sufficient clearing tolerance through which the control shaft extends. This results in a leaky aperture. The inside wall of the panel hole forms an outer conductor to a coaxially-situated internal control shaft (i.e., the inner conductor). In other words, potential EMI can enter or exit through this effective short coaxial line, and the extended shaft beyond the panel acts either as a receiving or radiating antenna.

To preserve the shielding integrity of otherwise leaky control-shaft situations, one method of minimizing the degradation of SE is to design a supporting bushing extender to act as a circular WBCO attenuator [cf. Eq. (6.11)]. For 100 dB attenuation in a circular waveguide, the length of the waveguide must be somewhat more than three times its diameter [$l_d/g > 3$ in Eq. (6.12)]. Figure 6.28 shows an acceptable use of a metal tube bonded to the wall containing the clearance aperture for control shafts.

If the preceding situation were implemented without regard to the control shaft properties and relations to the added metal tube, little improvement would result for typical metal shafts. This situation corresponds to a low-impedance coaxial line in which an intervening dielectric may result from contaminants such as oil films or oxides. To preclude this from happening, one of two techniques is followed:

1. Replace the metallic control shaft with a nonconductive shaft as shown in Fig. 6.28.

2. Use a cylindrical-shim EMI gasket between the shaft and tube.

The latter method does not require modification of existing control shafts.

6.36

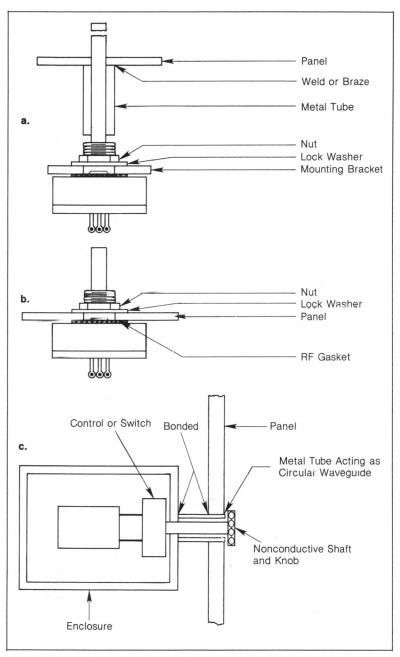

Figure 6.28—Use of Circular Waveguide in a Permanent Aperture for Control-Shaft EMI Leakage Control (Courtesy of USAFSC DH 1-4)

6.37

6.5.1.5 Indicator Buttons and Lamps

Some instruments or equipments require the use of push buttons, status indicator buttons or indicator lamps. These devices also provide another compromise of shielding integrity by virtue of the required apertures in a front panel or housing.

Two techniques are available to mitigate the EMI leakage through such devices:

1. Encase them in a shielded compartment behind the front panel when they are mounted as shown in Fig. 6.29. Feed-through capacitors or filter-pin conductors are used for hard wiring from outside the compartment to the buttons or indicator lamps since conducted EMI could exist on either side of the barrier.

2. Use special EMC-designed hardware where such devices are mounted directly to a front panel. Examples of this include wire mesh indicator lamps (which look like miniature photo flashbulbs). This mesh serves to reflect and absorb entering or exiting EMI energy.

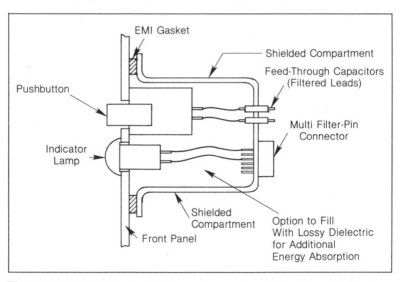

Figure 6.29—Shielded and Filtered Compartment Technique to Restore Shielding Integrity of Button and Lamp Apertures

6.5.2 EMC Gaskets

This section discusses the important class of techniques used to reinstate loss of shielding integrity at seams and joints where non-permanent fastening methods are permitted.

6.5.2.1 Gasketing Theory

Gaskets are employed for either temporary or semipermanent sealing applications between joints or structures such as:

Temporary RF Sealing Applications:
1. Securing access doors to enclosures, cabinets or equipments
2. Mounting cover plates or removal panels for equipment maintenance, alignment or other purposes

Semipermanent RF Sealing Applications:
1. Mounting either screen or conducted glass windows to housings containing electrical or electronic test equipment
2. Mounting honeycomb and other ventilation covers to enclosures, cabinets or equipment
3. Securing parallel members of an equipment housing to a frame structure using machine screws

All gaskets not of the spring-finger stock type, whether they seal EMI or higher-pressure fluid, make a container dunk proof or simply keep forced ventilating air from escaping at a door-to-cabinet joint, must conform to the unavoidable irregularities of the mating surfaces of a joint. Some examples are:

1. The joint between a garden hose and water faucet
2. The housing for an emergency radio or beacon to be dropped into the sea
3. The joint between the cover and enclosure of a radar pulse modulator

In each example, the joint has two relatively rigid mating surfaces, and neither surface is perfectly flat. When the surfaces are mated without a gasket, even high closing forces will not cause the two surfaces to mutually seal. Resultant gaps will allow leaks to exist. A gasket resilient enough to comply to both surfaces under reasonable force, however, will eliminate these leaks.

For example, through force alone, it is nearly impossible to prevent a leak in a garden hose coupling without a gasket. With a gasket placed in the hose fitting against a faucet, even hand torque results in a watertight joint. Realizing the same watertightness by accurate machining of both surfaces would be prohibitively expensive. Thus, in most cases, the least expensive way to obtain a tight joint (watertight, oil-tight or EMI-tight) is to make the mating surfaces to normal tolerances of flatness and rigidity, and then to add a gasket to compensate for mismatch between the two surfaces.

6.5.2.1.1 Joint Unevenness

The degree of misalignment or misfit of the mating surfaces is commonly called **joint unevenness** and is designated ΔH in Fig. 6.30a. It is the maximum separation between the two surfaces when they are just touching and in the limit becomes the sum of the peak irregularities of both surfaces. If the surfaces are not rigid, then the joint unevenness also includes any additional separation between the two surfaces due to joint distortion when pressure is applied.

Figure 6.30b shows the same joint with a gasket installed. The dashed lines indicate the gasket height, H_g, before compression. The compressed minimum gasket height, H_{min}, occurs at the point where the surfaces would touch without a gasket. Compressed maximum gasket height, H_{max}, is at the point of maximum joint separation. Thus, joint unevenness of the mating surface is:

$$\Delta H = H_{max} - H_{min} \qquad (6.16)$$

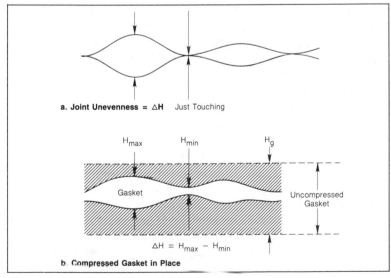

a. Joint Unevenness = ΔH Just Touching

H_{max} H_{min} H_g

Gasket

Uncompressed Gasket

$\Delta H = H_{max} - H_{min}$

b. Compressed Gasket in Place

Figure 6.30—Description of Joint Unevenness

6.5.2.1.2 Required Compression Pressure

Three factors determine the required compression pressure on a gasket: its resiliency, the minimum pressure required for a seal and the total joint unevenness. These are discussed below.

Resiliency

Resiliency is the amount by which a gasket compresses as a percentage unit of the original (uncompressed) gasket height divided by pressure in pounds per square inch (psi) or kilograms per square centimeter (kg/cm^2). A soft gasket will compress more than a hard gasket with the same applied pressure. Stated in another way, a soft gasket requires less pressure than a hard gasket to compress the same percentage of gasket height. For example, a sponge neoprene gasket might compress 10 percent under an applied compression pressure of 6 psi (17.4 kg/cm^2), but a solid neoprene gasket would require 40 psi (116 kg/cm^2) for the same 10 percent deflection as shown in Fig. 6.31.

Minimum Pressure for Seal

A gasket must at least make contact at the point of maximum separation between mating surfaces, i.e., $H_{max} \leqslant H_g$, as shown in Fig. 6.30. Actually, the pressure at this point must be a stated minimum amount to assure an EMI seal. This is easy to understand in the case of a high-pressure lubricating system. If there is not some required minimum pressure at the point of H_{max}, oil will leak between the flanges and the gasketing material. Thus, the pressure at the H_{max} point must be high enough to prevent leakage. For EMI gaskets, this minimum pressure (P_{min}) is determined by the pressure required to break through corrosion films and to make a suitable low-resistance contact. P_{min} is typically about 20 psi (58 kg/cm^2), but can be as small as 5 psi (15 kg/cm^2).

Average Pressure

The average pressure applied to the gasket must also be large enough to compress the overall gasket so that the difference between the minimum height and the maximum gasket height (determined by P_{min} from the previous paragraph) is equal to the joint unevenness, i.e., $\Delta H = H_{max} - H_{min}$, as previously presented in Eq. (6.16). In general, the average pressure should equal or exceed that corresponding to the average compressed gasket height, H_{avg}:

$$H_{avg} = (H_{max} + H_{min})/2 \qquad (6.17)$$

$$P_{avg} = (P_{min} + P_{max})/2 \qquad (6.18)$$

The required compression force, F, may be calculated from P_{avg} by determining the surface area, A, of the gasket to be sandwiched between the mating members:

$$F = P_{avg} \times A \qquad (6.19)$$

6.5.2.1.3 Required Gasket Height

To obtain the required EMI seal from a gasketed joint, the gasket height must meet these criteria:
1. The pressure at the point of maximum joint separation (H_{max}) must correspond to the minimum pressure to obtain the required EMI seal.
2. The difference between maximum and minimum compressed heights of the gasket must equal the joint unevenness of the mating surfaces.

If the average pressure available to compress the gasket is P_{avg}, the maximum pressure, P_{max}, is obtained from Eq. (6.17):

$$P_{max} = 2P_{avg} - P_{min} \qquad (6.20)$$

The perrcentages of uncompressed height corresponding to P_{min} and P_{max} in Fig. 6.31 are H_{max} and H_{min}, respectively. To calculate the required uncompressed gasket height, H_g, as a dimension:

$$H_g = \frac{\Delta H_{(in\ or\ cm)}}{\Delta H_{decimal}} \qquad (6.21)$$

Thus, the required height is the actual joint unevenness in inches or centimeters divided by the joint unevenness expressed in the decimal equivalent of percent gasket compression (see Fig. 6.31).

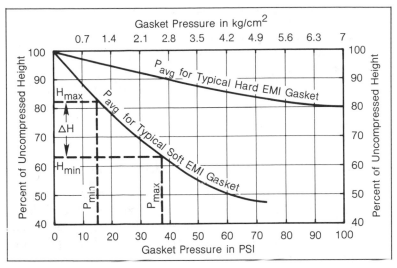

Figure 6.31—Typical Hard and Soft EMI Gasket Height vs. Pressure Relations

6.5.2.1.4 Compression Set

Some gaskets do not return to their original uncompressed height after release of compression. This is called **compression set**. It may be visualized by assuming that the lower curve shown in Fig. 6.31 applies for a particular soft gasket. When compression pressure is removed, the gasket returns to a lesser height whose properties might look somewhat like the upper curve in Fig. 6.31 (this is exaggerated for illustrative purposes). The importance of compression set depends upon how the gasket is to be used. The classes of use are now defined as:

1. Class A, permanently closed. Compression set is unimportant since the gasketed component will in all probability never be removed.
2. Class B, repeated identical open-close cycles (e.g., hinged door or symmetrical covers). Here, compression set problems are marginal; further examination of details, however, is indicated.

3. Class C, completely interchangeable (complete freedom to reposition gasket on repeat cycles; e.g., round gasket in waveguide). Since the compression set height at a point of maximum compression may end up being less than minimum compressed height, no contact at all would result between gasket and mating surfaces at this point. For Class C uses, do not reuse gaskets with compression set limits; instead, use a new gasket.

6.5.2.2 Gasket Types and Materials

There exists a plethora of EMI gasket types, shapes, binders and materials. In fact, the profusion of gaskets is so great that it is likely to be confusing to all but those who regularly specify or use them. To compensate, suppliers generally produce creditable application notes, design manuals and order guides.

For the convenience of discussion, EMI gaskets can be divided into four types:

1. Knitted wire mesh
2. Oriented, immersed wires
3. Conductive plastics and elastomers
4. Spring-finger stock

The last type is different in design and operation from the first three types. A brief summary of each is presented below, followed by a comparison of all four types.

6.5.2.2.1 Knitted Wire Mesh Gaskets

Figure 6.32 shows some examples of knitted wire mesh gaskets. They are made from resilient, conductive, knitted wire which resembles the outer jacket of a coaxial cable. Nearly any metal that can be produced in fine-wire form can be fabricated into these EMI gaskets. Typical materials used are monel; aluminum; silver-plated brass; and tin-plated, copper-clad steel. These gaskets may employ either an air core or, for maximum resiliency, they may use a spongy neoprene or silicone core. Cross sections may be round, rectangular or round with fins for mounting. They are generally applied to shielding joints having a periphery of greater than 102 mm (4") and cross sections between 1.6 and 19.1 mm (0.063" and 0.75").

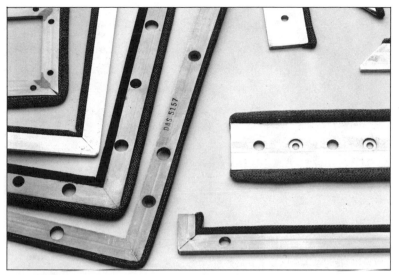

Figure 6.32—Typical Knitted Wire Mesh Gaskets

6.5.2.2.2 Oriented, Immersed-Wire Gaskets

Figure 6.33 shows some examples of oriented, immersed-wire gaskets. They are made with a myriad of fine, parallel, transverse-conductive wires whose parallel impedance across the gasket interface is very low. Each convoluted wire is insulated from its neighbor. They represent a density of about 1,000 wires per square inch (155 wires per square centimeter). Typical materials used are monel or aluminum embedded in either a solid silicone (hard gasket) or a sponge silicone (soft gasket) elastomer. As such, this gasket provides a simultaneous EMI and pressure seal. The embedded wires protrude a few mils on each side to assist in piercing any residual grease film and oxide on the surface of the mating numbers. This characteristic is especially good where aging and subsequent maintenance may result in a panel number being no longer clean and degreased. Available cross sections range from 3.175 mm square (0.125" square) to 15.875 × 12.7 mm (0.625" × 0.500"), and come in any length.

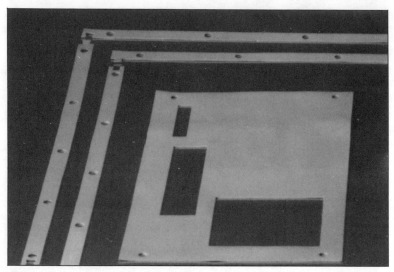

Figure 6.33—Typical Oriented Immersed-Wire Gaskets

6.5.2.2.3 Conductive Plastics and Elastomer Gaskets

Figure 6.34 shows some examples of conductive plastic and elastomer gaskets. They are made with a myriad of tiny silver balls immersed in a silicone rubber or vinyl elastomer binder and carrier. As such, this gasket provides a simultaneous EMI and hermetic seal. Offering volume resistivities from 0.001 to 0.01 ohm-meters (Ωm) and useful application over a wide range of temperatures, these gaskets are provided in sheets, die cuts, molded parts and extruded shapes. Some versions are operable down to cryogenic temperatures. They offer low closing pressures, low compression set and maintenance and long life.

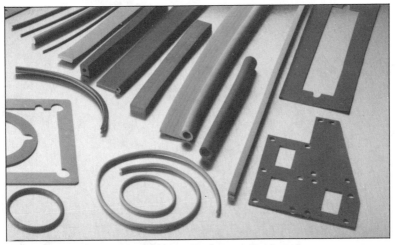

Figure 6.34—Typical Conductive Elastomer Gaskets

6.5.2.2.4 Spring-Finger Stock Gaskets

Figure 6.35 shows some examples of beryllium copper, spring-finger gaskets stamped into different configurations. Basically, gaskets similar to these were introduced over 40 years ago and were the first type of EMI gasket to appear on the market. Since there existed little elastomer technology in the 1940s, it is natural that joint unevenness could be accommodated by a series of individual fingers, each capable of flexing a different amount. Thus, shielded enclosures, cover plates and other heavy-duty applications used and still use this type of gasket.

Recent design changes, shown in Fig. 6.35, make this type of gasket more competitive with the others. The new spring-finger contact strips now offer self-adhesive backing to eliminate older mechanical fastening methods. They are available in a wide variety of sizes and shapes. The principal disadvantage is that the fingers tend to oxidize and break off.

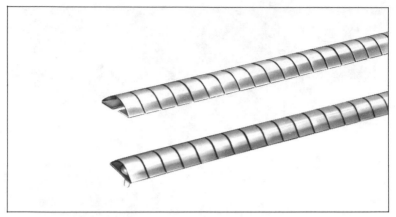

Figure 6.35—Typical Spring-Finger Strip Gaskets

6.5.2.2.5 Pressure-Sensitive, Foam-Backed Foil Gaskets

Another type of gasket differing from the above is a beryllium-copper foil backed by a highly compressible neoprene foam. The foam side, containing a synthetic-rubber, pressure-sensitive adhesive, is applied to cover plates. When placed over an electronics package containing shielded compartments, the foam-backed foil assumes the irregularities of the compartment heights, including outside plates to result in a continuous EMI seal. This 1.6 mm (1/16") gasket is available in sheets or in die-cut form. EMI SE of 90 dB to electric fields is claimed over the 1 kHz to 10 GHz frequency spectrum.

6.5.2.2.6 Comparison of Gasket Types and Materials

With the profusion of different gasket types and materials (over 1,000 variations), it is confusing to the design or specification engineer tasked with the responsibility of selecting one or more of the best candidates for his particular application. As a guide, Table 6.5 provides a comparison of some of the principal characteristics of EMI gaskets. (At least one manufacturer markets a pressure-sensitive, foam-backed shielding foil gasket, but insufficient information was available to include it in the table.) No single type is best for all applications. For example, those gaskets having relatively low cost tend to have relatively higher volume resistivity, resulting in a less impressive SE. Some gaskets are designed to operate down to cryogenic temperatures or up to 500°F (260°C), but not both. Since there exists several different methods of mounting, gaskets are available in sheets and strips, die cuts, molded shapes and extruded forms. At the risk of generalizing, conductive plastics and elastomers seem to offer the widest range of applications and price.

Table 6.5—Comparison of Gasket Types & Materials

Comparison Factors		Gasket Types	Knitted Wire Mesh	Oriented Immersed Wires	Conductive Plastics and Elastomers	Spring Finger Stock
Available Forms			Strips, Jointless Rings	Strips & Sheets. Jointless Rings Die-cut Shapes	Strips & Sheets. Die-Cut, Molded, Extruded Shapes	Strips
Size	Periphery		> 4'' (102 mm)			Any
	Cross Section	Min	0.063'' (1.6 mm)			
		Max	0.750'' (19 mm)			
Type of Seal	EMI only		Good to Excellent	Good	Also seals Hermetically	Good to Excellent
	EMI plus Hermetic		NA	Fair to Excellent	Good to Excellent	NA
Conductive Material			Silver Plate, Monel, Aluminum, Steel Sn/Cu/Fe	Monel, Aluminum	Many Tiny Silver Balls	Beryllium-Copper
Binder or Core Material			Rubber, Air Core, Neoprene, Silicone Sponge	Solid & Sponge-Silicone	Silicone or Plastic	NA
Temperature Range			Limited to Core	−70°F to 500°F (−57°C to 260°C)	−100°F to +400°F (−73°C to 204°C)	−65°F to 100°F (−54°C to 38°C)
Available Gasket Heights			0.062'' to 0.500''(1.57 to 12.7 mm)	0.062'' to 1.000''(1.57 to 25.4 mm)	0.020'' to 0.160'' (0.5 to 4.1 mm)	0.062'' to 0.400 (1.57 to 10.2 mm)
Joint Unevenness Accomodations			0.020'' to 0.160'' (0.5 to 4.1 mm)	0.010'' to 0.100'' (0.25 to 2.5 mm)	0.003'' to 0.030'' (0.076 to 0.76 mm)	0.035'' to 0.250'' (0.89 to 6.4 mm)
Compression Height Range						7:1
Compression Pressure			5 to 100 psi (14.5 to 290 kg/cm²)	20 to 100 psi (58 to 290 kg/cm²)	20 to 100 psi (58 to 290 kg/cm²)	
EMI Shielding Performance	10 kHz(H)		25 - 30 dB	> 45 dB	>35 dB	>10 dB
	10 MHz		>100 dB	>100 dB	>100 dB	>120 dB
	1 GHz		>90 dB	>90 dB	>95 dB	>100 dB
	10 GHz				>70 dB	>100 dB

6.5.2.3 Gasket Selection and Mounting

EMI gasket selection involves making suitable matches and tradeoffs between (a) available EMI gasket materials and their characteristics (see Table 6.5), and (b) equipment performance requirements and design constraints of mating surfaces. Gasket mounting (and hence selection) involves a number of alternatives.

6.5.2.3.1 Gasket Selection

In selecting suitable EMI gaskets for sealing mating surfaces, the major constraints (summarized in the following text) are:
1. Gasket characteristics
2. Application requirements and constraints
3. Price tradeoffs

Application Requirements
These usually are stated in the form of equipment performance specifications. They include amount of shielding, pressure sealing and environmental exposure (e.g., temperature, salt spray, ambient pressure and corrosive material).

Application Constraints
These usually are imposed by equipment housing design. They include space available, compression force, joint unevenness, contact surface characteristics and attachment possibilities.

Price Tradeoffs
The important tradeoffs between application requirements and constraints on one hand, and gasket characteristics and price on the other, are:
1. Gasket height and compressibility must be large enough to compensate for joint unevenness under the available force.
2. The gasket must be capable of providing the required EMI sealing and hermetic sealing (when applicable) when compressed by the available force.
3. There must be sufficient space for the gasket within the design limitations of the application.
4. The gasket must be attached or positioned by a means that fits in with the joint design.

5. The metal portion of the EMI gasket must be sufficiently corrosion resistant and compatible with the mating surfaces.
6. The EMI gasket must meet the temperature and other environmental needs of the equipment specifications.

Gasket manufacturers and suppliers provide design guide tables to assist the user to select the gasket most nearly meeting the application requirements and constraints.

6.5.2.3.2 Gasket Mounting

Several methods, summarized in the following text, are available to position the gasket to a metal mating surface:

1. Hold-in slots
2. Pressure-sensitive adhesives
3. Bonding the non-EMI portion of the gasket
4. Conductive adhesives
5. Bolt-through bolt holes
6. Special attachment situations

Hold-in Slots

This method is recommended if the slot can be provided at relatively low cost such as in a die casting. All solid elastomer materials, which embody the gasket material, are essentially incompressible. These products appear to compress because the material flows while it maintains a constant volume. Therefore, when these products are used in a slot, extra cross-sectional area must be allowed for the material to flow axially. At least 10 percent extra volume (more if possible) is recommended as shown in Fig. 6.36a.

Pressure-Sensitive Adhesives

This method of mounting is often the least expensive for attaching EMI gasket materials. Installation costs are substantially reduced with only a slight increase in gasket cost over a material without adhesive backing. Most sponge-elastomer materials are used for applications which do not require any hermetic sealing. The adhesive-backed rubber portion of this material serves only as an inexpensive attachment method for the EMI portion.

Bonding the Non-EMI Portion of the Gasket

Many good nonconductive adhesives are now available to bond an EMI gasket in position by applying the adhesive to the non-EMI

6.51

portion of the gasket. This can be insulated from the mating surfaces by a nonconductive material and is often a good way of
mounting EMI gaskets. This method is shown in Fig. 6.36b.

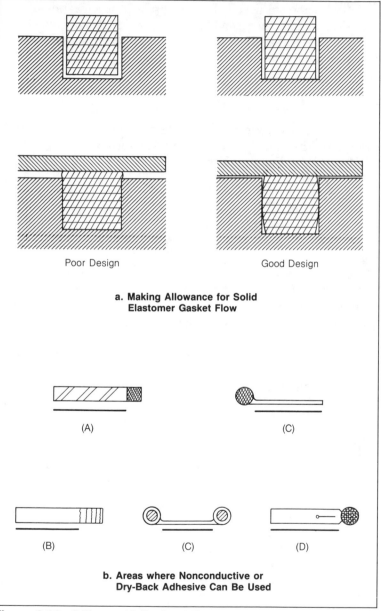

Poor Design   Good Design

**a. Making Allowance for Solid
Elastomer Gasket Flow**

(A)   (C)

(B)   (C)   (D)

**b. Areas where Nonconductive or
Dry-Back Adhesive Can Be Used**

Figure 6.36—Different Methods of Mounting Gaskets (continued next
page)

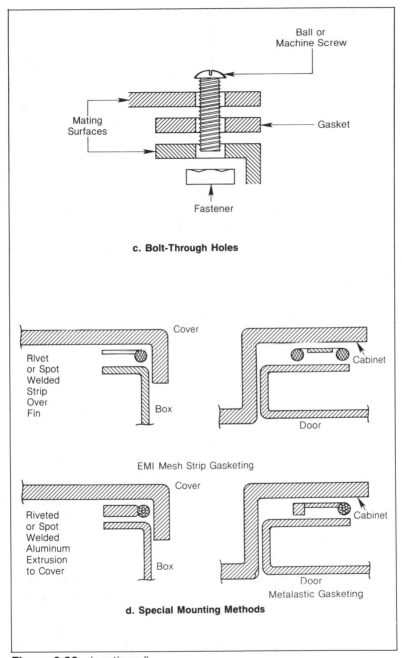

c. Bolt-Through Holes

EMI Mesh Strip Gasketing

Metalastic Gasketing

d. Special Mounting Methods

Figure 6.36—(continued)

The designer specifying nonconductive adhesive attachment must include adequate warnings in applicable drawings and standard procedures for production personnel. These cautions state that adhesive is to be applied to only the portion of the gasket material which is not involved with the EMI gasketing function. Experience indicates that installation workers, through carelessness or a misguided attempt to do a better job, will apply the nonconductive adhesive to the entire gasket, including the EMI gasket portion. It is not uncommon to hear, "This gasket would hold better if I glued all of it rather than half of it." This occurrence completely degrades the EMI performance.

Conductive Adhesives

Since good conductive adhesives can provide an adequate electrical contact between the EMI gasket and the mounting surfaces, they can also be used to mount the gaskets. However, the following cautions should be observed:

1. Most conductive adhesives are hard and incompressible. Thus, if too much adhesive is applied and it is allowed to soak too far into the EMI gasket material, the compressibility will be destroyed. Irregularly applied adhesive also has the effect of increasing joint unevenness.
2. The volume resistivity of the adhesive should be 0.01 Ωcm or less, preferably 0.001 Ωcm.
3. Most conductive adhesives do not bond well to either neoprene or silicone. This is why all products that have conductive paths in elastomer are poorly rated for conductive adhesive bonding by the manufacturers.
4. Applying a 3 to 6 mm (1/8" to 1/4") diameter spot of conductive adhesive every 25 to 50 mm (1" to 2") is preferred over a continuous bead.
5. Conductive epoxies will attach the gasket permanently. Thus, removal of an EMI gasket without destroying it is almost impossible.

Bolt-Through Bolt Holes

This is a very common and inexpensive way to hold gaskets in position as shown in Fig. 6.36c. For most products, providing bolt holes involves only a small initial tooling charge. There is generally no extra cost for bolt holes in the piece price of the gasket. Bolt holes can be provided in the fin portion of EMI strips or in rectangular cross section EMI strips if they are sufficiently wide, such as over 9.5 mm (3/8").

Special Attachment Situations

The knitted-mesh fins provided on some versions of EMI strips and the aluminum extrusions in aluminum gasketing were designed to attach these products as shown in Fig. 6.36d. The mesh fins could be clamped under a strip of metal which is held down by riveting or spot welding, or the mesh fins can be bonded with an adhesive or epoxy. The aluminum extrusions of aluminum gasketing can also be held in position by riveting or bolting.

EMI gaskets should be positioned so they receive little or no sliding motion when being compressed. This is illustrated in Fig. 6.37. The EMI gasket shown in Fig. 6.37a is subject to sliding motion when the door is closed. This may cause it to tear loose or to wear out quickly. In Fig. 6.37b, the gasket is subjected to almost pure compression-only forces. This is the preferred position.

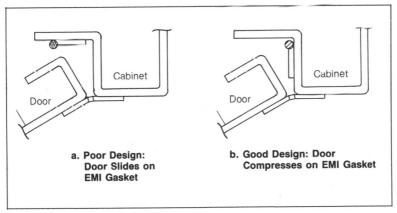

a. Poor Design: Door Slides on EMI Gasket

b. Good Design: Door Compresses on EMI Gasket

Figure 6.37—Proper Method of Mounting Gasket in Cabinet Door Well

6.5.3 EMC Sealants

This section discusses EMC shield integrity protection in the form of conductive epoxies and caulking.

6.5.3.1 Conductive Epoxies

Conductive epoxies are used to join, bond and seal two or more metallic mating surfaces. The silver-epoxy resins replace soldering and other bonding techniques and cure at room temperatures.

The conductive epoxy adhesives are used in the following applications:

1. Electrical connections to heat-sensitive components, capacitor slugs, ferrites and ICs
2. Electroluminescent panel connections
3. Bonding bus bars and strips to conductive glass
4. Bonding flanges to waveguides
5. Bonding waveguide sections
6. Bolt holes and fasteners on electronic enclosures
7. Joining dissimilar metals
8. Sealing IC packages against moisture and EMI
9. Repairing printed circuits
10. Interconnecting conductive metal gaskets
11. Field repairs to circuits
12. Permanent seam shielding
13. Sealing EMI shields

6.5.3.1.1 Preparation and Curing

Conductive epoxies are easily mixed on a volumetric basis, eliminating much time and equipment that would otherwise be necessary for weighing the components. Most epoxies can be prepared with either equal volumes or weights of the components. They are formulated with mixed viscosities to produce a light, creamy paste which is easily and accurately applied with standard dispensing equipment. Typical cure time is one day at room temperature or 30 minutes at 200°F (93°C).

6.5.3.1.2 Typical Properties

Depending upon the type of silver-epoxy resin used, typical volume resistivity will range from 0.001 to 0.02 Ωcm. The operating temperature range is about −80°F to +250°F (−62°C to 121°C). Shear strength is about 1,200 psi. Tensile strength varies with type, but averages about 2,500 psi (7,250 kg/cm^2). It exhibits excellent moisture resistance. The cured specific gravity is about two, suggesting its relative light weight for many payload-limited applications.

6.5.3.2 Conductive Caulking

Conductive caulking is used to EMI shield and seal two or more metallic mating members mechanically held by other means. Silver particles are suspended in resin to provide conductive sealing. Conductive caulking is used in the following applications:

1. Caulking EMI-shielded shelter panels
2. Caulking EMI-tight cabinets and enclosures
3. Improving joint and seam integrity of electronic enclosures
4. Protecting mating members of shielded conduits
5. EMI sealing and grounding bulkhead panel fittings
6. Moisture sealing of mating members
7. Adhering metal-foil tape to shielded room joints
8. Repairing damaged conductive gaskets
9. Caulking fasteners, panels and handles

6.5.3.3 Preparation and Use

The conductive caulking compounds, like all EMI sealants and bonds, require surfaces which are thoroughly degreased and cleaned of oxide coatings. The caulking may be applied with conventional caulking guns and dispensing equipment such as small bead-orifice syringes, or it may be applied with a spatula or putty knife.

The caulking is free of any corrosive binders. It is used at room temperatures, and most caulking will not cure (permanently non-setting). This feature permits easy disassembly of caulked parts for mobility and maintenance.

6.5.3.4 Typical Properties

Depending upon the type of silver resin used, typical volume resistivity will range from 0.005 to 0.02 Ωcm. The operating temperature is -80°F to 400°F (−62°C to 204°C). Moisture resistance is excellent. The final specific gravity is about 1.8, suggesting its relative light weight for many payload-limited applications.

6.5.4 Conductive Grease

Conductive grease is not an immediate member of the EMI gasket and sealant family discussed in this chapter. However, it is related in that one of its functions is to provide a low-resistivity contact to mating members. Here, mating members may engage and disengage more often than in most EMI gasketing applications, excepting finger stock used in shielded enclosures.

Conductive grease is a low-resistivity, silver-silicone grease which contains no carbon or graphite fillers. The material will maintain its electrical and lubricating properties over a broad environmental range. These conditions include high and low temperatures, resistance to moisture and humidity and inertness to many chemicals, ozone and radiation. Most conductive greases exist in the form of a viscous paste which can be applied at elevated operating temperatures to vertical or overhead surfaces without dripping or running.

Conductive grease is used on power substation switches and in suspension insulators to reduce EMI noise. It also reduces make-break arcing and pitting of the sliding metal contact surfaces of switches, and fills in pitted areas with silver-silicone. In addition, normally-closed switches are prevented from sticking due to corrosion or icing. The grease is effective in maintaining a continuous electrical path between contact surfaces which must be free to move. These include ball-and-socket connections of power insulators which, if allowed to arc, can generate EMI. Conductive grease is designed to maintain low resistance electrical contact and thereby maintain equipment operating over extended environmental conditions, helping to deliver continuous electrical service.

Conductive grease is used on the contacting surfaces of circuit breakers and knife-blade switches. It reduces localized overheating and hot spots, thereby in turn maintaining the spring properties of the blades and the current rating of the switch or breaker at original equipment level. Conductive lubrication prevents freeze-up in operating equipment and permits restoration of marginal or discarded breakers to rated capacity.

Typical volume resistivity is about 0.02 Ωcm. Operating temperature range is $-65°F$ to $450°F$ ($-54°C$ to $232°C$). Conductive grease provides excellent moisture resistance and has no corrosive effect on metals. Its pot life is unlimited, and unused portions can be returned to the container.

6.6 References

1. Lasitter, Homer A., "Low Frequency Shielding Effectiveness of Conducted Glass," *IEEE Transactions on Electromagnetic Compatibility*, Vol. EMC-6, No. 2, July, 1964, pp. 17-30.

6.7 Bibliography

Blake, Christopher L., "Electromagnetic Problem Associated with the Use of Advanced Composites," *IEEE International EMC Symposium Record* (New York: IEEE, 1976).

Butler, C.M., "A Review of Electromagnetic Diffraction by Small Apertures in Conducting Surfaces," *IEEE International EMC Symposium Record* (New York: IEEE, 1978).

Casey, K.F., "Advanced Composite Materials and Electromagnetic Shielding," *IEEE International EMC Symposium Record* (New York: IEEE, 1978).

Chow, T.Y. and Adams, A.T., "The Coupling of Electromagnetic Waves through Long Slots (with Editorial Summary)," *IEEE Transactions on EMC*, Vol. EMC-19, no. 2, May 1977.

Duncan, D., "A Low Cost Method of RFI/EMI Shielding," *EMC Technology, October 1984, p. 75.*

EMI Shielding Engineering Handbook (Woburn, Mass.: Chomerics, Inc., 1986).

Furman, S., "Conductive Coating Considerations for Electronics Engineers," *EMC Technology,* October 1984, p. 49.

Graves, B.D.; Crow, T.T. and Taylor, C.D., "On the Electromagnetic Field Penetration through Apertures (with Editorial Summary," *IEEE Transactions on EMC*, Vol. EMC-18, no. 4, November 1976.

Kunkel, G.M., "Introduction—An Overview of Problems Associated with the Design of EM Shields," *IEEE International EMC Symposium Record* (New York: IEEE, 1976).

Kunkel, G.M., "Introduction to Shielding of Electromagnetic Fields and the Application of EMI/RFI Gaskets," *IEEE International EMC Symposium Record* (New York: IEEE, 1975).

Liao, S.Y., "Light Transmittance and RF Shielding Effectiveness of a Gold Film on a Glass Substrate," *IEEE Transactions on EMC,* Vol. EMC-17, no. 4, November 1975.

Liao, S.Y., "Light Transmittance and RF Shielding Effectiveness of a Metallic Film Coating on a Plastic Substrate," *IEEE International EMC Symposium Record* (New York: IEEE, 1977).

Liao, S.Y., "RF Shielding Effectiveness and Light Transmittance of Copper or Silver Film Coating on Plastic Substrate," *IEEE International EMC Symposium Record* (New York: IEEE, 1976).

Madle, P.J., "Panel Assemblies, Honeycomb Air-Vent Assemblies and Thin Metallic Foils," *IEEE International EMC Symposium Record* (New York: IEEE, 1976).

Mauriello, A.J., "Selection and Evaluation of Conductive Plastics," *EMC Technology,* October 1984, p. 59.

Mendez, H.A., "Shielding Theory of Enclosures with Apertures (with Editorial Summary)," *IEEE Transactions on EMC,* Vol. EMC-20, no. 2, May 1978.

MIL-G-83528, "Gaskets, Shielding, Elastomer Electrical, EMI/RFI, General Specification for."

MIL-STD-285, "Attenuation Measurements for Enclosures, Electromagnetic Shielding, for Electronic Test Purposes, Method of."

Mullin, A.J., "Penetration of Shielding Barriers, Low-Frequency Effects," *IEEE International EMC Symposium Record* (New York: IEEE, 1978).

Nablo, J.C. and Tolokan, R.P., "Stainless Steel, the Invisible Conductive Filler for Plastics," *EMC Technology,* October 1984, p. 43.

Neff, R., "Trends in Applications of Advanced Composites in Military Hardware," *IEEE International EMC Symposium Record* (New York: IEEE, 1976).

Nichols, F., "Trends in Applications of Advanced Composites in Military Hardware," *IEEE International EMC Symposium Record* (New York: IEEE, 1976).

Rostek, P.M., "Techniques of Shielding and Filtering Digital Computers for EMI Emissions and Susceptibility," *IEEE International EMC Symposium Record* (New York: IEEE, 1975).

Simon, R.M., "EMI Shielding with Aluminum Flake Filled Polymer Composites," *Proceedings of the 1984 International Symposium on EMC,* Tokyo, Vol. 1, p. 732.

Simon, R.M. and Stutz, D., "Test Methods for Shielding Materials, *EMC Technology,* October 1983, p. 39.

Soltys, J.J., "Maintaining EMI/RFI Shielding Integrity of Equipment Enclosures with Conductive Gasketing," *IEEE International EMC Symposium Record* (New York: IEEE, 1978).

Szekers, B., "Building Attenuation: A Factor to Improve EMC Calculations," Electromagnetic Compatibility 1977—Second Symposium and Technical Exhibition on EMC, Montreux, Switzerland, June 28-30, 1977.

Various articles, EMC Technology, special issue on shielded plastics, October-December, 1985.

Wait, J.R., "Comments on 'Shielding Performance of Metallic Cylinders and Comments by C.W. Harrison, Jr. and Reply by D. Schieber'," *IEEE Transactions on EMC,* Vol. EMC-16, no. 1, February 1974.

Walker, W.F. and Heintz, R.E., "Conductivity Measurements of Graphite/Epoxy Composite Laminates at UHF Frequencies," *IEEE International EMC Symposium Record* (New York: IEEE, 1977).

White, D.R.J., *Electromagnetic Shielding Materials and Performance* (Gainesville, Virginia: Interference Control Technologies, Inc., 1980).

Wilson, P.F. and Ma, M.T., "A Study of Techniques for Measuring the Electromagnetic Shielding Effectiveness of Materials," NBS Technical Note 1095 (Boulder, Colorado: National Bureau of Standards, 1986).

Wu, Chang-Yu and Cheng, D.K., "Field Distribution Inside a Box with Aperture," *IEEE International EMC Symposium Record* (New York: IEEE, 1977).

Wu, T.K. and Tsai, L.L., "Shielding Properties of Thick Conducting Cylindrical Shells," *IEEE Transactions on EMC,* Vol. EMC-16, no. 4, November 1974.

Chapter 7

Filters

An electrical filter is a network that transforms an input signal in some specified way to yield a desired output signal. The signals may be considered in the time domain or in the frequency domain and, correspondingly, the output requirements of the filter may be stated in terms of time or frequency. In the latter case, a filter is often a frequency-selective device which passes signals of certain frequencies and blocks or attenuates signals of other frequencies.

A frequency-selective filter is one that passes signals whose frequencies are in certain ranges or bands, called the **passbands**, and blocks or attenuates signals whose frequencies are in other ranges, called the **stopbands**. The nature of the amplitude function or the loss function may be used to classify the various types of filters according to the location of their passbands and stopbands. An ideal filter is one which has a linear phase response in its passband, zero loss in its passband and infinite loss in its stopband. Although an ideal filter response is physically unrealizable, it is possible to design filters that have low loss in the passband and significant attenuation in the stopband.

The most often encountered types of frequency-selective filters are defined as follows:

1. A **low-pass filter** is one with a single passband between 0 Hz and a cutoff frequency, f_C, with all frequencies higher than f_C constituting the stopband. The bandwidth is defined as BW $= f_C$.

2. A **high-pass** filter is one with a single passband extending from cutoff frequency f_C to infinity, with $f_C > 0$.

3. A **bandpass** filter is one with a passband between two lower and upper cutoff frequencies, f_L and f_U, with f_L being greater than 0 and f_U less than infinity. The two stopbands are 0 to f_L and f_U to infinity. The bandwidth is defined as $B = f_U - f_L$.

4. A **band-reject** filter is one with a stopband ranging between f_L and f_U and two passbands, 0 Hz to f_L and f_U to infinity. (They are also called **band-elimination** or **band-stop** filters.)

5. An **all-pass** filter is one which passes all frequencies equally well. That is, the amplitude response is constant for all frequencies, with the phase response generally a function of frequency.

Electrical filters used to control EMI may be divided into two types: communication or wave filters used in intersystem EMI control and power line filters used in intrasystem EMI control. This chapter presents a summary of communication filters and EMI power line filters.

Filters are used to control intersystem EMI in one or more of the following ways:

1. Selectivity in superheterodyne receivers via the IF bandpass response formed by a combination of a fixed-tuned filter and IF amplifier

2. RF selectivity in superheterodyne receivers via a tunable preselector which both suppresses the image response and provides additional out-of-band rejection to strong unwanted emissions

3. RF selectivity in both tuned radio-frequency (TRF) and crystal-video receivers via either tunable preselectors or fixed-tuned, bandpass filters to reject out-of-band emissions

4. Band-rejection or notch filters in receivers to suppress EMI from strong adjacent-channel emissions or for use in wide-band amplifiers

5. Low-pass (or high-pass) filters to protect the front end of receivers and other susceptible circuits or equipments from emissions existing above (or below) the base band of operation

6. High-power, low-pass filters in the output of transmitters to suppress unwanted harmonic radiations

With few exceptions, these intersystem filters are characterized by having equal input and output impedances in the passband of their operational networks. Typical impedance levels are 50 or 72 Ω, but 600 Ω or other impedances occasionally may be used at audio frequencies, and 300 Ω may be used at VHF and lower UHF. They are also characterized by protecting low-level susceptible circuits, especially receivers, having sensitivities ranging from − 150 dBm to about − 30 dBm. One exception is item 6, in which transmitter outputs may operate with peak-pulse powers from + 20 dBm to about + 100 dBm. Here, filters must have very low insertion losses in the passband to readily dissipate any absorbed power.

Filters are also used in intrasystem EMI control in one or more of the following ways but with a different emphasis:

1. RF suppression of unwanted signals otherwise entering or exiting the power lines of ac power mains
2. RF isolation of common-impedance coupled circuitry, such as several networks fed from common power supplies, via low-pass filters
3. Conducted broadband noise suppression from power tools, appliances, industrial machinery, office equipment and other devices developing transients due to arc discharge at the brush-commutator interface of motors
4. Conducted broadband noise suppression from non-motor, transient-developing devices such as fluorescent lamps, electric ignition systems, industrial controls, relays, solenoids and other switching action devices
5. Protection of susceptible devices such as transducers, computers and electro-explosive devices

With some exception, intrasystem filters are characterized by having unequal input and output impedances when installed in their operational environments. For example, impedance sources of power mains are frequently less than 1 Ω at low frequencies, while their loads represent high impedances. Furthermore, both source and load impedances are frequency dependent. Emphasis for intrasystem filtering is to suppress the source rather than protect susceptible circuits such as mentioned in item 5.

7.1 Filter Performance Characteristics

Filters may range in rate of attenuation beyond cutoff frequency from 20 dB per decade, corresponding to a simple feedthrough capacitor or series inductor, to 200 dB or more per decade for a 10-stage (or more) inductance-capacitance (LC) network. This is illustrated in Fig. 7.1 for n = 1 to 20 stages. The abscissa is shown in normalized units of frequency with the 0 dB notch cutoff frequency appearing in the upper left corner.

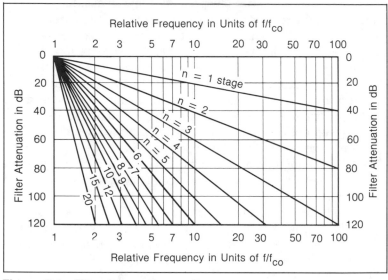

Figure 7.1—Filter Attenuation vs. Frequency

One danger in using Fig. 7.1 as a general model of stopband rejection of filters is that (1) attenuations of more than 100 dB are difficult to achieve due to input-output (I/O) crosstalk coupling, and (2) the filter may completely degenerate in performance a few decades above cutoff due to parasitics. Where open circuitry is used, involving neither connectors nor filter shields, it is common to have direct I/O coupling on the order of 40 to 60 dB, especially in miniature and integrated circuits. Regarding parasitics, unless special precautions are taken in the filter design and fabrication, a filter may offer little to no attenuation at two or more decades above cutoff.

As a result of the foregoing, it is recommended that installation-measured attenuation performance data always be used wherever available. The next best data source is either nominal performance data or attenuation measurements of the filter when out of its installed position. Finally, if all else fails and the only known data are (1) the filter type and number of stages, (2) the physical size and whether a shield and connectors are used and (3) the general installation plan, then the maximum performance suggested in Table 7.1 may be used.

Table 7.1—Model of Maximum Average Attenuation of Electrical Filters Outside Thier Passbands

Rejection-Band Frequency Range	Shield and Connectors	Shield Only	No Shield or Connectors
Microminiature or IC Filters			
$f_{co} \leqslant f \leqslant 10\ f_{co}$	NA	60 dB	50 dB
$10\ f_{co} \leqslant f \leqslant 100\ f_{co}$	NA	40 dB	30 dB
$f > 100\ f_{co}$	NA	20 dB	10 dB
Communication Filters (No Special EMI Precautions)			
$f_{co} \leqslant f \leqslant 10\ f_{co}$	80 dB	70 dB	60 dB
$10\ f_{co} \leqslant f \leqslant 100\ f_{co}$	60 dB	50 dB	40 dB
$f \geqslant 100\ f_{co}$	40 dB	30 dB	20 dB
Communication Filters (EMI Hardened)			
$f_{co} \leqslant f \leqslant 10\ f_{co}$	90 dB	NA	NA
$10\ f_{co} \leqslant f \leqslant 100\ f_{co}$	80 dB	NA	NA
$f > 100\ f_{co}$	70 dB	NA	NA
Power-Line Filters $\leqslant$ 10 A (EMI Type)			
$f_{co} \leqslant f \leqslant 10\ f_{co}$	80 dB	NA	NA
$10\ f_{co} \leqslant f \leqslant 100\ f_{co}$	80 dB	NA	NA
$f > 100\ f_{co}$	70 dB	NA	NA
Power-Line Filters $>$ 10 A (EMI Type)			
$f_{co} \leqslant f \leqslant 10\ f_{co}$	100 dB	NA	NA
$10\ f_{co} \leqslant f \leqslant 100\ f_{co}$	100 dB	NA	NS
$f > 100\ f_{co}$	90 dB	NA	NA

7.2 Power Line Filters

Most conducted forms of intrasystem EMI result from equipment or systems sharing the same source of ac power mains. Here, an electrical noisy source may pollute the power distribution wiring by injecting broadband emissions into wires which also feed other potentially susceptible equipments. Another mechanism involves **common-impedance coupling** in which two or more circuits are fed from a common regulated or unregulated power supply. On the other hand, it frequently develops that a potentially susceptible equipment sharing a common power bus with an EMI source may not be affected thereby. Rather, the power line may have been electromagnetically contaminated to begin with, and the mutual connection thereto is academic.

Power lines feeding a given area can act as pickup antennas for broadcast, shortwave, HF, FM, TV, communication emissions, radar, etc., across the frequency spectrum. Furthermore, these lines can conduct wideband ignition and overhead fluorescent lamp noise, harmonics from the ac power mains, nearby office and machine noise and virtually any electrical noise which couples to the input power lines by electric, magnetic or electromagnetic means. Since these potentially disturbing noises can cause EMI to sensitive equipment, it is paramount to filter them out, preferably before they get to user areas. This is accomplished by the use of power line filters. They must pass the dc, 60 Hz and/or 400 Hz power-main frequencies with very little attenuation (e.g., 0.2 dB or less) and provide perhaps 60 dB or more attenuation from a low frequency such as 10 kHz to 1 GHz, 10 GHz or other frequency, depending upon the EMI bounds of potential susceptibility.

If EMI is to be removed from a power line, one first must establish if the EMI is common-mode or differential-mode. These modes are defined as follows:

Common-Mode EMI:

A signal which appears equally and in phase on both black (hot) and white (neutral) lines, but not on the green (safety) line. Thus, there exists little or no differential EMI between black and white lines, but a significant EMI exists between either black or white and green lines. To be effective, filters must be placed between black and green or white and green, or both.

Differential-Mode EMI:

A situation in which noise exists on either the black or white line, but not both, changing the potential of one line relative to the other. To be effective, filters must be placed between the black and white lines, with or without involving the green line.

To address the above EMI situations, filters are generally placed between both the black and green lines and the white and green lines. If the EMI is common-mode, it will be filtered out to the green line, whereas if it is differential-mode, it will be filtered out between the black and white lines quite independently of the presence of EMI on the green line. However, should all three wires contain the same common-mode noise, EMI will not be removed by the above filtering action. A differential-mode input circuit (the situation for nearly all networks) will greatly reduce the impact of nearly equal common-mode inputs.

Attenuation over a prescribed frequency range is perhaps the most common way of specifying filter spectrum performance and is also one of the most abused terms in EMI filters. Filter attenuation refers to the ratio of output voltages, before and after filter insertion, as a function of frequency. Attenuation, A, expressed in decibels (dB) is derived in the following manner:

$$A_{dB} = 10 \log (P_b/P_a) \tag{7.1}$$

where,

P_b = power delivered to the load before insertion of the filter

P_a = power delivered to the load after insertion of the filter

Since the load impedance, Z, remains unchanged in both the "before" and "after" cases, the respective powers of Eq. (7.1) may be substituted by their voltages and impedances:

$$P = (V^2/Z_1) \tag{7.2}$$

Thus,

$$A_{dB} = \log \left(\frac{V_b^2/Z_1}{V_a^2/Z_1} \right) \tag{7.3}$$

$$= 10 \log (V_b/V_a)^2$$

$$= 20 \log (V_b/V_a) \tag{7.4}$$

Note that Eq. (7.4) represents true insertion loss expressed in dB and requires that measurements at any frequency be made by removing and inserting the filter.

For power filters, however, the above attenuation measurement method is invalid because the impedances of both the source and terminations of real-life installations are significantly different from the 50 Ω used in a convenient measuring system. Since the filter's frequency response behavior is impedance-level dependent, the test method is nearly meaningless except to compare filters on a relative basis. For example, 115 Vac power supply mains may provide a 100 A service with not more than 5 percent voltage drop. This corresponds to an impedance source, Z_g, at 60 Hz of:

$$V_g = e_g - IZ_g = e_g(1 - 0.05)$$

or,

$$Z_g = \frac{0.05e_g}{I} = \frac{0.05 \times 115 \text{ V}}{100} = 0.06 \text{ } \Omega \qquad (7.5)$$

For a 55 A load, for example, the termination impedance, Z_L, is:

$$Z_L = V_L/I_L = 110/55 = 2 \text{ } \Omega \qquad (7.6)$$

for,

$$V_L \text{ in volts and } I_L \text{ in amperes}$$

The previous example illustrates one typical low-frequency power-source impedance of 60 mΩ and a termination load of 2 Ω at 60 Hz. Now, if a typical single-element filter (e.g., capacitor or inductor) were measured in an impedance system of this amount and compared to the 50 Ω system generally used for rating purposes, the results of the spectrum attenuation performance would be significantly different. Figure 7.2 illustrates this situation in which either a single shunt capacitor (C = 0.63 μF) or a single series inductor (L = 1.6 MHz) results in a cutoff frequency of 10 kHz when measured in a 50 Ω system. Beyond cutoff, the rate of attenuation is 6 dB per octave or 20 dB per decade. Thus at 10 MHz, for example, the measured attenuation would be 60 dB.

If the series-inductor or shunt-capacitor filter element were placed in the above Z_g = 0.06 Ω and Z_L = 2 Ω system, which is more closely related to an actual installation, entirely different results would follow. Figure 7.2 shows that the cutoff frequency of the capacitor filter has increased from 10 kHz to 4.3 MHz and the attenuation thereafter is 52 dB poorer than when measured in a 50 Ω system. In a like manner, Fig. 7.2 shows that the cutoff frequency of the inductor filter has increased to 490 kHz, and the attenuation thereafter is 33 dB poorer than when measured in a

50 Ω system. Thus, it is concluded that attenuation measurements made with fixed terminating impedances are somewhat meaningless. Both source and load impedance are pertinent to the filter's performance.

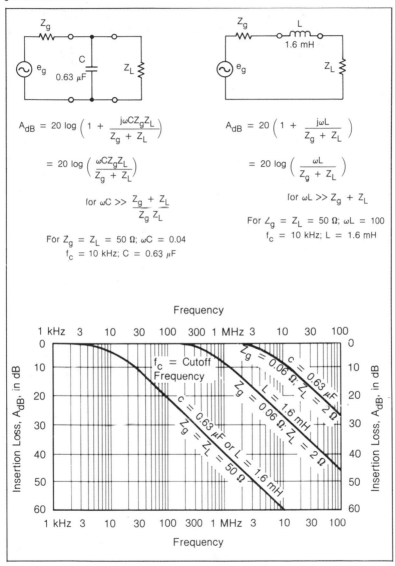

Figure 7.2—Attenuation (Insertion Loss) of a Single-Element Filter in a 50 Ω and in a Low-Impedance Source and Load System

It develops that the actual performance situation for three or more stages of LC filtering is not quite as bad as implied above for one stage. Depending upon both source and termination impedance, one or more filter stages may be offered as sacrificial elements to establish either a source or load impedance or both. This results in a different number of equivalent filter stages, n, as shown in Table 7.1.

Figures 7.3 through 7.6 illustrate different filter configurations which may be selected to work into or out of either a high or low source or load impedance (relative to 50 Ω). All filters shown are of the low-pass type (i.e., they use series inductors and shunt capacitors). The philosophy is to connect either (1) a filter series inductor to a low-impedance source or (2) a shunt capacitor to a high-impedance source such that the impedances of source and filter elements are about equal at the desired cutoff frequency.

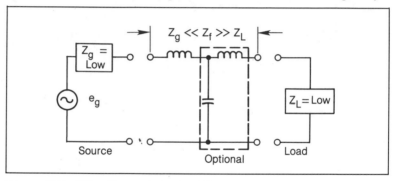

Figure 7.3—Filter Network for Low Source and Load Impedances

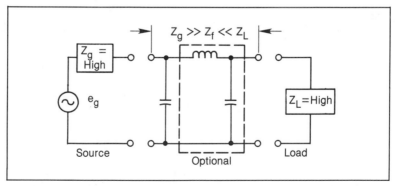

Figure 7.4—Filter Network for High Source and Load Impedances

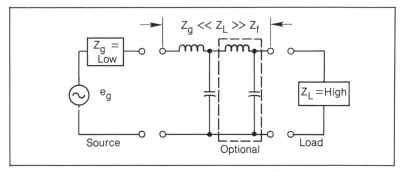

Figure 7.5—Filter Network for Low Source and High Load Impedances

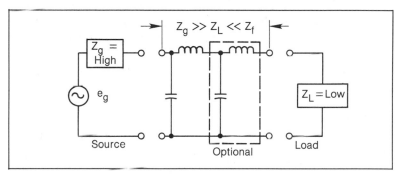

Figure 7.6—Filter Network for High Source and Low Load Impedances

Similarly, a series inductor should face a low-impedance load, and a shunt capacitor should face a high-impedance load. This assures optimum use of filter elements and in part compensates for some source and load impedances of typical power mains, varying over wide ranges starting at about 100 times the power frequencies.

Crosstalk between the filter input and output terminals may be significant (60 dB or even lower, i.e., greater coupling) unless an infinite baffle is used between the two terminal pairs. Consequently, when the manufacturers rate the filter attenuation with frequency, it is understood that the filter is mounted in a suitable bulkhead. For shielded enclosure filters, where attenuation is rated up to 100 dB or more, the entire assembly is shielded in a permeable case. Thus, after filtering, there is reasonable assurance that there will be no cross coupling of magnetic, electric or electromagnetic fields to the filter output leads which are located inside the enclosure.

Nearly every EMI power line filter on the market is of the low-pass type, passing dc to 60 Hz or 400 Hz power mains, and cutting off above these frequencies. There are a number of manufacturers of power line filters which are used either to filter the power mains into an open area, a shielded enclosure or to an instrument, equipment or device.

7.3 Isolation Transformers

Typical transformers isolate one circuit from another while magnetically coupling desired energy from one to the other. Such a transformer is adequate for use with low-gain circuits or insensitive instruments. However, if the transformer must couple into high-gain circuits or sensitive instrumentation, noise potentials between the primary circuit and ground must be prevented from affecting the secondary circuits due to capacitive and resistive coupling between the transformer's windings.

Traditional techniques for keeping electrical noise from reaching the transformer secondary, e.g., the standard Faraday shield (a grounded conducting foil between the windings), will divert most of the primary noise current to ground. Electrical noise still can be coupled into the secondary because of the electrostatic field around the Faraday shield. Unique box shielding techniques employed in some isolation transformers effectively overcome this problem. There, the impedances between windings are extremely high.

Isolation transformers must be conservatively rated so that they remain cool under full-load conditions and exhibit good voltage regulation, i.e., they do not generate a common-mode impedance coupling problem. They are especially designed for these important applications:

1. Isolating sensitive instrumentation from noisy power lines
2. Providing maximum common-mode noise rejection
3. Isolating noisy equipment from noise-sensitive equipment when they share the same power line
4. Minimizing differential-mode noise (noise across winding) resulting from common-mode noise (noise between winding and ground)
5. Rendering complete electrostatic blocking: When the complete shield surrounding the transformer secondary is extended around the equipment being guarded, shielding effectiveness is maximized.

7.3.1 Common-Mode Noise Rejection

Box shielding techniques employed in the construction of isolation transformers achieve maximum impedance between windings while offering a very low-impedance path for common-mode noise to ground. To accomplish this, the leakage resistance is kept at a high level (e.g., 10,000 MΩ) and the effective interwinding capacitance is maintained at the low values stated below. This provides a significant advantage over the typical isolation transformer using traditional shielding methods as shown in Figs. 7.7 and 7.8.

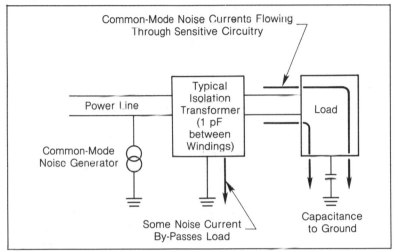

Figure 7.7—Typical Isolation Transformer

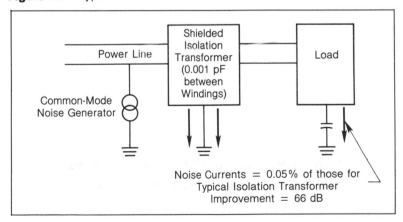

Figure 7.8—Specially-Shielded Isolation

7.13

Three basic levels of quality shielding performance that are commercially available are rated in terms of interwinding capacitance.
1. 0.005 pF $(5 \times 10^{-15}$ F)
2. 0.001 pF $(1 \times 15^{-15}$ F)
3. 0.0005 pF $(0.5 \times 10^{-15}$ F)

Common-mode noise voltage, V_c, in dB is measured relative to input noise voltage, E, as shown in Fig. 7.9. Measurements are made over the audio frequency band from 20 Hz to 50 kHz.

For each level of interwinding capacitance, C_x, the common-mode noise rejection is shown below. V_c is measured across C, a 0.01 μF capacitor to ground. Thus:

C_x in pF	$V_c/E = C_x/C$
0.005	-126 dB
0.001	-140 dB
0.0005	-146 dB

For noise across capacitances to ground other than C = 0.01 μF, add -20 dB to above numbers for each factor of 10 increase in C, or add $+20$ dB for each factor of 10 decrease in C.

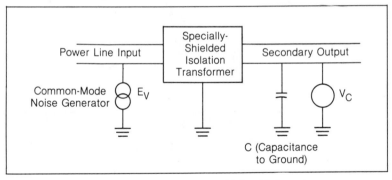

Figure 7.9—Measuring Common-Mode Noise Voltage

7.3.2 Suppression of Differential-Mode EMI Generated by Common-Mode Noise Input

The shielding should minimize differential mode EMI caused by a common-mode noise source. Figures 7.10 and 7.11 illustrate how the special shielding techniques achieve a reduction of differential-mode voltage greater than 40 dB below the value attainable by the normally best box shielding methods. The ordinary shielded isolation transformer (including a box-shielded type) will itself generate a differential-mode voltage between either primary or secondary terminals due to a common-mode noise voltage appearing between any of these terminals and ground.

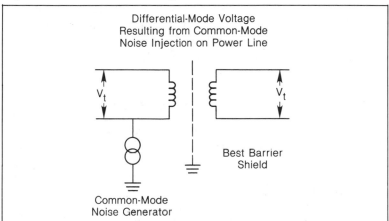

Figure 7.10—Normal Transverse Voltage from Common-Mode Noise

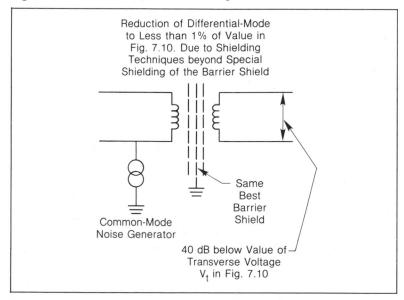

Figure 7.11—Reduction of Transverse Noise Voltage with Special Shield

7.15

In Fig. 7.10, differential-mode appears as a voltage (V_t) across both primary and secondary windings of an isolation transformer when a common-mode noise causes current to flow in the primary winding and from there to ground via capacitance to a grounded shield. Similarly, common-mode noise generated by noisy equipment in the secondary environment can be transformed into a differential mode which appears across the secondary and is magnetically coupled to the primary, thereby contaminating the power line. A good isolation transformer can reduce this differential-mode to less than 0.004 times the amount encountered in standard box-shielded isolation transformers.

7.3.3 Magnetic-Noise Suppression

Instrumentation in the secondary circuits often is sensitive enough to be affected by electromagnetic noise fields emanating from the isolation transformer itself. In competent EMI design practices, precautions are taken in isolation transformers to keep these stray fields to a minimum. For example, a typical magnetic flux density level at a distance of 46 cm (18") from the geometric center of the transformer is 0.1 gauss (140 dBpT). This flux decreases with the cube of the distance. Thus at a 2 m distance, the level would be about 119 dBpT.

7.3.4 High-Frequency Performance

The performance of EMI-type isolation transformers is in part predicated upon keeping the secondary capacitance to ground to a definable level. However, it is possible that this capacitance may become self-resonant at some high frequencies such that the secondary impedance is high. Under these conditions, the common-mode rejection will become very poor.

One solution is to use EMI filters to suppress EMI at the higher frequencies. However, these may unbalance the secondary and result in an undesirable differential mode. A better solution would be to twist the secondary output lines and cover them with lossy EMI suppressant tubing. This converts any HF differential-mode noise to heat.

7.4 Lossy Line Filters

Lossy line filters are based on one of two principles of operation: dielectric losses and permeable losses. In Fig. 7.12, the dielectric medium intentionally corresponds to a high dissipation factor or loss tangent. The equivalent circuit shown in Fig. 7.13 shows that the dielectric conductive losses convert the RF energy into heat. In ordinary transmission lines, these losses are negligible, since low dissipation factor dielectrics are used, but for EMI filter design, the high dissipation factor corresponds to a cutoff frequency of about 10 MHz when used in a 50 Ω system. Thus, lumped-element EMI filters which would fail to perform above, say, 100 MHz, perform well to 10 GHz when the lossy graphite is used as a potting compound.

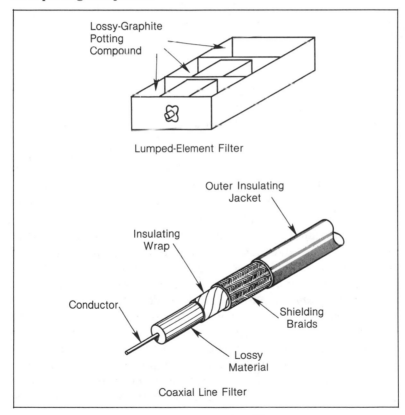

Figure 7.12—Two Examples of Lossy Line Filters

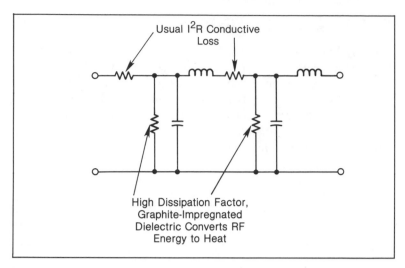

Figure 7.13—Equivalent Circuit of Fig. 7.12

The other technique is based on an extension of some of the advantages of ferrite beads and rods, and it eliminates some of the disadvantages. Here, a flexible tubing material may be slipped over an insulated or uninsulated conductor of any standard size as shown in Fig. 7.14. Because a lower permeability of the flexible tubing is used compared with beads and rods, little attenuation of EMI is offered below about 10 MHz. On the other hand, no saturation or resonant-frequency properties are exhibited, and attenuation above 100 MHz becomes significant.

The operating principle of the EMI suppressant tubing is similar to that of beads and rods. Having an equivalent permeability of about 10, the self-inductance of a wire covered with the tubing is increased so that it acts as a one-stage distributed filter with series inductance as shown in Fig. 7.15. By avoiding the alternating high and low incremental inductance of beads and rods, the tendency to radiate between elements is avoided. The suppressant tubing is also available with a shielded layer of metalized mylar for capacitance shielding (electric-field pickup) at lower frequencies. The tubing exhibits no saturation to any dc, 60 Hz or 400 Hz power line current when shipped over power main busses for low-pass filter operation.

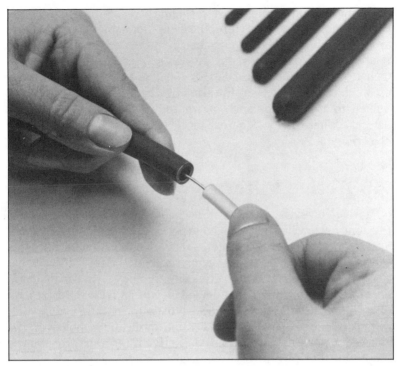

Figure 7.14—Permeable Flexible Wire Tubing (Courtesy of Lundy Electronics)

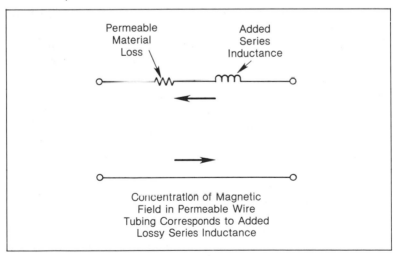

Permeable Material Loss

Added Series Inductance

Concentration of Magnetic Field in Permeable Wire Tubing Corresponds to Added Lossy Series Inductance

Figure 7.15—Equivalent Circuit of Fig. 7.14

7.19

A combination of the above techniques results in a dissipative coaxial-line, ferrite filter. Here, the dielectromagnetic loss tangents are very high, the relative permeability is in excess of 10^3 and the relative permittivity is about 10^5. Schiffress has shown that attenuations on the order of 20 dB at 100 kHz and 100 dB at 10 MHz are achievable.[1] However, the use of this kind of a ferrite filter is limited to applications such as squib initiators (electro-explosive devices) where a low dc resistance between conductors is not objectionable.

7.5 Active Filters

Passive, low-pass, LC filters will become very large as the cutoff frequency is lowered into the audio region. While the capacitor can be chosen with lower values (e.g., 0.01 μF), the inductor becomes enormous in size and weight. Thus, an inductorless filter is needed for ELF applications. An active filter is a device in which operational amplifiers transfer the impedance of an RF network to appear as an inductor. Active parallel or twin-Tee tuned audio networks are one example. For power line applications, however, the main power will have to bypass the active filter translator if large supply currents are to be processed (EMI removed).

When the passband power cannot pass through transistors in active filters, then verters and separators may be used. The term **verter** represents an impedance converter or inverter with impedance transformations having either positive or negative values. The separator passes no energy except for those frequencies for which the feedback of the active elements is made inoperative by low-power filters.

Active low-pass power line filters have been designed with supply currents up to 100 A. In the case of one 24 Vdc unit furnishing 30 A, 40 dB of attenuation existed at 1 Hz and 60 dB at 20 Hz. The physical size compared to a comparable passive LC network is about 10^{-3} in ratio.

7.6 References

1. Schiffress, P., "A Dissipative Coaxial RFI Filter," *IEEE Transactions on EMC*, Vol. EMC-6, January, 1964, pp. 55-61.

7.7 Bibliography

Converse, M.E., "Time Domain Filters—Principles and Applications," *IEEE International EMC Symposium Record* (New York: IEEE, 1975).

Favors, H.A., "Trade-Off Considerations in the Design of Wave Filters for TEMPEST, EMP and Communications Applications," *IEEE International EMC Symposium Record* (New York: IEEE, 1975).

Ha, I.W. and Yarbrough, R.B., "A Lossy Element for EMC Filters," *IEEE Transactions on EMC,* Vol. EMC-18, no. 4, November 1976.

Kendall, C.M. and Hebson, B., "Microfiltering of I/O Cables: A New Solution to High Frequency I/O Cable Radiation and Susceptibility Fields," *IEEE International EMC Symposium Record* (New York: IEEE, 1978).

Mayer, F., "Distributed Filters as RFI Suppression Components," *IEEE International EMC Symposium Record* (New York: IEEE, 1975).

Mayer, F., "RFI Suppression Components: State of the Art; New Developments," *IEEE Transactions on EMC,* Vol. EMC-18, no. 2, May 1976.

Neufeldt, D., "Radiation Masks Conducted RFI Power Line Filter Testing," *EMC Technology,* April-June 1984.

Rostek, P.M., "Techniques of Shielding and Filtering Digital Computers for EMI Emissions and Susceptibility," *IEEE International EMC Symposium Record* (New York: IEEE, 1975).

Schlicke, H.M., "Assuredly Effective Filters," *IEEE Transactions on EMC,* Vol. EMC-18, no. 3, August 1976.

Schneider, L.M., "Modeling Takes the Guesswork out of Filter Design and Selection," Power Sources Users Conference, Anaheim, CA, October 1984.

Schneider, L.M., "Noise Source Equivalent Circuit Model for Off Line Converters and Its Use in Input Filter Design," IEEE Symposium on EMC, Arlington, VA, August 1983.

Schneider, L.M., "Take the Guesswork Out of Emissions Filter Design," *EMC Technology,* April-June, 1984.

Schneider, L.M., "Theory and Application of Power Line EMI Filters," *EMC Expo 86 Symposium Record* (Gainesville, Virginia: Interference Control Technologies, Inc., 1986).

Chapter 8

EMC Rules, Regulations and Standards

There are many situations in both civilian and military applica
tions where it is necessary for a number of equipments to work
together in close proximity. To avoid EMI in these situations, it
is necessary to limit the emissions and susceptibilities of the individual equipments. By properly limiting emissions and susceptibilities, it is possible for equipments to operate together in a dense
environment with a minimum of EMI problems.

EMC rules, regulations and standards have been developed and
are imposed on equipments and systems intended for both civilian
and military applications. This chapter introduces and reviews
government rules and regulations pertaining to industrial, consumer and commercial products. This chapter also introduces and
reviews current military directives, regulations and standards
relating to EMI. The most commonly used documents, with ex-
planatory text, can be found in Volumes 9 through 12 of this handbook series.

8.1 FCC Rules and Regulations

The Federal Communications Commission (FCC) regulates all
industrial, commercial, consumer and other non-federal government use of the radio frequency spectrum within the United States

of America. The authority for the FCC to impose rules and regulations on industrial, commercial and consumer devices which may radiate electromagnetic energy originates from the Communications Act of 1934 and its subsequent amendments.

For many years, the FCC has controlled the generation of electromagnetic emissions which might interfere with communications. As communication equipment became more complex and utilized larger segments of the frequency spectrum, and as the spectrum became more crowded with radiation from electronic, industrial, commercial and consumer equipment, the FCC increased the scope and effectiveness of its regulations.

RF devices subject to FCC authority and included under the rules and regulations range from radio transmitters used in broadcasting, common carrier, marine, aviation and land-mobile services to restricted radiation devices (e.g., radio receivers, CATV systems) and low-power communication devices such as wireless microphones, phonograph oscillators, radio-controlled garage door openers and radio-controlled models and toys. Also included are industrial, scientific and medical (ISM) equipment such as ultrasonic instruments, industrial heating, medical diathermy, RF stabilized arc welders and miscellaneous emitting equipment.

Public Law 90-379 amends the Communications Act of 1934, as amended, to give the Federal Communications Commission authority to prescribe regulations for the manufacture, import, sale, shipment and use of devices which cause interference which is potentially harmful to radio reception. Previously, the FCC could only pursue the offending users of such devices, who often were helpless and innocent parties with little or no technical knowledge. With few exceptions, the manufacturers and distributors of offending devices such as walkie talkies, garage-door openers, industrial heaters and some licensed transmitters could not be held accountable. However, the manufacturer is generally in a much preferred position to take early corrective action to avoid electrical interference.

Public Law 90-379 extends the responsibility for EMI control from the users to manufacturers, importers, vendors, shippers, etc. With this added muscle, the FCC can now issue Cease and Desist Orders to any offending party. If necessary, it can get a court injunction for compliance or even petition the Justice Department to prosecute the offenders. In 1982, legislation was enacted that provided the FCC with the additional authority to regulate the susceptibility of consumer electronic products.

The FCC Rules and Regulations are contained in the Code of Federal Regulations, Title 47—Telecommunication. Title 47 is composed of five volumes as shown in Table 8.1. Each volume is further organized into parts and subparts. The parts of the FCC Rules and Regulations that are of most interest from the standpoint of EMI are Parts 15 and 18, which are contained in Volume 1. Table 8.2 lists the various subparts of Parts 15 and 18.

Table 8.1—FCC Rules and Regulations

Volume 1	Parts 0 through 19
Volume 2	Parts 20 through 39
Volume 3	Parts 40 through 69
Volume 4	Parts 70 through 79
Volume 5	Parts 80 to End

Table 8.2—FCC Parts 15 and 18

Part 15: RF Devices
    Subpart A: General
    Subpart B: Administrative Provisions
    Subpart C: Radio Receivers
    Subpart D: Low-Power Communication Devices:
        General Requirements
    Subpart E: Low-Power Communication Devices:
        Specific Devices
    Subpart F: Field Disturbance Sensors
    Subpart G: Auditory Assistance Devices
    Subpart H: TV Interface Devices
    Subpart I: Measurement Procedures
    Subpart J: Computing Devices, Class A and B
Part 18: ISM Equipment
    Subpart A: General Information
    Subpart B: Applications and Authorizations
    Subpart C: Technical Standards

Part 15 deals specifically with RF devices. As shown in Table 8.3, this includes a variety of products. The specific portion of Part 15 that is of most interest to the electronics industry is Subpart J, which deals with computing devices. The FCC rules define a computing device as "Any electronic device or system that generates and uses timing signals or pulses at a rate in excess of

10,000 pulses (cycles) per second and uses digital techniques...."
Computing devices are divided into two classifications as defined
below.

Class A: A computing device that is marketed for use in a commercial, industrial or business environment, exclusive of a device which is marketed for use by the general public, or which is intended to be used in the home.

Class B: A computing device that is marketed for use in a residential environment notwithstanding use in commercial, business and industrial environment. Examples of such devices include, but are not limited to, personal computers, calculators and similar electronic devices that are marketed for use by the general public.

Table 8.3—FCC Rules and Regulations, Part 15: RF Devices

Subpart C—Radio Receivers (Restricted Radiation Devices)
- FM Broadcast Receivers
- VHF TV Broadcast Receivers
- UHF TV Broadcast Receivers
- Other 30-890 MHz Receivers
- LO Radiation
- Sweep-Circuit Radiation
- Other Radiated Emissions
- Power Line Conducted Emisssions

Subpart D and E—Low-Power Communication (Restricted Radiation) Devices
- Wireless Microphone
- Phonograph Oscillator
- Biomedical Telemetry
- Radio-Controlled Door Openers
- Radio-Controlled Toys and Models
- 100 mW Walkie Talkies
- Carrier-Current Systems

Subpart F—Field Disturbance (Restricted Radiation) Sensors
- Microwave Intrusion Sensors
- Production-Line Sensing and Counting

Subpart G—Auditory Training (Restricted Radiation) Devices
- For Auricular Instruction

Subpart H—Class I TV (Restricted Radiation) Devices
- Cable Connected at TV Frequencies
- Carrier-Modulated Video Recorders
- Carrier-Modulated TV Camera Video

  Excludes:
- Cable TV Equipment
- Equipment Producing Signals at Other than TV Frequencies

Subpart J—Computing Equipment

Both classes of computing devices must comply with limits on radiated and conducted emission limits as specified in Table 8.4. Furthermore, the device must also meet FCC requirements on labeling and instruction manuals.

Table 8.4—FCC Limits for Computers: Part 15J

Class A Radiation Limit
(Computers for Use in Industry/Commercial Areas)

f(MHz)	d(m)	E(μV/m)	E (dBμV/m)
30-88	30	30	30
88-216	30	50	34
216-1,000	30	70	37

Class A Conduction Limit

f(MHz)	RF Voltage (μV)	V (dBμV)
0.45-1.6	1,000	60
1.6-30	3,000	70

Class B Radiation Limit
(Computers for Use in Residential Areas)

f(MHz)	d(m)	E(μV/m)	E (dBμV/m)
30-88	3	100	40
88-216	3	150	43
216-1,000	3	200	46

Class B Conduction Limit

f(MHz)	RF Voltage (μV)	V(dBμV)
0.45-30	250	48

Note: For conducted limits, a 13 dB reduction is allowed if the noise is demonstrated to be impulsive broadband.

Several different procedures are specified by the FCC for demonstrating that a device complies with the regulations. Among these procedures are:
1. Verification
2. Certification
3. Type Acceptance
4. Type Approval

The specific procedures to be followed depend on the device classification.

For devices requiring **verification**, it is necessary to measure the radiated and conducted emissions to verify performance within the FCC limits, and the test records must be kept on file and submitted to the FCC if requested. The verification process applies to all Class A computing devices and those Class B computer devices considered to present a minimal interference potential.

For devices that require **certification**, it is necessary to measure the radiated and conducted emissions to demonstrate that they comply with the applicable FCC limits. A test report must be submitted to the FCC which reviews the test data and grants the certification if the test results are acceptable. The FCC reserves the right to request that the manufacturer provide the equipment to the FCC laboratory to check the test results and certify compliance. Certification is applicable to most Class B computing devices, low-power communication devices and most other devices regulated under FCC Part 15 with the exception of radio transmitters.

Type acceptance applies to licensed radio transmitters. For devices requiring type acceptance, the test data must be submitted to the FCC by the manufacturer or prospective licensee. The FCC reviews the test data and grants the type acceptance. The FCC may request the equipment be supplied to an FCC laboratory for measurement to check compliance.

For equipment requiring **type approval**, the equipment must be provided to the FCC, which performs the tests and grants the type approval. Type approval applies to certain low-power communication devices, medical diathermy equipment, etc.

8.2 European Regulations and Standards

The nations of Western Europe are bound together under the Treaty of Rome, which requires harmonization of national standards so that equipments manufactured in one country will conform with the national standards and requirements of other nations. The western European nations are members of the European Common Market (European Economic Community or EEC) and are bound by Common Market regulations. In matters concerning technical standards, an EEC directive is superior to national law.

EEC directives exist for electromagnetic emissions from household appliances and fluorescent lights and telecommunications terminal equipment (EEC Directives 82/499, 82/500 and 86/361). Under the Treaty of Rome, International Electrotechnical Commission (IEC) standards prevail in instances where specific EEC directives do not exist, and the applicable IEC standards have the presumption of law.

8.2.1 International Special Committee On Interference (CISPR)

When standards are required, the IEC selects a professional organization like the Institute of Electrical and Electronics Engineers (IEEE) to develop the standard. In areas of great importance, like emissions control, the IEC will not use an independent voluntary organization to write a standard. Rather, it will set up its own standards writing subgroup within CISPR (French initials for the "International Special Committee on Radio Interference"). CISPR serves as a committee dedicated to interference-related issues within the IEC. Since the mid-1930s, this organization has been putting together international standards on EMI compliance.

The standards are written by subcommittees whose power and influence to shape international law is quite significant. When their work is finished, documents are forwarded to the IEC for eventual adoption as an IEC Standard. If accepted by the ministers of the EEC, the document can become embodied in an EEC Directive. Many CISPR documents, through this procedure, have become elevated to EEC Directive status.

The makeup of the subcommittees reveals much about the European attitude toward radio interference, and the way that they classify the equipment is important in understanding national regulations. The subcommittees are as follows:

1. Subcommittee A works on radio interference measurements and statistical methods. It prepares specifications on measuring apparatus as well as methods.
2. Subcommittee B works on developing standards for measuring interference from industrial, scientific and medical (ISM) equipment and was involved in drafting the standard for digital computing equipments.

3. Subcommittee C is involved with interference from overhead high-voltage power lines, high-voltage equipment and electric traction systems.
4. Subcommittee D deals with interference relating to motor vehicles and internal combustion engines.
5. Subcommittee E concerns itself with interference of radio receivers.
6. Subcommittee F deals with interference from motors, household appliances, lighting apparatus and similar devices.
7. Subcommittee G has authority over what CISPR terms "Information Technology Equipment (ITE)" and equipment "which predominantly generates a multiplicity of periodic binary electrical/electronic waveforms which can be unintentionally coupled via mains, cables, signals or other leads, or by direct radiation [and] can constitute a potential source of interference to radio reception." The phrase is reminiscent of the definition of "computing equipment" in FCC Part 15, Subpart J, and was designed to encompass all electronic data processing (EDP) equipment, giving Subcommittee G jurisdiction over these devices.

The United States has a major voice in CISPR and therefore, indirectly, a major voice in the content of European EMI regulations. The United States National Committee to the IEC is an American National Standards Institute (ANSI) organization. An ANSI Technical Advisory Group (TAG) has been assigned to CISPR.

There are three directives of the EEC which are of direct interest to manufacturers of electronic equipment. There are also several CISPR specifications of importance.

The Europeans have traditionally treated equipment which had the potential to cause interference as being in one of five categories, corresponding to the CISPR committees. These are:
1. Industrial, scientific and medical (ISM) equipment, construed under European law to include EDP equipment (Note that this differs dramatically from the United States ISM classification.)
2. Vehicles, motor boats and spark ignited engine-driven devices
3. Radio receivers and television receivers
4. Electrical appliances, portable tools and similar electrical apparatus
5. Fluorescent lamps and luminaries

Of these, categories 4 and 5 are currently covered by EEC Directives, and it is therefore EEC law, not national law, that applies. Unfortunately, measurement procedures in Europe often attempt to cover the devices mentioned in all five categories above, causing great confusion. For example, West German VDE standards had to be rewritten because of newly adopted EEC Directives 82/499, covering household appliances, and 82/500, covering fluorescent lights.

CISPR 22 covers ITE, which it divides into Class A and Class B equipment. Class A devices are defined as "equipment which satisfies the Class A interference limits and Class B devices are defined as equipment that satisfies the Class B interference limits." CISPR 22 mentions that countries may restrict the sale of Class A equipment to commercial environments, but it does not require it.

The document describes recommended limits for **terminal interference voltage**, known in the United States as **conducted interference**. The limits are shown for both quasipeak and average-mode detection. Devices which meet the average limit while in the quasipeak or peak mode are considered to comply. However, a device which is tested in the average mode and meets the average limits must be tested a second time in the quasipeak mode to the quasipeak limits. The device must pass both to be considered compliant. Conducted interference is specified for the ac line only.

CISPR 22 also sets limits for radiated field strength. A quasipeak detector is specified, although peak measurements are also acceptable. The test distance is specified as 30 m for Class A equipment and 10 m for Class B, but a shortened test distance, as short as 3 m, can be used.

8.2.2 West German Regulations on Emissions From Digital Devices (VDE)

West Germany was one of the first industrialized nations to regulate emissions from computing devices. In the process of developing the regulations for electronic data processing equipment, Germany has relied heavily on the private organization known as the German Institute of Electrical Engineers or VDE. Standards VDE 0871, VDE 0875, VDE 0876 and VDE 0877 describe the procedures and the EMI limits applied to electronic devices in Germany, including EDP equipment.

West Germany specifies radiated and conducted emission limits for both Class A and Class B devices. The VDE limits are provided in Figs. 8.1 and 8.2. A Class A device is defined simply as a device that meets the less stringent Class A limits. A Class B device is one that complies with the stricter Class B limits. Equipments which meet the Class A limits are subject to strict scrutiny. Each individual user of a Class A device must obtain an "Individual Permit" to use the device. Equipments which meet the Class B limits are issued a "General Permit," and it is not necessary for each user to obtain an "Individual Permit."

Germany requires radiated (broadcast into space) and conducted (passed down the ac line) measurements, referring to them as **RFI field strength** and **RFI voltage** measurements, respectively. The limits differ considerably, however, from those in the United States, and they go down to lower frequencies. Class A limits go down to 150 kHz, while Class B go all the way down to 10 kHz. Furthermore, both radiated and conducted measurements have to be run down to these low frequencies, whereas the United States requires radiated emission measurements to be run only down to 30 MHz.

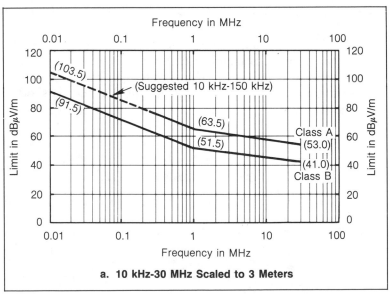

a. **10 kHz-30 MHz Scaled to 3 Meters**

Figure 8.1—VDE Radiated Emission Limits (continued next page)

8.10

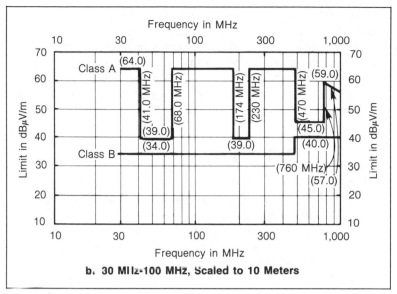

b. 30 MHz-100 MHz, Scaled to 10 Meters

Figure 8.1—(continued)

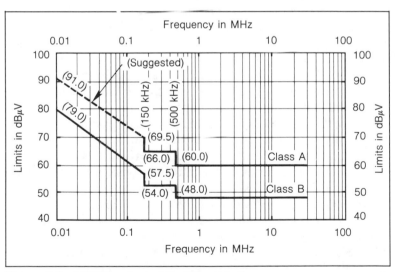

Figure 8.2—VDE Conducted Emission Limits

8.11

The requirement that radiated emissions cover 10 kHz to 30 MHz for Class B devices imposes a serious restraint on devices such as monitors and printers. Conducted signals must also be measured on I/0 cables as well as the power mains. Fortunately, this cumbersome requirement has many exceptions and does not apply to cables which interconnect parts of a system and are two meters in length or less, or which are properly designed shielded cables.

8.3 MIL-STD-461

MIL-STD-461 is a DoD issued standard entitled "Electromagnetic Interference Characteristics Requirements for Equipment." As of this writing, the current version is MIL-STD-461C. It covers the requirements and test limits for the measurements and determination of the electromagnetic interference (EMI) emission and susceptibility characteristics of electronic, electrical and electromechanical equipments and subsystems which are used independently or become part of other subsystems or systems.

Figure 8.3 illustrates the various categories of radiated and conducted emissions and susceptibilities that are required for MIL-STD-461. The requirements and test limits contained herein are applicable to the extent specified in the individual equipment or subsystem specification contract issued. Accordingly, when invoking this standard, the requirements and limits contained herein must be analyzed to verify suitability and applicability for the specific procurement. When it is known that the equipment or subsystem will encounter maximum operational conditions, more or less severe than the levels contained herein, the individual specification may modify the limits in this standard.

The requirements specified in MIL-STD-461 are established to:
1. Ensure that interference control is considered and incorporated into the design of equipment and subsystems
2. Provide a basis for evaluating the electromagnetic compatibility of equipments and systems which will operate in a complex electromagnetic environment

MIL-STD-461 is typically used in conjunction with the following standards which round out the MIL-STD-460 series:
1. MIL-STD-462: Electromagnetic Interference Characteristics, Measurements of
2. MIL-STD-463: Definitions and System of Units, Electromagnetic Interference Technology

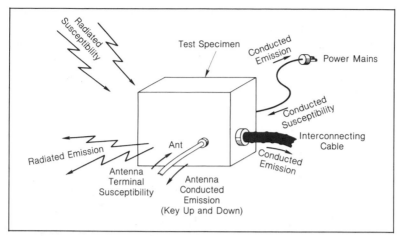

Figure 8.3—Conceptual Illustration of Interference and Susceptibility of Test Specimen

MIL-STD-461 has undergone an extended process of evolution since its original introduction as MIL-STD-461A in August 1968. The initial modifications to MIL-STD-461A and its companion MIL-STD-462 occurred in the form of notices which provided corrections, classifications or exceptions to certain of the requirements included in MIL-STD-461A. Figure 8.4 illustrates the evolution of MIL-STD-461A and 462 and the subsequent notices.

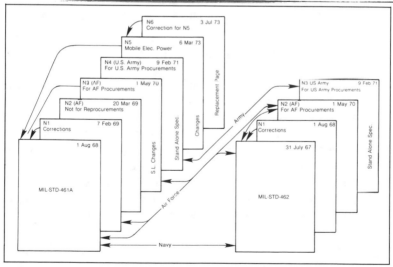

Figure 8.4—Employment of MIL-STD-461A and MIL-STD-462 by the Military Services

Figure 8.5 organizes the EMI tests into a family tree in order to get a better picture of how the tests are grouped. The first principal dichotomy is by test type, viz., emission (E) or susceptibility (S). The next level split is by mode of EMI coupling path, i.e., conducted (C) or radiated (R). Thus, a radiated susceptibility test is designated by the prefix RS.

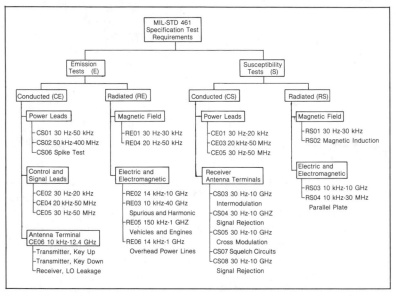

Figure 8.5—Organization Tree of MIL-STD-461 Test Specifications

Only certain of the EMI tests specified in MIL-STD-461A need to be performed on specific test specimens. Equipments are grouped into various classes is shown in Table 8.5. The specific tests required for each equipment class are identified in Table 8.6.

As a result of the various notices that have been released to modify MIL-STD-461A, various services have elected to omit certain of the tests required in the overall standard. Table 8.7 lists the various tests which are included in MIL-STD-461A, states whether that specific test is required by each of the services and provides the applicable charge notice which provides the authority for omitting tests where applicable.

Table 8.5—Classes of Equipment for Determining Applicable Test Requirements (continued next page)

Class No.	Description
I	Communication-electronic (CE) equipment: any item, including subassemblies and parts, serving functionally generating, transmitting, conveying, acquiring, receiving, storing, processing or utilizing information in the broadest sense. Subclasses are:
IA	Receivers Using Antennas
IB	Transmitters Using Antennas
IC	Non-Antenna CE Equipment (e.g., counters, oscilloscopes, signal generators, RF and audio test equipment, computers, power supplies, digital equipment, electrically operated cameras and projectors, wire terminal image interpretation facilities, photographic processing equipment and other electronic devices working in conjunction with classes IA and IB)
ID	Electrical and electronic equipment and instruments which would affect mission success or safety if degraded or malfunctioned by internally generated interference or susceptibility to external fields and voltages (e.g. autopilots, infrared devices, flight instruments, autocompasses and electronic engine control devices)
II	Non-communication equipment. Specific subclasses are:
IIA	Non-communication-electronic equipment: equipment for which RF energy is intentionally generated for other than information or control purposes. Examples are ultrasonic equipment, medical diathermy equipment, induction heaters, RF stabilized arcwelders, RF power supplies and uninterruptible power units (both rotary and solid state).
IIB	Electrical equipment: electric motors, hand tools, office and kitchen equipment, laundry and repair shop equipment and lithographic processing equipment.
IIC	Accessories for vehicles and engines: electrically and mechanically driven and engine electrical accessories such as gauges, fuel pumps, regulators, windshield wipers, turret motors, magnetos and generators, when tested off of the vehicle or engine. Applicable only to accessories for use on items of Classes IIIA and IIIB.

**Table 8.5—Classes of Equipment for Determining
Applicable Test Requirements (continued)**

Class No.	Description
III	Vehicles, engine-driven equipment
IIIA	Tactical vehicles: armored and tracked vehicles, off-the-road cargo and personnel carriers, assault and landing craft, amphibious vehicles, patrol boats, mobile railway and maintenance-of-way equipment and all other vehicles intended for installation of tactical CE equipment.
IIIB	Engine generators: those supplying power to, or closely associated with CE equipment.
IIIC	Special-purpose vehicles and engine-driven equipment: those intended for use in critical communication areas such as airfields, missile sites, ships' forward areas or in support of tactical operations. Examples are fire engines, aircraft service vehicles, pumps, blowers, bulldozers and other construction equipment, harbor tugs, floating repair shops, self-propelled barges and fork lift trucks.
IIID	Administrative vehicles: those of basically civilian character not intended for use in tactical areas or in critical areas covered by Class IIIC, and not intended for installation of communication equipment. Examples are sedans and other material handling equipment, whether engine-driven or electrically driven.
IV	Overhead power lines

8.16

Table 8.6—Test Requirements Applicable to Equipment Classes

Test	IA	IB	IC	ID	IIA	IIB	IIC	III A	III B	III C	III D	IV	Description of Test Method
CE01	Y	Y	Y	Y	Y	N	N	N	N	N	N	N	30 Hz to 20 kHz, Power Leads
CE02	Y	Y	Y	Y	Y	N	N	N	N	N	N	N	30 Hz to 20 kHz, Control and Sig. Leads
CE03	Y	Y	Y	Y	Y	Y	Y	Y	Y	N	N	N	20 kHz to 50 MHz, Power Leads
CE04	Y	Y	Y	Y	Y	N	N	N	N	N	N	N	20 kHz to 50 MHz, Control and Sig. Leads
CE05	Y	Y	Y	Y	Y	Y	N	N	N	N	N	N	30 Hz to 50 MHz, Inverse Filter Method
CE06	Y	Y	N	N	N	N	N	N	N	N	N	N	10 kHz to 12.4 GHz, Antenna Terminal
CS01	Y	Y	Y	Y	N	N	N	N	N	N	N	N	30 Hz to 50 kHz, Power Leads
CS02	Y	Y	Y	Y	N	N	N	N	N	N	N	N	50 kHz to 400 MHz, Power Leads
CS03	Y	N	Y	N	N	N	N	N	N	N	N	N	30 Hz to 10 GHz, Intermodulation
CS04	Y	N	Y	N	N	N	N	N	N	N	N	N	30 Hz to 10 GHz, Rej. of Undesirable Sig.
CS05	Y	N	Y	N	N	N	N	N	N	N	N	N	30 Hz to 10 GHz, Cross-Modulation
CS06	Y	Y	Y	Y	N	N	N	N	N	N	N	N	Spike, Power Leads
CS07	Y	N	Y	N	N	N	N	N	N	N	N	N	Squelch Circuits
CS08	Y	N	Y	N	N	N	N	N	N	N	N	N	30 Hz to 10 GHz, Rej. of Undesirable Sig.
RE01	Y	Y	Y	N	Y	N	N	N	N	N	N	N	30 Hz to 30 kHz, Magnetic Field
RE02	Y	Y	Y	Y	Y	Y	Y	N	N	N	N	N	14 KHz to 10 GHz, Electric Field
RE03	N	Y	N	N	N	N	N	N	N	N	N	N	10 kHz to 40 GHz, Spurious & Harmonics
RE04	Y	Y	Y	N	Y	N	N	N	N	N	N	N	20 kHz to 50 kHz, Magnetic Field
RE05	N	N	N	N	N	N	N	Y	Y	Y	N	N	150 kHz to 1 GHz, Vehicles and Engine Driven Eq.
RE06	N	N	N	N	N	N	N	N	N	N	N	Y	Overhead Power Line Test
RS01	Y	Y	Y	Y	N	N	N	N	N	N	N	N	30 Hz to 30 kHz, Magnetic Field
RS02	Y	Y	Y	Y	N	N	N	N	N	N	N	N	Mag. Induction Field
RS03	Y	Y	Y	Y	N	N	N	N	N	N	N	N	14 kHz to 10 GHz, Electric Field
RS04	Y	Y	Y	Y	N	N	N	N	N	N	N	N	14 kHz to 30 MHz

Table 8.7—Tri-Service EMI MIL-STD-461A/462 Tests
(continued next page)

Test	Test Identification	Frequency Range	Army	Navy	A.F.	Authority
Conducted Emission (CE)						
CE01	DC Power Leads	30 Hz—50 kHz	Yes	No	No	N4/461A
CE01	AC and DC Power Leads	30 Hz—20 kHz	NA	Yes	Yes	461A
CE02	AC Power Leads	10 kHz—50 kHz	Yes	No	No	N4/461A
CE02	Control and Signal Leads	30 Hz—20 kHz	NA	Yes	Yes	461A
CE03	Control and Signal Leads	30 Hz—50 kHz	Yes	NA	NA	N4/461A
CE03	AC and DC Power Leads	20 kHz—50 MHz	NA	Yes	Yes	461A
CE04	AC and DC Power Leads	50 kHz—50 MHz	Yes	NA	NA	N4/461A
CE04	Control and Signal Leads	20 kHz—50 MHz	NA	Yes	Yes	461A
CE05	Control and Signal Leads	50 kHz—50 MHz	Yes	NA	NA	N4/461A
CE05	Inverse Filter Method	30 Hz—50 MHz	NA	Yes	NA	N2/462
CE06	Antenna Terminal	10 kHz—12.4 GHz	Yes	Yes	Yes	N4 and 461A
CE07	Power Source Tactical Vehicle	1.5 MHz—65 MHz	Yes	NA	NA	N4/461A
Conducted Susceptibility (CS)						
CS01	DC Power Leads	30 Hz—50 kHz	Yes	No	No	N4/461A
CS01	AC and DC Power Leads	30 Hz—50 kHz	No	Yes	Yes	461A
CS02	AC and DC Power Leads	50 kHz—400 MHz	Yes	Yes	Yes	N4 and 461A
CS03	Intermodulation	30 Hz—10 GHz	Yes	Yes	Yes	N4 and 461A
CS04	Rejection Undes. Sig. (2 Gen)	30 Hz—10 GHz	Yes	Yes	Yes	N4 and 461A
CS05	Cross Modulation	30 Hz—10 GHz	NA	Yes	Yes	461A
CS06	AC and DC Power Leads	Spike Gen.	Yes	Yes	Yes	N4 and 461A
CS07	Ant. Input-Squelch Cir.	Impulse Gen.	Yes	Yes	Yes	N4 and 461A
CS08	Rejection Undes. Sig. (1 Gen)	30 Hz—10 GHz	NA	Yes	Yes	USE ES04
Radiated Emission (RE)						
RE01	Magnetic Field	30 Hz—30 kHz	Yes	Yes	No	N2/462
RE02	Electric Field, Broadband	14 kHz—1 GHz	Yes	No	No	N4/461A
RE02.1	Electric Field, Narrowband	14 kHz—12.4 GHz	Yes	No	No	N4/461A

Table8.7—Tri-Service EMI MIL-STD-461/462 Tests (continued)

Test	Test Identification	Frequency Range	Army	Navy	A.F.	Authority
Radiated Emission (RE) (Continued)						
RE02	Electric Field	14 kHz—10 GHz	No	Yes	Yes	N2/462
RE03	Spurious and Harmonics	10 kHz—40 GHz	Yes	Yes	Yes	N4 and 461A
RE04	Magnetic Field	20 Hz—50 kHz	Yes	Yes	Yes	N4 and 461A
RE05	Veh. and Eng.-Driven Equip.	150 kHz—1 GHz	Yes	Yes	Yes	N4 and 461A
RE06	Overhead Power Lines	14 kHz—1 GHz	Yes	Yes	Yes	N4 and 461A
Radiated Susceptibility (RS)						
RS01	Magnetic Field	30 Hz—30 kHz	Yes	Yes	No	N2/462
RS02	Induction Field Spike	Spike Only	Yes	No	No	N4/461A
RS02	Mag. Induction Field	Power and Spike	NA	Yes	Yes	461A
RS03	Electric Field	10 kHz—400 MHz	Yes	No	No	NA/461A
RS03.1	Electric Field	2 MHz—12.4 GHz	Yes	No	No	N4/461A
RS03.2	Electric Field	0.1 xf—10 f etc.	Yes	No	No	N4/461A
RS03	Electric Field	14 kHz—10 GHz	No	Yes	Yes	461A
RS04	Electric Field	14 kHz—30 MHz	No	Yes	Yes	461A

In April 1980, MIL-STD-461B was issued. MIL-STD-461B reflects a major change in philosophy from MIL-STD-461A. Under MIL-STD-461B all military purchased equipment is required to meet testing requirements that involve equipment type or class as well as the intended installation and mission criticality. MIL-STD-461B is organized into parts, as shown in Fig. 8.6, that correspond to the various types of installations in which equipments may be employed. In MIL-STD-461B, the equipments are grouped into classes depending on their intended application or installation as shown in Table 8.8.

The multipart structure of MIL-STD-461B tailors the requirement to both the equipment and the application. Further tailoring of the specifications may be provided by contractors if thorough justification is given. Table 8.9 provides a comparison between MIL-STD-461A and MIL-STD-461B. It should be noted that many of the test requirements are the same for both standards. The most significant changes in requirements between MIL-STD 461A and MIL-STD-461B are that several of the requirements have been combined, several requirements have been deleted and several have been added, as identified in the table. Some of the major changes between MIL-STD-461A and MIL-STD-461B are described below.

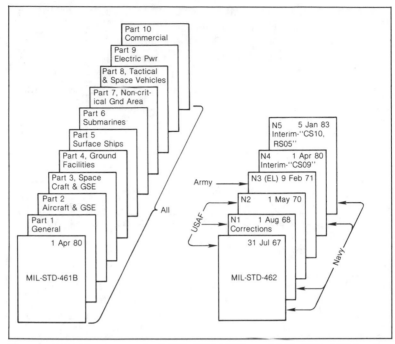

Figure 8.6—Employment of MIL-STD-461B and MIL-STD-462 by the Military Services

There are several requirements that are contained in MIL-STD-461A that have been deleted from MIL-STD-461B. Specifically, the inverse filter method of measuring conducted emissions (CE05) has been deleted, as has the radiated emission requirement for overhead power lines (RE06). Radiated emission requirements (RE05) for vehicles and engine-driven equipment has been replaced by UM03, whereas CE02 and CE04 have been combined with CE01 and CE03. The requirement to measure magnetic fields over the 0.2 to 50 kHz frequency range has been dropped, as has the one-signal-generator method of measuring receiver rejection of undesired signals from 30 Hz to 10 GHz (CS08). The two-signal-generator method (CS04) is still in effect.

Table 8.8—Equipment and Subsystem Classes vs. Applicable Part of MIL-STD-461B and 461C

Class	Description	Applicable Part
A	Equipments and subsystems which must operate compatibly when installed in critical areas, such as the following platforms or installations:	
A1	Aircraft (including associated ground support equipment)	2
A2	Spacecraft and Launch Vehicles (Including associated ground support equipment)	3
A3	Ground facilities (fixed and mobile, including tracked and wheeled vehicles)	4
A4	Surface Ships	5
A5	Submarines	6
B	Equipments and subsystems which support the Class A equipments and subsystems but which will not be physically located in critical ground areas. Examples are electronic shop maintenance and test equipment used in non-critical areas; aerospace ground equipment used away from flightlines; theodolites, navaids and similar equipments used in isolated areas.	7
C	Miscellaneous, general purpose equipments and subsystems not usually associated with a specific platform or installation. Specific items in this class are:	
C1	Tactical and special purpose vehicles and engine-driven equipent	8
C2	Engine generators and associated components, uninterruptible power sets (UPS) and mobile electric power (MEP) equipment supplying power to or used in critical areas	9
C3	Commercial electrical or electro-mechanical equipment	10

Table 8.9—Comparison of MIL-STD-461A and MIL-STD-461B Test Methods (continued next page)

461A Test Method	461A Short Title of Test-Method	Frequency Range	Test Method	461B Short Title of Test-Method	461B Frequency Range
CE01	Power Leads	30 Hz - 20 kHz	CE01	Power and Interconnect Leads	To 15 kHz
CE02	Control and Signal Leads	30 Hz - 20 kHz	CE02		
CE03	Power Leads	20 kHz- 50 MHz	CE03	Power and Interconnect Leads	0.015-50 MHz
CE04	Control and Signal Leads	20 kHz- 50 MHz	CE04		
CE05	Inverse Filter Method	30 Hz - 50 MHz	(Dropped)		
CE06	Antenna Terminal Conducted	10 kHz- 10 GHz	CE06	Antenna Terminals	10 kHz-26 GHz
CS01	Power Leads	20 Hz - 50 kHz	CS01	Power Leads	30 Hz- 50 kHz
CS02	Power Leads	50 kHz-400 MHz	CS02	(Same)	(Same)
CS03	Intermodulation	15 kHz- 10 GHz	CS03	(Same)	(Same)
CS04	Rej. of Undesired Signals	15 kHz- 10 GHz	CS04	(Same)	(Same)
CS05	Cross Modulation	15 kHz- 10 GHz	CS05	(Same)	(Same)
CS06	Spike, Power Leads	NA	CS06	(Same)	(Seme)
CS07	Squelch Circuits	NA	CS07	(Same)	(Same)
CS08	Rej. of Undesired Signals	30 Hz - 10 GHz	(Dropped)		
RE01	Magnetic Field	30 Hz - 30 kHz	RE01	(Same)	(Same)
RE02	Electric Field	14 kHz- 10 GHz	RE02	(Same)	(Same)
RE03	Spurious and Harm. Radiation	10 kHz- 40 GHz	RE03	(Same)	(Same)
RE04	Magnetic Field	20 Hz - 50 kHz	(Dropped)		
RE05	Veh. and Eng. Driven Eqmt.	150 kHz- 1 GHz	(Dropped)		
RE06	Overhead Power Lines	14 kHz- 1 GHz	(Dropped)		

Table 8.9—Comparison of MIL-STD-461A and MIL-STD-461B Test Methods (continued)

461A Test Method	461A Short Title of Test-Method	Frequency Range	Test Method	461B Short Title of Test-Method	461B Frequency Range
RS01	Magnetic Field	30 Hz - 30 kHz	RS01	(Same)	(Same)
RS02	Mag. Induction Field	Pwr. Line and Spike	RS02	(Same)	(Same)
RS03	Electric Field	14 kHz - 10 GHz	FS03	(Same)	(Same)
RS04	Parallel Line Fields	14 kHz - 30 MHz	(Dropped)		
			CE07	Power Leads, Time Domain	
			CS09	Structure (Common Mode)	
			UM03	Tactical and Special Vehicles	
			UM04	Engine Generators and UPS and MEP Equipment	
			UM05	Common Electrical/Mechanical Equipments	

CE = Conducted Emission

CS = Conducted Susceptibility

RE = Radiated Emission

RS = Radiated Susceptibility

UM = Unique, Miscellaneous

In addition to the above, there are requirements in MIL-STD-461B that were not included in MIL-STD-461A. In particular, MIL-STD-461B provides for a time domain transient limit (CE07) which is applicable to conducted emissions on the power lines for Navy and Air Force procurements. This requirement limits conducted switching transients to ±50 percent of nominal rms voltage on ac leads and +50 to −150 percent of nominal line voltage on dc leads. MIL-STD-461B also provides a requirement to inject noise currents (CS09) between the equipment case and the structure. This requirement applies only to Navy procurements and is for equipments and subsystems that have an operating frequency range of 100 kHz or less and an operating sensitivity of 1 μV or less. The injected current starts at 1 A at 60 Hz and decays in a varied fashion until it reaches 100 mA at 100 kHz.

MIL-STD-461C was released in August 1986. The new MIL-STD-461C version retains the same format, Part/Class identification of platforms and organization used in MIL-STD-461B. MIL-STD-461C contains several minor modifications to MIL-STD-461B, and several of the requirements and/or limits have been relaxed. The major difference between MIL-STD-461B and MIL-STD-461C is that new requirements have been added to limit conducted and radiated susceptibility to an electromagnetic pulse (EMP). The specific tests that have been added are EMP Injection Tests and EMP Electromagnetic Field Tests as described below.

EMP Injection Tests are to be performed by injecting a pulsed sinusoidal signal into equipment pins (CS10) and interconnecting cables (CS11) and observing performance to ensure that permanent malfunction beyond the specified recovery time does not occur.

EMP Electromagnetic Field Tests (RS05) are performed by using a parallel plate line or Transverse Electromagnetic (TEM) cell to subject the equipment under test to high-level EMPs to demonstrate that the equipment is capable of surviving in an EMP environment. This test only applies to equipment or subsystems that are essential for the success of a mission and are located outside of an intentionally hardened (shielded) area.

It should be noted that the EMP requirements that have been added to MIL-STD-461C are Navy requirements only and are required for all Navy platforms except in space. With the addition of these new EMP requirements, an additional notice (Notice 5) to MIL-STD-462 has been issued to define the test methods used to establish adherence to the specifications. The MIL-STD-461C limits imposed by these EMP requirements will be presented later in this section.

MIL-STD-461A, 461B and 461C are all currently in use and, therefore, it is important to be knowledgeable about all three versions. In general, MIL-STD-461A applies to:

1. Equipment for which the procurement was initiated prior to the existence of 461B or 461C
2. Equipment that will be used in systems that were originally developed when MIL-STD-461A was in effect
3. Reprocurement of equipment for use in systems that were originally procured under MIL-STD-461A

MIL-STD-461B applies to new procurements that were initiated between April 1980 and August 1986. MIL-STD-461C, in general, applies to new procurements that were initiated after August 1986. The following paragraphs present examples of the various radiated and conducted emission and susceptibility limits imposed by MIL-STD-461A, 461B and 461C. The reader is cautioned that the limits shown in this section are only examples of the limits provided by the standards. Refer to the appropriate standard to determine the limits that should apply in a particular situation. For a detailed treatment of the MIL-STD-460 series and other military standards, see Volumes 11 and 12 of this handbook series.

MIL-STD-461A, 461B and 461C impose limits on conducted emissions on power leads, connected leads and interconnecting cables between parts, sources and loads of an equipment. Figure 8.7 provides typical limits for both narrowband and broadband emissions over the applicable frequency ranges. Intentional transmissions of electrical energy by conduction on their intended leads, at their specified power levels, and within their necessary information bandwidths are exempt from the requirements of this standard.

MIL-STD-461 also limits the level of emissions that may appear at the antenna input terminals of transmitters and receivers as a result of conducted emissions on the antenna cable. For transmitters in the "key-up mode" and for receivers, the following MIL-STD-461C limits apply:

1. 34 dBμV into a matched load for narrowband emissions
2. 40 dBμV/MHz for broadband emissions.

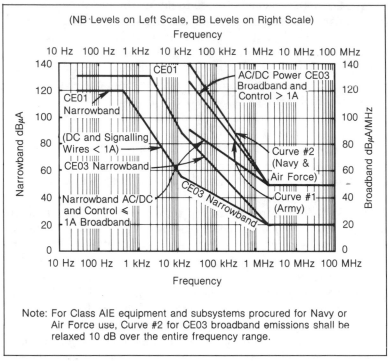

Figure 8.7—MIL-461C Conducted Emission Limits, CE01 and CE03

Harmonic and all other spurious emissions (except the second and third harmonics) shall have peak powers 80 dB down from the peak power at the fundamental. The second and third harmonics are limited to the peak power levels shown in Fig. 8.8. These limits do not apply within the test sample's designed emission bandwidth or ±5 percent of its center frequency.

Under MIL-STD-461, the performance characteristics of the equipment or subsystem must not be degraded beyond the tolerances given in the individual equipment specification or test plan when subjected to electromagnetic energy injected on the power leads equal to or less than the limits. Figure 8.9 illustrates typical limits for power-line conducted susceptibility in the frequency range from 30 Hz to 50 kHz. The requirements for this limit are considered to be met if the required test voltages cannot be generated by 50 W dissipated in a 0.5 Ω load. In the frequency range of 50 kHz to 400 MHz, a typical limit for power-line conducted susceptibility is 1 volt from a 50 ohm source applied to the equipment power input terminals. When a 1 W source of 50 Ω impedance cannot develop the required voltage at the test sample power-input terminals (excluding power cable) and the test sample is not susceptible to the output of this signal source, then the equipment may be considered nonsusceptible.

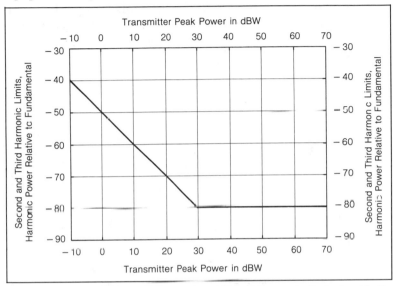

Figure 8.8—MIL-STD-461C Second and Third Harmonic Emission Limits

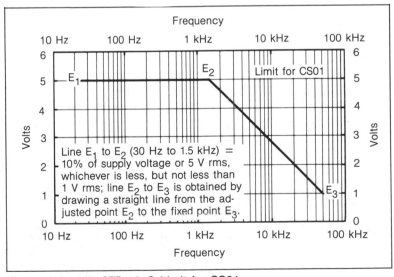

Figure 8.9—MIL-STD-461C Limit for CS01

In addition to the power line conducted susceptibility requirements described above, communication-electronic equipments are also required by MIL-STD-461 to function without exhibiting any malfunction, degradation of performance or deviation from specified indication beyond the tolerances given in the test sample's individual equipment specification or approved test plan when the spike shown in Fig. 8.10 is applied to the ac power input lines of the test sample.

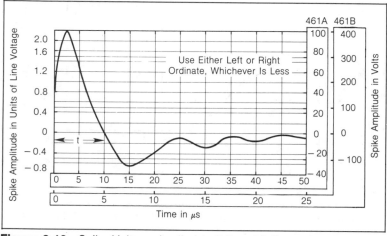

Figure 8.10—Spike Voltage Applied to DC or AC Power Leads of Test Item for CS06 Specification Limit

For receivers, MIL-STD-461A, 461B and 461C impose limits on the susceptibility to conducted signals at the antenna input terminals as a result of spurious responses, cross modulation and squelch circuits. The conducted susceptibility limits for two signal intermodulations cover the frequency range from 30 Hz to 10 GHz and require that intermodulation products must not be present when the two signal generators are set 66 dB above the level required to produce the standard reference output. The intermodulation susceptibility limits are illustrated in Fig. 8.11. The limits for conducted susceptibility to spurious responses require that the receiver must not exhibit any undesired responses when subjected to the signal levels indicated in Fig. 8.12. Receivers must not exhibit any malfunction, degradation of performance or deviation from specified indications beyond the tolerances given in the individual equipment specification or approved test plan as a result of cross modulation when subjected to an interfering signal 66 dB above the level required to produce the standard reference output. The cross modulation conducted susceptibility limits are illustrated in Fig. 8.13.

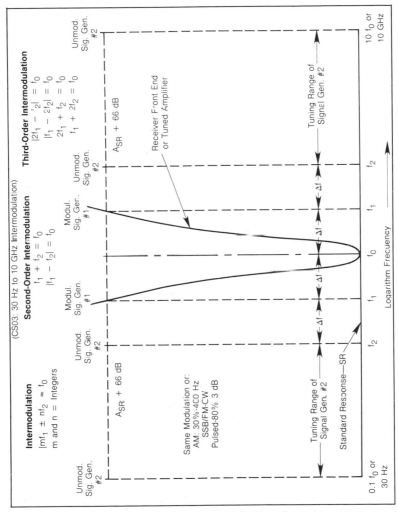

Figure 8.11—Intermodulation: Conducted Susceptibility Measurements

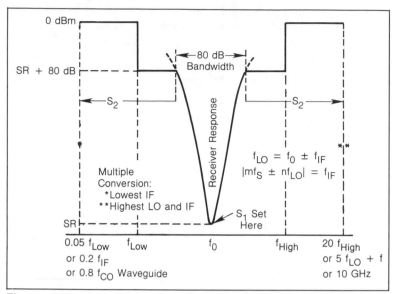

Figure 8.12—Rejection of Undesired Signals: CS04 and CS08

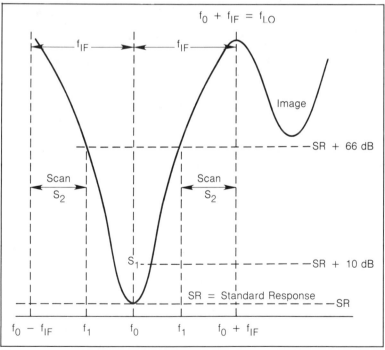

Figure 8.13—Cross Modulation, Conducted Susceptibility: CS05

The conducted susceptibility limits for receiver squelch circuits as a result of interference at the antenna input terminals are as follows.

Test 1

Squelch circuits must not open when the output of a 50 Ω source impedance impulse generator, set at 90 dBμV/MHz, is applied and matched to the input terminals of the test sample.

Test 2

The squelch circuit must not open when two signals are applied at the input of the test sample. One signal must be an unmodulated RF signal at f_o whose amplitude is 2/3 of the RF voltage used to adjust the squelch threshold. The second signal is an impulse signal having a level of 50 dBμV/MHz.

The conducted susceptibility limits for the EMP requirements as a result of a damped sinusoidal transient on the pins and cables are provided in Fig. 8.14.

MIL-STD-461A, 461B and 461C impose limits on both the magnetic and electric field levels that may be radiated from equipments. Magnetic field emissions in the frequency range from 30 Hz to 30 kHz must not be generated and radiated in excess of the values shown in the "Acceptable Radiation" portion as shown in Fig. 8.15. Narrowband electric-field emissions in the frequency range of 14 kHz to 10 GHz must not be generated and radiated in excess of the values shown in Fig. 8.16. These limits may be relaxed for certain classes of equipment and installations as also indicated in Fig. 8.16.

Radiated susceptibility limits for magnetic fields require that the test sample shall not exhibit any malfunction, degradation of performance or deviation from specified indications beyond the tolerances specified in the individual equipment specification, in the frequency range of 30 Hz to 30 kHz when subjected to the magnetic fields less than those shown in the "Acceptable Susceptibility" portion of Fig. 8.15.

Radiated susceptibility limits for induction fields require that the test sample must not exhibit any malfunction, degradation of performance or deviation from specified indications beyond the tolerances given in the individual equipment specification or approved test plan when subjected to the following fields:

1. Power frequency test: 20 A applied to the test wire at the power frequency or frequencies
2. Spike test: the same spike shape shown in Fig. 8.10 where E = 100 V across 5 Ω applied to the test wire

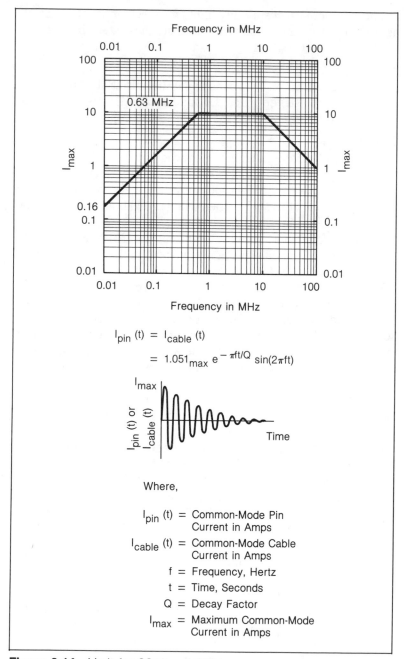

Figure 8.14—Limit for CS10 and CS11

8.32

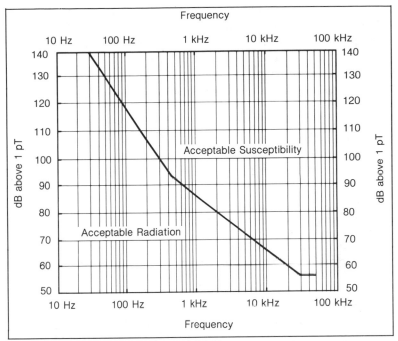

Figure 8.15—Limit for RE01 and RS01

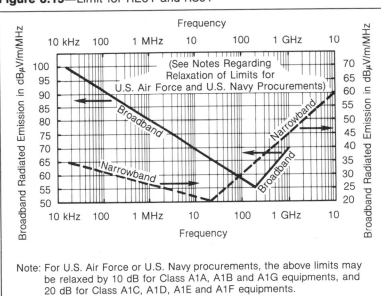

Note: For U.S. Air Force or U.S. Navy procurements, the above limits may be relaxed by 10 dB for Class A1A, A1B and A1G equipments, and 20 dB for Class A1C, A1D, A1E and A1F equipments.

Figure 8.16—MIL-STD-461C Specification Limits for RE02

8.33

Radiated susceptibility limits for electric fields require that the test sample must not exhibit any malfunction, degradation of performance or deviation from specified indication beyond tolerances given in the individual equipment specification or approved test plan in the frequency range from 14 kHz to 10 GHz when the test sample is subjected to a radiated field intensity of 1 V/m or more. For certain classes of equipment and installation, the radiated susceptibility limits are increased to levels as high as 200 V/m. Figure 8.17 illustrates the MIL-STD-461B and 461C electric field radiated susceptibility limits for various classes of equipment. For EMP radiated susceptibility, MIL-STD-461C limits are given in Fig. 8.18.

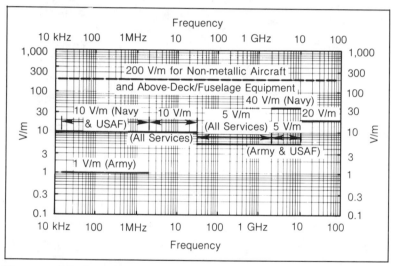

Figure 8.17—RS03 Limits for 461B and 461C for Class A and B Equipments

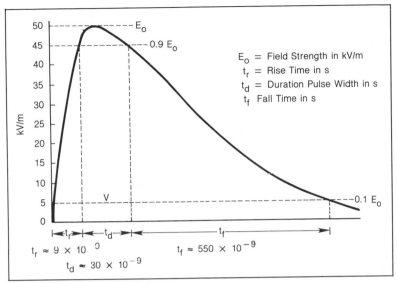

Figure 8.18—Limits for RS05

8.4 MIL-E-6051D System-Level EMC Specification

MIL-E-6051D is a composite system specification. As such, it is applicable to all items of equipment within the total system which utilizes or may be affected by electrical-electronic phenomena. The major objective of this specification is to assure a compatible total system under operational conditions. Figure 8.19 illustrates the relationship between MIL-STD-461/462, which are equipment-level standards, and MIL-E-6051D, which is a system-level specification. The emphasis in MIL-E-6051D is on intrasystem compatibility, regardless of whether any equipment within the system conforms to other applicable specifications. The test procedures in MIL-E-6051D are general, and they do not specify individual equipments or detailed procedures to be followed. Instead, they require the preparation and use of a detailed test plan by the contractor.

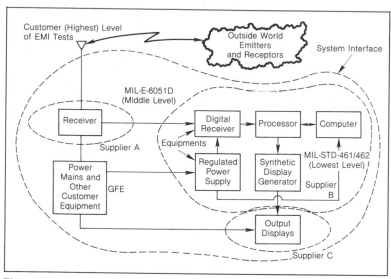

Figure 8.19—System Diagram Showing Level of EMI Specification Compliance Testing

To assure that it is understood what constitutes a system, a system is defined as an assemblage of subordinate systems, subsystems, equipments, devices and interconnecting or interfacing elements, housed in or on a structure of some type to permit the performance of one or more missions. Systems are either mounted on a vehicle or situated at fixed locations. Vehicular systems may be mounted on cars, trucks, tanks, aircraft, missiles, ships and trains. Fixed systems, which are often subordinated to and are part of vehicular systems, include computers, radar, communications, telemetry, weapons fire control, navigation and the like.

The MIL-E-6051D test serves as the final check on the EMI characteristics of a complete system. These tests are specifically designed to investigate every potential EMI susceptibility of the actual system via the mechanism inherent in the actual operational environment. Because the tests include the basic system equipments (i.e.; receivers, transmitters, control equipment, etc.) as well as all of the electrical and electronic equipment in the system installation (i.e.; transmitters, receivers, computers, generators, motors, etc.), the tests are lengthy in both preparation and implementation.

The test procedures and instrumentation necessary to conduct realistic system electromagnetic compatibility tests are not defined by the MIL-E-6051D specification. Instead, it is the responsibility of the system contractor to prepare a detailed test plan. There are three basic approaches that may be followed in setting up the procedures for the compatibility demonstration tests required by MIL-E-6051D. These basic approaches may be used either singly or collectively to fulfill the specification requirements.

The first approach that may be used to satisfy the requirements of MIL-E-6051D is to inject emissions into the system at critical points. The injected conducted emissions must be at a level that is 6 dB higher than predetermined environment levels created by the system, per se. Appropriate system test points must then be monitored for malfunction indications.

A second approach that may be used to test for a 6 dB margin between equipment susceptibility levels and the noise levels created by the system, is to increase the sensitivity level of the system so that its susceptibility level to interference is increased by the required 6 dB. With this approach, it is also necessary to monitor appropriate system points to determine if a malfunction(s) occurs. This increase in sensitivity by 6 dB is often difficult to impossible to achieve and therefore this approach is seldom used.

A third approach that may be used is to measure the interference susceptibility of key subsystem and system circuits and compare these measured susceptibility levels with existing noise emission levels to determine if the required 6 dB margin exists.

Each of the three approaches outlined has certain advantages and disadvantages. The best approach for a particular system will depend on the characteristics of the system and must be determined by the contractor as the test plan is prepared. In some cases, it may be desirable to use a combination of the three approaches.

Basically, the electromagnetic compatibility requirements of MIL-STD-6051D are that all elements of a system operate properly (individually and collectively) and that the susceptibility level of each equipment is such that there is at least a 6 dB margin between the susceptibility and the electromagnetic noise emission environment resulting from the operation of the total system. This means that any and all elements of the system must operate as designed with twice the noise level that actually exists within the system regardless of its frequency, duration, modulation, waveform, repetition rates, duty cycle, sequence, time, amplitude or any other characteristic that may be used to define noise. The primary concern is the manner in which the noise affects the operation of the system if indeed it does.

It is conceivable that there may be extreme differences in the effects that any given type of noise will have on an element, circuit or subsystem within a total system. For example, a given element of a complex system is affected differently by a burst of noise than is a voltmeter, a field- intensity meter or other measurement device. Also, the susceptibility characteristics (i.e.; sensitivity, bandwidth, etc.) of a system element may vary as a function of time, signal level or other programmed changes so that the reaction of the element to noise would not be constant. These effects may or may not have a synchronous relation. For example, transients may or may not coincide with clock pulses. Random transients would find random coincidence with periodic ON gates.

Therefore, in order to properly evaluate the effectiveness of the system under test, it is necessary to evaluate existing noise levels in terms of how the system is affected by the noise. In many cases, this can be accomplished by measuring the effect of noise upon functional elements and circuits within the system. However, in order to determine by tests whether the system can indeed operate as designed, within the required safety margin, it is necessary to utilize test methods and instrumentation that permit close and accurate time and event correlation of all the quantities measured.

There are several other important factors that must be considered in developing test methods and procedures. First, the instrumentation must include the capability to measure directly or indirectly the effects of noise on critical elements and subsystems. Second, it must be possible to analyze all data on a time and event basis. Third, test procedures must include system checkout and support equipment when the checkout and support equipment are capable of contributing to the electromagnetic environment. Fourth, test procedures must encompass the total operational profile of a system and must ensure that all circuits and subsystems are exercised through their total dynamic range.

8.5 Comparison of Limits

A comparison of the FCC, VDE and MIL-STD-461 limits will reveal that MIL-STD-461 is the more stringent standard. In general, the radiated and conducted emission limits of MIL-STD-461 are lower than the limits imposed on commercial equipment. Of course, when comparing the radiated emission limits, it is necessary to consider that the MIL-STD-461 limits are imposed at a 1 m distance, whereas the FCC and VDE limits are imposed at distances ranging from 3 to 30 m. When the differences are considered, MIL-STD-461 radiated emission limits are considerably more stringent than either FCC or VDE limits. Therefore, equipments that satisfy MIL-STD-461 emission limits will, in general, satisfy the FCC and VDE limits. On the other hand, equipments that meet the FCC or VDE emission limits may not satisfy the MIL-STD-461 requirements. In addition, it should be acknowledged that MIL-STD-461 also imposes limits on device susceptibility, whereas susceptibility of most commercial products is not regulated.

8.6 Other EMC Standards and Publications

In addition to the EMC standards discussed in this section, there are numerous other standards and design manuals which are of interest to the EMC engineer. Table 8.10 provides a list of some of the more widely referenced military EMC standards and design manuals. Many of these can be found in Volumes 11 and 12 of this handbook series. In addition, Volumes 9 and 10 cover a range of U.S. and foreign commercial EMC standards.

Table 8.10—Military EMC Standards and Design Manuals

SPECIFICATIONS

Military

MIL-B-5087	Bonding, Electrical and Lightning Protection, for Aerospace Systems
MIL-W-5088	Wiring, Aircraft Installation of
MIL-E-6051	Electromagnetic Compatibility Requirements, Systems
MIL-W-83575 (USAF)	Wiring Harness, Space Vehicle, Design and Testing
MIL-STD-105	Sampling Procedures and Tables for Inspection by Attributes
MIL-STD-188	Military Communication System Technical Standards
MIL-STD-220	Method of Insertion Loss Measurement
MIL-STD-285	Attenuation Measurements for Enclosures, EM Shielding for Electronic Test Purposes, Method
MIL-STD-454	Standard General Requirements for Electronic Equipment
MIL-STD-462	Electromagnetic Emission and Susceptibility, Test Methods for
MIL-STD-463	Definitions and System of Units, Electromagnetic Interference Technology
MIL-STD-469	Radar Engineering Design Requirements, Electromagnetic Compatibility
MIL-STD-480	Configuration Control—Engineering Changes, Deviations and Waivers
MIL-STD-704	Electric Power, Aircraft Characteristics and Utilization
MIL-STD-831	Test Reports, Preparation of
MIL-STD-863	Wiring Data, Preparation of
MIL-STD-1310 (NAVY)	Shipboard Bonding and Grounding Methods for Electromagnetic Compatibility and Safety
MIL-STD-1337 (SHIPS)	Electric Portable Handtools, General Suppression, System Design Requirements
MIL-STD-1377 (NAVY)	Effectiveness of Cable, Connector and Weapon Enclosure Shielding and Filters in Precluding Hazards of Electromagnetic Radiation to Ordnance, Measurement of
MIL-STD-1385 (NAVY)	Preclusion of Ordnance Hazards in Electromagnetic Fields; General Requirements for
MIL-STD-1512 (USAF)	Electroexplosive Subsystems, Electrically Initiated, Test Methods and Design Requirements
MIL-STD-1541 (USAF)	Electromagnetic Compatibility Requirements for Space Systems
MIL-STD-1542 (USAF)	Electromagnetic Compatibility (EMC) and Grounding Requirements for Space System Facilities

Military Design Manuals

AD 619666	Interference Reduction Guide for Design Engineers, Volume 1
AD 619667	Interference Reduction Guide for Design Engineers, Volume 2
AFSC DH 1-4	Design Handbook, Electromagnetic Compatibility
AFSC DH 2-5	Design Handbook, Armament
NAVELEX 0101,106	Naval Shore Electronics Criteria, EMC/EMR Hazards
NAVSEA OD 30393	Design Principles and Practices for Controlling Hazards of Electromagnetic-Radiation to Ordnance
NAVSEA 0967-266-1010	RF compatibility and Electromagnetic Interference Reduction for Forces Afloat
NAVSEA 0967-000-0150	Electronics Installation and Maintenance Book, Radio Frequency Interference Reduction
NAVSEA 0967-283-5010	Submarine Electromagnetic Shielding Practices
AMC Pamphlet 706-235	Hardening Weapon Systems Against RF Energy

Chapter 9

EMC Control Plans, Test Plans and Test Reports

The **EMC Control Plan** is a formal document prepared early in a project to provide EMC design guidelines for all pertinent personnel and to meet contractual requirements for military or government procurements where applicable. It is important to recognize that there are different types of EMI control plans. First, in programs involving the development of a large system such as an aircraft, spacecraft, ship, etc., a system-level EMI Control Plan should be prepared and implemented. This type of system-level EMC Control Plan is required by MIL-E-6051D. Second, for individual equipments or subsystems, a separate EMC Control Plan may be required to define equipment-level engineering design procedures and techniques. Equipment-level Control Plans are required by MIL-STD-461C.

It is emphasized that the EMC Control Plan is one of the most effective and important means of assuring that proper attention is given to EMC throughout the entire system or equipment development cycle. Therefore, an EMC Control Plan should be prepared and implemented for any equipment or system development program (government or commercial) even if there is no contractual requirement for such a plan.

The **EMI Test Plan** describes the measurement program that will be employed to demonstrate that a system, subsystem or equipment complies with the contractual EMI requirements. The EMI

9.1

Test Plan also describes how the general test requirements, methods and procedures described in the applicable specifications or standards will be applied on the specific system, subsystem or equipment.

The **EMI Test Report** describes the results of the EMI tests performed to demonstrate compliance with the contractual EMI requirements imposed on a system, subsystem or equipment.

This chapter discusses the purpose and contents of system-level and equipment-level EMC Control Plans, Test Plans and Test Reports.

9.1 The Role of the EMC Control Plan

The EMC Control Plan should place into effect the methods and procedures that are to be used throughout the development cycle of an equipment or system to ensure that proper attention is given to EMC. The EMC Control Plan should, as a minimum, perform the following functions:

1. Communicate to all pertinent personnel the management responsibilities and controls for achieving EMC
2. Define EMC design requirements and provide detailed design guidelines
3. Identify documents that are applicable to EMI control and provide an interpretation of EMC specifications
4. Describe EMC test requirements
5. Provide criteria for continued EMC quality assurance throughout the production process

The importance of the EMC Control Plan cannot be over-emphasized. Simply stated, it describes the entire EMC Program by which all subsequent EMC documentation, requirements, specifications, test methods and criteria are controlled and enforced. Thus, it is obvious that the management requirements, organizational responsibilities, design criteria, test procedures and limits and related matters must be clearly defined to assure acceptance of the plan.

9.1.1 System-Level EMC Control Plan

An EMC Control Plan should be prepared and implemented for any large system development project. If the system is being developed for military or certain other government applications, MIL-E-6051D will most likely be imposed as a contractual requirement, and an EMC Control Plan will be required. If the system is being developed for commercial or other government applications that do not require adherence to MIL-E-6051D, an EMC Control Plan still should be prepared and implemented. In either situation, the purpose and content of the EMC Control Plan would be the same. Although the discussion that follows relates specifically to system development projects that require adherence to MIL-E-6051D, these procedures should be observed on all major system development projects.

The most widely invoked system EMC specification is MIL-E-6051D, "Military Specification, Electromagnetic Compatibility Requirements, Systems." MIL-E-6051D outlines overall requirements for systems EMC, including control of electromagnetic environment, lightning protection, bonding, grounding and static electrification. This specification is applicable to systems and all associated subsystems. Fulfilling system-level EMC requirements of MIL-E-6051D is the ultimate goal of other EMC specifications and standards such as MIL-STD-461C and MIL-STD-462.

MIL-E-6051D requires the prime contractor to establish an overall integrated compatibility program for most system development projects. The EMC Program should include the prime contractor's approach, planning, technical criteria and management control based on the governing documents. Vendors, subcontractors, and others involved in the program should follow the same criteria as the prime contractor in accomplishing their EMC Program.

MIL-E-6051D outlines overall requirements for system electromagnetic compatibility programs, including the Electromagnetic Compatibility Board, EMC System Requirements, the EMC Control Plan and EMC for commercial subsystems/equipment, government-furnished equipment, subsystems equipment installations and redesign of systems.

The details of the system EMC Program shall be included in the system EMC Control Plan that is submitted for review and approval by the procuring activity. The EMC Control Plan shall be prepared and submitted in accordance with the requirements of the contract. Compliance with it, after approval, is a contractual requirement. The control plan shall include, but not be limited to, the following elements of the overall program and shall be updated during the contract as necessary.

1. Responsibility and authority of the individual who will direct and implement the contractor's electromagnetic compatibility program
2. Number and experience of full-time and part-time EMC personnel available for the program
3. Methods and requirements for ensuring that contractor-developed subsystems/equipments will not be adversely affected by interference from sources within the system nor be sources of interference that might adversely affect the operation of other subsystems (implementation of MIL-STD-461C and 462)
4. Predicted problem areas and proposed methods for solution of problems not resolved by compliance with MIL-STD-461C and 462
5. Radiation characteristics from system antennas, including fundamental and spurious energy and antenna-to-antenna coupling
6. General approach to cable design including wire categorization criteria for identifying, labeling and installing interference-generating or susceptible wires; shielding techniques; and wire routing
7. Impact of corrosion control requirements on EMC and recommendations for resolution of problem areas
8. Design criteria and required tests for lightning protection and design impact on individual subsystems
9. Design criteria and required tests for electrification, including precipitation static and propulsion subsystem charging
10. Methods of implementation of design changes required for EMC
11. Special requirements, test methods and limits necessary for the system and associated subsystems/equipments
12. Facilities that will be required and made available for the EMC program
13. Methods of accomplishing design review and coordination with subcontractors and vendors
14. Spike protection requirements for subsystems/equipments connected to the power bus
15. Bonding criteria
16. Grounding criteria

17. EMC requirements for contractor-furnished, off-the-shelf equipment
18. Application of interference control specifications and standards through the phases of definition, design and production
19. Proposed charter and details of operation of the EMC Board
20. Criticality category and degradation criteria for each subsystem/equipment, including safety margins (where necessary)
21. Spectrum utilization design provision measures, including control of emitters and frequencies, harmonics thereof, bandwidth control of oscillator frequencies, rise times, etc.
22. Scheduling and milestones

The final objective of the EMC Control Plan is to confirm by testing that no undesirable response, malfunction or degradation of performance due to EMI will occur in, or be produced by, electrical or electronic equipment in the system. Maximum feasible system and subsystem operational compatibility and overall system effectiveness, obtained by competent design, are the criteria to be considered in developing the EMC Control Plan.

If the EMC Program is to be accomplished by a contractor, an enforceable EMC Control Plan is normally assured by making MIL-E-6051D a part of the basic contract. If the program is to be accomplished in house, a directive from program management stipulating MIL-E-6051D as an applicable document usually assures an enforceable EMC Control Plan, but other approaches may be used.

It is suggested that the plan be presented in sections as enumerated below. Following these guidelines will help to obtain acceptance or approval of the EMC Control Plan.

1. Introduction
2. Applicable documents
3. Specification interpretations
4. Program management requirements
5. Design requirements
6. Test requirements
7. Quality assurance tests
8. Definition of terms

The contents of the EMC Control Plan are described in the following paragraphs.

9.1.1.1 Introduction to the EMC Control Plan

The introduction to the EMC Control Plan should contain a brief statement of the scope and objectives of the plan. It should introduce the system to which the plan is applied and state the objectives of the plan and the military specification to which it was prepared. The introduction should also stipulate a time for review and updating of the EMC Control Plan. A period of not more than six months is recommended.

9.1.1.2 Documents Applicable to the EMC Control Plan

The list of documents applicable to the EMC Control Plan should include the standards, specifications, drawings, plans and reports to be used in meeting the requirements of the plan. Applicable EMC documents developed by the military, the contractor and vendors should be included. Effective dates of the listed documents and all restrictions or limitations affecting the incorporation of the documents should be included.

Section Two of MIL-E-6051D, "Applicable Documents," refers to other specifications, standards and manuals that form an integral part of the standard. The reference specifications, with the exception of MIL-B-5087 and MIL-P-24014, are documents covering capacitors and filters.

MIL-B-5087, "Bonding, Electrical and Lightning Protection for Aerospace Systems," should be used by the design group through final fabrication.

MIL-P-24014, "Preclusion of Hazards from Electromagnetic Radiation to Ordnance, General Requirements for," establishes general requirements for weapon systems to preclude hazards from electromagnetic fields to ordnance systems.

MIL-STD-454, "Standard General Requirements for Electronic Equipments" lists 63 detailed requirements concerned with military specifications for electronic equipment. It promulgates uniform requirements applicable to electronic equipment, with the intent that they be incorporated by reference in general equipment specifications.

MIL-STD-461C, "Electromagnetic Emission and Susceptibility Requirements for the Control of Electromagnetic Interference," and MIL-STD-462, "Electromagnetic Interference Characteristics,

Measurement of," are documents applicable to components and subsystems as MIL-I-6051D applies to systems.

Other pertinent reference documents are:

1. MIL-STD-704, "Electrical Power, Aircraft Characteristics and Utilization"
2. MIL-STD-831, "Test Reports, Preparation of"
3. MIL-STD-2584, "Plug, Fuel Nozzle, Grounding"
4. MIL-STD-33645, "Receptacle Installations, Fuel Nozzle Jumper, Aircraft to Servicing Hose"
5. MIL-STD-90298, "Connectors, Receptacle, Electrical Fuel Nozzle Jumper Plug"
6. Air Force Manual AFSM 80-7, *Handbook of Instructions for Aerospace Vehicle Equipment Design*
7. Air Force Manual AFSM 80-9, Vol. IV, *Electromagnetic Compatibility*

9.1.1.3 Specification Interpretation

It is mandatory that the commonly used EMC specifications be interpreted for application to each overall program. Interpretation is necessary because, in some cases, the specifications are several years old and were written for applications that may differ from present ones. In these cases, the frequency ranges specified, test configurations shown, etc., do not always fit the ranges and configurations of present-day equipments. Interpretation is also required because, in all instances, the specifications have been prepared to apply to as wide a range of conditions as possible. In this respect, a system-level specification may be applied to a ground station consisting of one rack of equipment or to a space vehicle consisting of multiple stages and their associated ground support equipment. Therefore, because of the age and broad scope of the commonly used specification, interpretation by competent EMC specialists for each overall program is mandatory. It is also important that, within an overall program, all specification interpretations be the responsibility of one organization.

When specifications have been interpreted and their applicability established, the result may be the modification of some requirements and the imposing of other requirements not called for in the specification. The basic requirement is to satisfy the intent of the specification rather than to be dogmatic about compliance with each detailed stipulation. The intent of MIL-E-6051D may be stated as being "to assure that the system is electromagnetically compatible." The intent of MIL-STD-461C may be stated as being "to assure that the EMI and susceptibility characteristics of subsystems and individual equipments fall within specified limits." As such, any interpretation of MIL-E-6051D or MIL-STD-461C should be adequate for accomplishment of these intentions.

MIL-B-5087 is primarily a design specification, and the requirements are much more specific than those of either MIL-E-6051D or MIL-STD-461C. The EMC Control Plan should delineate the applicability of this specification to contractor designed equipment, government equipments, mechanical interfaces, equipment installation mountings, etc. Particular attention must be devoted to the fact that a satisfactory RF ground plane is as mandatory as a satisfactory dc ground plane. Problems related to proper grounding of equipments or maintenance of ground-plane continuity will develop during system-level testing without this attention.

In addition to the above requirements, this portion of the EMC Control Plan should include any requirement not specifically stated in the applicable specifications but which the contractor deems necessary for an adequate EMC program. These extra requirements should receive particular attention in view of the fact that the applicable specifications require extensive interpretation.

9.1.1.4 Management of the EMC Control Program

The effectiveness with which an EMC Control Program can be implemented is obviously affected by all elements of the program. These elements include management, organization, technical capability, etc. For these reasons, the control plan should contain positive statements of program management's intent to fully support an effective EMC Control Program, and sufficient organizational information to assure implementation. Normally, this portion of the control plan will present a chart of work statement presenting organizational elements and responsibilities such as:

1. The single organization responsible for all EMC matters and having final authority in all EMI/EMC policy, concept, philosophy and technique matters
2. The organization responsible for preparation of EMI/EMC procedures, plans and other associated documentation such

as the General Test Plan, End Item Test Plan, process specifications, etc. Where more than one organization provides inputs to the documentation, the organizational chart should reflect this.

3. The organization responsible for EMI/EMC testing at all levels. This organization chart should show equipment/subsystem-level testing activity such as development, qualification, engineering, etc., as well as system-level testing activity such as qualification, acceptance, compliance, etc.

4. The organization that will provide EMI/EMC representation during the various program reviews. These reviews might logically be held immediately after the program conceptual phase, flight equipment design phase, ground equipment design phase or various testing phases. If the review is performed by a designated team, one of the team members should be an EMI/EMC engineer.

5. The organization responsible for the preparation, approval and submittal of deviation requests against EMI/EMC requirements or specifications. As a general rule, the responsible design organization prepares needed deviation requests, and the central EMI/EMC coordination organization approves and makes the formal submittal to the procuring agency.

In addition to the organizational elements, the management portion of the EMC Control Plan should specify all applicable EMC documentation. If documents are classified into various levels such that some are submitted to the procuring agency for approval, others for review and maybe others for general information, this shall be shown specifically. Special attention should be directed to the time intervals between preparation and submittal of EMI/EMC documentation. This is particularly important in the case of test results. Within the documentation to be prepared as a result of the EMC Control Program, the documents that are to show the status of the EMC efforts in relation to the milestones in the EMC program and in relation to the milestones of the entire program, should be specifically shown.

The management portion of the EMC Control Plan should also include program milestones. These milestones and target dates should be shown relative to the schedules applicable to the overall program. Typical milestones are:

1. Preparation and submittal of the control plan
2. Qualification testing of equipment to interference and susceptibility requirements

3. Preparation of the EMC Test Plans
4. Preparation of EMC test procedures
5. Initiation of the electrical/electronic compatibility test
6. Initiation of the general acceptance test
7. Any other milestones which the contractor or procuring agency considers pertinent

The means by which satisfactory EMI/EMC design control is to be assured should also be presented in the management portion. This includes the EMI/EMC design guidelines that are to be employed, how these design guidelines are to be effectively presented to the design organizations, the control methods used to assure that the design guidelines are being followed, the means by which the design organizations are to be made knowledgeable of the overall program EMI/EMC philosophies of the control plan, etc.

As a recommendation, EMI/EMC design guidelines should be prepared by one of the responsible contractor organizations. These guidelines should be written so that various portions apply to company management as well as the individual designers. Design organizations should be made knowledgeable of these guidelines by formal training sessions and periodic publications prepared by the EMC organization and should be distributed to the design organizations by an EMC committee which meets regularly with representatives from all affected organizations. The total purpose of this effort is to assure that every possible EMI/EMC control measure is incorporated as early as possible in the design of equipments. Otherwise, costly time delays, major redesigns and serious compromises of equipment operation may result.

In many large companies, several different organizations are involved in testing equipments, subsystems and systems. Where this is the case, the EMC Control Plan should reflect particular tests to be performed by the various organizations and how the results of these tests are to be coordinated. Active liaison between testing organizations performing subsystem/equipment (MIL-STD-461C/462) and system (MIL-E-6051D) tests is especially important. This is true because the results of the subsystem/equipment-level tests are used to define both points to be monitored and to establish tolerable limits for the system-level testing.

Additional active liaison is necessary in cases where system-level testing is performed at more than one location. In these cases, the test results from one location are used to define test requirements at a different location, and the results from tests performed at all locations are combined to show compliance with the applicable system-level specification. Without this active liaison between testing efforts, EMC tests are duplicated, excessive time is consumed in performance of EMC tests and test results lack validity because tolerable limits cannot be established.

In some large system development projects, there is a requirement for an **Electromagnetic Compatibility Advisory Board** (EMCAB). The EMCAB assists in implementing the EMC Control Plan, expedites solutions to EMC problems and establishes high-level channels of coordination. The EMCAB works to ensure that each participating associate, subcontractor and vendor works in accordance with the overall program EMC objectives, that effective methods of monitoring EMC efforts and progress are established and followed, that periodic EMC Program design reviews are scheduled and that noted deficiencies are promptly corrected.

It is the responsibility of the EMCAB to review the EMC Program, initiate studies, make recommendations and otherwise assist in achieving electromagnetic compatibility among similar or dissimilar electrical and avionic systems, subsystems and equipments. EMCAB activities would include the following:

1. Group discussion by EMCAB and design personnel to reveal potential problem areas
2. Continuing review and updating of the EMC Program
3. Examination of potential problems and definition of specific problems
4. Determination of possible solutions and selection of the best one
5. Recommendations of corrective measures to the performing activity
6. Review of the effects of the recommended solution

The proposed charter of the EMCAB and details of its operation are included in the EMC Control Plan. Members of the board are typically the contractor, subcontractor, vendor, **Electromagnetic Compatibility Analysis Center (ECAC)** and procuring activity representatives who are qualified in EMC requirements. Procedures for appointing members are prepared carefully to ensure that each representative has adequate experience and authority to participate in, concur with and implement board recommendations and agreements.

9.1.1.5 Design Considerations

The EMC Control Plan, as required by MIL-E-6051D, does not require detailed EMC design guidelines. Rather, the intent of the MIL-E-6051D EMC Control Plan is to require submittal of overall design policies from a systems point of view. It should be realized that, even though the requirement is for overall design policy, there still must be sufficient depth of exploration to discern what these policies are. In other words, a statement to the effect that "grounding, shielding, testing and other related aspects of the EMC design effort will be managed in a matter adequate to assure a compatible final system" is clearly insufficient.

In many cases, the system from one organization ultimately will be joined with another system from another organization. The design portions of the EMC Control Plans submitted by these two different organizations must present EMC design policy in sufficient detail to allow the procuring agency to be assured that policies implemented on one system will not be violated by policies implemented on the mating system.

One measure of controlling system interference and susceptibility is to ensure adequate EMC design of each equipment associated with the system. This specifically includes equipment using antennas or sensing elements operating in all their modes and performing their intended function. Unless otherwise specified, each equipment shall be designed to meet the requirements of MIL-STD-461C and MIL-STD-462.

Subsystems and equipments used in aircraft installations must operate without malfunction when supplied with electrical power conforming to MIL-STD-704, including surges, ripple voltages and other electrical abnormalities.

Bonding and grounding provisions must meet the requirements of MIL-B-5087 and the National Electrical Code. All elements of systems and ground sites must provide adequate lightning protection in accordance with MIL-B-5087. Special emphasis and testing are given to ordnance and personnel protection.

System design incorporates provisions for keeping static electricity from degrading system effectiveness. Static dischargers are required as specified by the procuring activity. Conductive coating must be used on all nonmetallic material on the external surfaces of the aircraft that are exposed to airflow.

Systems, subsystems and equipments are designed to protect personnel from electromagnetic hazards. System design includes provisions to protect ordnance systems, subsystems and equipments from premature ignition. Good EMI design should be used in laying out wiring, cabling and hardware associated with the ordnance system, which includes weapons, rockets, explosives, electroexplosive devices, squibs, flares, igniters, explosive bolts, destruct devices and similar items.

In system design, the external electromagnetic environment must be considered. Thought must be given to individual mission profiles, available electromagnetic environmental data and the effect of the external environment on system effectiveness.

Some of the areas for which EMC design specifications must be prepared are:

1. Electrical bonding and grounding: Equipment-to-ground reference plane, electrical interface with other equipments or systems and subsystems, electrical power returns and conductor shields

2. Shielding: Equipment and subsystem case shielding, shielding provisions of the system structure, shielding and twisting of conductors and anticipated electromagnetic and electrostatic environments

3. Transient control: Suppression of transients from inductive sources, suppression of conducted transients and surge limiting within the system power profile

4. Radiated signal control: Spurious signals from intentional radiation sources, unintentional radiation sources, control of response to radiation signals and projected intentional radiation environment created by the system

5. Interference and susceptibility prediction: Frequency allocations, antenna locations, antenna patterns and signal levels.

6. Cable and conductor routing consideration: Conductor separation and isolation and location of equipments and subsystems

7. Electromagnetic radiation hazard (RADHAZ) and hazards of electromagnetic radiation to ordnance (HERO): Design policy and test procedures to prevent electromagnetic radiation hazard to personnel or harmful operation of weapon systems and electroexplosive devices

8. Special EMC considerations: Conditions peculiar to the type of system or to the nature of its intended mission and installed equipments may call for more stringent EMC control or variations to the cited specifications

In addition to citing EMC specifications and standards, the system EMC Control Plan should include all requirements necessary for an adequate EMC Program, even though they may not be stated in the specifications and standards. These extra requirements should receive particular attention, and the applicable specifications and standards themselves often require extensive interpretation to fit the particular procurement. Typical of some of the extra requirements that should be presented are:

1. Transient susceptibility testing of equipments and subsystems
2. Audio frequency susceptibility over the range of 15 to 150 kHz for equipments and subsystems
3. EMI emission or susceptibility of interface, ancillary or interconnection devices that may not appear in equipment or subsystem requirement lists
4. Direct current resistance measurements with an approximate limit of 0.0025 Ω to assure a continuous ground reference plane
5. Susceptibility testing of equipments to determine the threshold of susceptibility. This will require a higher signal level than the 100,000 μV generally used.
6. Visual inspection of grounding techniques to assure that there is an adequate RF grounding system
7. Initial system-level EMC testing performed on individual subsystems to define a data base for subsequent system-level tests, familiarization with EMC monitoring equipment and familiarization with the operation of the system

9.1.1.6 EMC Test Requirements

As part of the EMC control program of MIL-E-6051D, the contractor is required to present an EMC Test Plan. EMC Test Plan details, together with a discussion of a sample plan, are presented in a following section.

Test requirements of the EMC Control Plan should provide for:

1. Preparation of an EMC Test Plan that defines equipment, subsystem and system-level testing to be performed and that is a contractual requirement over which the procuring activity has approval authority
2. A statement of criteria used in determining which equipments and subsystems shall be tested

3. Identification, by nomenclature and serial number if possible, of equipments and subsystems to be tested
4. A statement of criteria used in determining the extent of EMC tests to be performed
5. A design review to assure that the equipments and subsystems have complied with the applicable design requirements of the EMC Control Plan

9.1.1.7 Quality Assurance Criteria

Once the efficiency of the EMC control measures has been proved by detailed tests on a test model of the system or subsystem, a simplified test procedure will assure continued quality in production models. It is therefore required by MIL-E-6051D that each production model be given a general acceptance test to ensure compliance with EMC requirements. This portion of the EMC Control Plan sets forth the responsibility for the test and directs attention to applicable portions of the EMC Test Plan.

9.1.1.8 Definitions and Other Pertinent Information

Additional information normally included in the EMC Control Plan includes definitions of terms used, methods to be used in the education of design, management and test personnel to EMC awareness, system quality assurance and production control or any studies that will be initiated for improvement of the EMC control program.

The "definitions" portion of the EMC Control Plan is a small part of the total volume, but it is implicitly necessary to establish the extent and scope of the EMC effort. Words and phrases have various meanings to different persons. Some common terms that often are not assigned exact meanings and therefore require precise definition are: engineering tests, acceptance tests, ground, interference, susceptibility, ambient environment, compatibility, safety margin and other such general, unspecific terms.

The EMC Control Plan outline and content described in this section is a systems plan in accordance with the requirements of MIL-E-6051D. For individual equipments or subsystem, a separate EMC Control Plan may be required to describe the engineering design procedures and techniques which comply with equipment standards MIL-STD-461C and 462. It is desirable that these control plans be separate sections of a single document. The emphasis of the equipment control plan is on equipment design practices, procedures and guidelines.

All the information stipulated for inclusion in the EMC Control Plan may not be available by the submission date specified in the contract. The rest of the information will become known as the program progresses. Therefore, the EMC Control Plan must be reviewed periodically and updated as necessary. The EMC Advisory Board should logically assist in this updating. The suggested period for review is semiannually. Even if no update is necessary every six months, the review will benefit all concerned as a reminder of basic requirements of the EMC Control Plan. The EMC Control Plan is kept updated by the use of supplements or revised pages as specified by the contract.

9.1.2 Equipment-Level EMC Control Plan

The previous section discussed the purpose, requirements and contents for a system-level EMC Control Plan. This section provides a similar discussion for the equipment-level EMC Control Plan. If an equipment or subsystem is being developed for military or certain other government applications, MIL-STD-461C will most likely be imposed as a contractual requirement, and an EMC Control Plan will then be required. If the equipment is being developed for commercial or other government applications that do not require adherence to MIL-STD-461C, an EMC Control Plan should still be prepared and implemented.

If MIL-STD-461C is a contractual requirement, the EMC Control Plan must conform to the DoD Data Item Description Number DI-EMCS-80199. The equipment-level EMC Control Plan should be a detailed plan outlining the interference control or *a priori* reduction program, the engineering design procedures and proposed techniques that will be used to determine conformance with the requirements of military EMI Standards. This will enable the equipment to perform its operational function without interference or compromise from its parts and subassemblies.

Approval of the EMI Control Plan and compliance thereto does not relieve the contractor of the responsibility of meeting the applicable requirements of the military EMI standards. Technically

9.16

justifiable deviations which are or will be formally processed through contractual channels may be included in the control plan.

As set forth in the applicable Data Item Description, the EMI Control Plan should contain, but is not to be limited to, the major categories covered in Sections 9.1.2.1 through 9.1.2.9.

9.1.2.1 Management Controls

Specific organizational responsibilities, lines of authority and control and the implementation plan, including milestones to be used by the contractor, are included in the EMI Control Plan. This section also includes a definition of responsibility for associate contractor equipments, government-furnished equipments and subcontractor vendor items. For example, test requirements placed upon independent testing laboratories and a complete listing of all EMC/EMI requirements in suppliers purchase orders, work statements and equipment and subsystem specifications are enumerated. The purpose behind the foregoing is to assure that lines of responsibility and authority are known to all parties concerned, i.e., that communications are well established.

9.1.2.2 Spectrum Conservation

Frequency management is employed and consists of minimizing emission spectrum and receiver bandwidths and controlling oscillator frequencies, pulse rise times, harmonics, sidebands and duty cycle. In general, frequency management attempts to establish the lowest transmitting power, out-of-band emissions and receiver bandwidth required to transfer intelligence. It reduces spectrum pollution and hardens receivers to susceptibility. An **Application for Frequency Allocation Data Form (DD Form 1494)** is to be included for informational purposes when applicable.

9.1.2.3 EMI Mechanical Design

The materials and construction methods selected for design should inherently reduce electromagnetic emissions and susceptibilities while still meeting the requirements contract end item specification and without compromising other mechanical requirements of the individual equipment specifications. The EMI

Control Plan describes the material and construction used and the criteria for this selection. Some specific data to be included are as follows:

1. Type of metals, casting, finishes and hardware employed in the design
2. Type of construction, such as compartmentizing; filter mounting and isolation of other parts; dimensions of access ports, windows and ventilation ports; type and characteristics of filtering used on openings including such items as ventilation ports, access hatches, windows, meter faces and control shafts; and type and attenuation characteristics of RF gaskets used on all internal and external mating surfaces
3. Shielding and design practices employed for determining shielding effectiveness
4. Corrosion control procedures

9.1.2.4 Electrical/Electronic Wiring Design

The EMI Control Plan includes a description of any proposed electrical and electronic wiring designs. For example, cables are separated and routed to minimize EMI and susceptibility in accordance with the classification procedures of the standard. The plan, therefore, describes the practices to be used with regard to grouping of signal, logic and control and power cables and the criteria to be employed with regard to shielding and grounding of cable shields. Diagrams of equipments or subsystems, consisting of a number of boxes or chassis will be supplied showing the interconnecting cabling.

9.1.2.5 Electrical/Electronic Circuit Design

This section describes the EMI suppression techniques which are to be applied to all parts and circuitry, whether capable of generating undesirable emanations or suspected of being susceptible to the coupling fields and voltage levels specified. Some specifically required design data includes the following:

1. Choice of component parts and circuitry, the criteria for use of standard parts and circuitry and bonding and grounding techniques

2. Justification of selected filter characteristics, including type and attenuation, technical reasons for selecting types of filters (for example, absorptive vs. nonabsorptive filters) and specific circuit applications

3. Part location and separation based on orientation of electric and magnetic fields for reduction of emissions, susceptibility or both

4. Discussion indicating valid technical reasons for selection of pulse shape. The pulse shapes to be considered for example, are to include rectangular, trapezoidal, triangular, binomial and cosine squared. The pulse shapes utilized will minimize the electromagnetic spectrum occupancy consistent with achieving the design performance.

5. Location of critical circuits and decoupling techniques employed for each

6. Shielding and isolation of critical circuits

9.1.2.6 Analysis

Prediction and analysis techniques employed to determine the adequacy of contractor's conclusions are included. Specific aspects of the mechanical, electrical and electronic design to be included are as follows:

1. Adequacy of mechanical construction and an analysis of the shielding afforded by the proposed designs over the specified frequency range and energy level

2. Complete frequency matrix of all frequencies associated with receivers and transmitters, expected spurious responses of receivers at input signal levels and frequency range(s) specified in the standard and expected spurious outputs of items such as transmitters, local oscillators and frequency synthesizers. The frequency matrix could be used to formulate a subsystem test matrix of source and victim equipments. The test matrix is included in the subsystem test plan.

3. Worst-case analysis (Fourier) of multivibrators, switching (single and repetitive) and logic circuits, clock signals and strobe signals

4. Analysis of circuitry, subassemblies and total equipment or subsystem including cabling and loads for:
   a. The prediction of susceptibility to internally and externally generated fields and voltages, whether below or above the limits specified
   b. The prediction of emissions whether below or above the limits specified
5. Subsystem analysis for mobile or fixed installations with two or more antennas. This includes a description of radiation characteristics from antennas covering fundamentals and spurious energy and discussion of minimizing antenna coupling and isolation achieved by placement and location of antennas.

9.1.2.7 R&D Testing

Discussions of a proposed testing program during development and breadboard construction stages are required.

9.1.2.8 Problem Areas

Plans and procedures for identifying and resolving potential EMI problems shall be discussed. Also, the methods for testing and implementing solutions shall be discussed.

9.1.2.9 Revisions

The method and frequency for revising the control plan shall be discussed.

9.2 The EMC Test Plan

The EMC Test Plan is intended to provide the procuring activity with specific techniques by which the contractor will assure compliance with the appropriate EMC specifications and standards. It is important to recognize that there are different types of EMC specifications and standards. As a result, there are different requirements for EMC Test Plans. First, MIL-E-6051D applies to the development of large systems and imposes requirements for system-level testing. Second, MIL-STD-461C and MIL-STD-469 apply to the development of equipment and impose requirements for equipment-level testing. This section discusses the purpose and content of both types of EMC Test Plans.

9.2.1 System-Level EMC Test Plan

MIL-E-6051D specifies that the contractor shall develop and prepare a system-level test plan. The test plan must be submitted to the procuring agency for approval prior to the initiation of tests. As a minimum, the Test Plan should include the following information:

1. Methods to be used in selecting critical circuits to be monitored for compliance with the degradation criteria and safety margin
2. Procedures used for developing failure criteria and limits
3. Test conditions and procedures for all electronic and electrical equipment installed in, or associated with, the system and the sequence for operations during tests, including switching
4. Implementation and application of test procedures which shall include modes of operation and monitoring points for each subsystem and equipment
5. Use of approved results from laboratory interference tests on subsystems and equipment
6. Flight test program (manned systems only)
7. Methods and procedures for data readout and analysis
8. Means of testing design adequacy of vehicle electrification (static electricity) and lightning protection
9. Means of simulating and testing electro-explosive subsystems and devices
10. Demonstration of the approval safety margin for electro-explosive devices and for systems whose degradation affects safety-of-flight or mission success
11. Electrical power voltage limits and methods for monitoring ac and dc power buses to assure that voltages are within the proper limits
12. Test locations and descriptions of arrangements for simulating operational performance in cases where actual operation is impractical
13. Adjustments and settings of variable controls such as audio gain, video gain, sensitivity, squelch settings, etc.

14. Details concerning frequency ranges, channels and combinations to be specifically tested such as image frequencies, intermediate frequencies, local oscillator and transmitter fundamental and harmonically related frequencies. Subsystem susceptibility frequencies identified during laboratory testing shall be included.
15. Personnel required: government, contractor and vendor
16. Calibration schedules and description of unique EMC instrumentation for measuring electrical, video and mechanical outputs of equipments and subsystems to be monitored during the testing including applicable safety margins
17. Means of simulating signal inputs such as doppler, radar altimeter, etc.
18. Evaluation and degradation criteria for each subsystem and equipment

9.2.2 Equipment-Level EMC Test Plan

MIL-STD-461C specifies that the contractor shall develop and prepare equipment-level test plans in accordance with the requirements of Data Item Description DI-EMCS-80201. The equipment-level EMI Test Plan should conform to the content and format requirements described in the following sections.

9.2.2.1 Introduction

The EMI Test Plan shall contain an introduction which shall cover the following:
1. The purpose of the plan and its relationship to the overall electromagnetic control program for the equipment or subsystem
2. A table listing the tests to be performed, the paragraph number of the plan and the corresponding test method of the basic standards MIL-STD-461C and MIL-STD-462
3. Description of the test sample, including operating frequency, line current and so forth

9.2.2.2 Applicable Documents

Applicable documents shall be listed as follows:
1. Military (standards, specifications and so forth)
2. Company (in-house documents for calibration or quality assurance)
3. Other government or industry standards, specifications or documents

9.2.2.3 Test Site

A description of the test site, covering the following:
1. Description of test facility, shielded enclosure or anechoic chamber (size, power availability, filters and attenuation characteristics of room to electric, magnetic and plane waves)
2. Description of ground plane (size and type) and methods of grounding or bonding the test sample to the ground plane to simulate actual equipment installation
3. Evidence of spot-check measurements of the ambient electromagnetic emission profile of the test facility, both radiated and conducted, to determine ambient suitability

9.2.2.4 Test Instrumentation

Test instrumentation to be used shall be described as follows:
1. Test equipment nomenclature and bandwidth
2. Scanning speed used to drive the measuring equipment
3. The characteristics of matching transformers and band rejection
4. Antenna factors of specified antennas, transfer impedances of current probes, impedance of line impedance stabilization network (LISN) and insertion losses and impedance curves of 10 μF capacitors

9.2.2.5 Test Sample Setup

A description of test sample setup shall cover the actual physical layout of the equipment under test, the position of the feedthrough capacitors or LISNs on the ground plane and the location of bond straps, loads and test sets. Notes may be used to indicate height above ground plane for leads.

9.2.2.6 Test Sample Operation

The description of the test sample's operation shall cover:
1. Modes of operation for each test and operating frequency
2. Control settings on the test sample
3. Control settings on any test sets employed or characteristics of input signals
4. Test frequencies at which oscillators, clocks and so forth may be expected to approach requirements and limits
5. Performance checks initiated to designate the equipment as meeting minimal working standard requirements
6. An enumeration of circuits, outputs and displays to be monitored during susceptibility testing as well as the criteria for monitoring for performance degradation
7. Normal, malfunction and performance degradation criteria for susceptibility testing

9.2.2.7 Measurements

The measurements to be employed to demonstrate compliance with the contractual requirements shall be described. As a minimum, the following shall be indicated for each test:
1. Block diagram depicting the test setup
2. Test equipment used in performance of the test, and the methods of grounding, bonding or achieving isolation for the measurement instrumentation
3. Procedures for:
   a. Probing the test sample
   b. Determining placement and orientation of probes and antennas
   c. Selecting measurement frequencies and detector functions

4. Information to be recorded during the test, including frequency and units of recorded information. Sample data sheets, test logs and graphs, including test limits may be shown.
5. Modulation characteristics of the susceptibility test signals, such as amplitude, waveform, type of modulation and so forth

9.3 EMI Test Reports and Certifications

The EMI Test Report contains the necessary data and discussion of results to demonstrate that the equipment or system being tested complies with the applicable EMC specification or standard. The following sections discuss the report requirements for tests performed to demonstrate compliance with military standards and FCC rules and regulations.

9.3.1 EMI Test Reports for Military Standard Testing

The report requirements for EMI tests performed to demonstrate compliance with military standards (e.g., MIL-STD-461C or MIL-E-6051D) are given in MIL-STD-831, "Test Reports, Preparation of." In addition, MIL-STD-461C imposes specific requirements as described in Data Item Description DI-EMCS-80200. The EMI Test Report requirements, as specified by these documents are described below.

9.3.1.1 MIL-STD-831 Test Reports

MIL-STD-461C, MIL-E-6051 and some other EMI and related specifications state that the test report shall follow the format of MIL-STD-831, "Test Reports, Preparation of." Accordingly, MIL-STD-831 is reproduced in part here.

9.3.1.1.1 General

Scope
This standard delineates the format and content criteria to be used in the preparation of test reports covering tests on systems, subsystems, equipments, components and parts.

Purpose

The purpose of this standard is to foster uniformity in the portrayal of test results on items of material. They also provide for greater ease in the evaluation of the design suitability and performance capability of test items for use in new applications.

9.3.1.1.2 Applicable Documents

Not applicable.

9.3.1.1.3 Definitions

Universal Document Number

That number which shall identify each test report and will be furnished by the procuring activity when it is required. This number is to be assigned in addition to any existing originator's report number.

Appendixes

An appendix is defined as any portion of a report which is necessary to its completeness but which is separated from the balance of the report for convenience or because it does not logically fall under one of the preceding headings.

Exhibits

An exhibit is defined as any document which is furnished with a report but is not an integral portion thereof. It might consist of a separate test report on the same or similar item or pertinent correspondence or vendor data sheets or a memo reporting important conversations.

9.3.1.1.4 General Requirements

Basic Data

All test reports shall contain all the collected data and all conclusions resulting therefrom for the tests performed.

Test File

A test file shall be established and maintained which shall include original log sheets, wiring and piping diagrams, schematics and block diagrams which are required to completely describe the purpose, conduct and results of tests. Upon creation, this file shall be given a permanent identifying number which shall appear on all subsequent documents associated with a particular test.

Notes

Notes of all incidents of the testing, such as adjustments made, service performed, leaks, vibrations and any other irregular functioning of the product and corrective measures taken shall be placed on log sheets and included in the test report.

Use of Supporting Documents

When applicable data has been previously submitted as a result of similar or related government-funded tests, these shall be quoted, excerpted or used in whatever manner possible to direct, guide, support, substantiate or shorten test reports.

Authentication

The test report shall provide for the following signatures:

1. **Responsible Officer**

   The test report shall be signed by a responsible officer of the contractor's organization.

2. **Government Representative**

   A Government representative may witness the test and countersign the report. The latter signature shall constitute verification of the data contained in the report and shall not necessarily indicate concurrence with the conclusions presented.

9.3.1.1.5 Detail Requirements: Format

Test reports shall be prepared in accordance with the following criteria:

Paper

Copies of documents intended for technical data repositories or data exchange programs shall be designated **Data Interchange Submittal Copies** and shall be on white opaque paper. Complete text shall be clear and sharp, of consistent high contrast and preferably black on white. "Brownline" transparencies and "blue lines" shall not be used for the above purposes. All other copies shall be on carbon-backed vellum, parchment, ozo-parchment, 14 pound bond or equivalent translucent material for reproduction purposes.

Page Size

The size of each finished page shall be 8" by 10.5" or 8.5" by 11". The universal document number, page number and issue or revision date shall be included on all sheets. Sketches, drawings and diagrams may exceed the 8" or 8.5" dimension to form foldouts where the alternative would be extreme reduction in size of graphic material.

Margins

Adequate margins shall be allowed so that the complete text can be easily read when the report is in bound form.

Numbering

Beginning with the first page, all pages of the test report shall be numbered consecutively. The page number shall be placed in the center of the bottom margin.

Binding

The test report shall be bound in such a manner that the pages can be removed without damage or mutilation to the pages. Full page tables, illustrations, etcetera, shall be arranged so that the bottom of the table or illustration will be either at the bottom or at the right-hand edge of the bound document.

Illustrations

Where practical, illustrations shall be provided when such would serve to clarify or otherwise aid in understanding the report. Illustrations shall fit the required dimensions of the report. Illustrations may include sketches, drawings, graphs, photographs, etc. and may be included in the main body of the report as applicable and shall have dark line work on light background. Drawings over "C" size shall be avoided. However, inclusion of illustrations as appendixed under a proper group heading is preferred, provided references are indicated in the main body of the report. All photographic prints shall be of high contrast and definition and shall be page-size. When photographs are in the bond copy, a positive transparency shall be provided with the reproducible copy. In data interchange submittal copies, negatives are not acceptable in lieu of prints.

Color Differentiation
Color differentiation shall not be used for graphs, diagrams, etc.

Abbreviations
Abbreviations shall be held to a minimum.

Required Elements
The report shall contain the following elements in the degree of detail applicable to the size and complexity of the test item and the test performed, in the order specified:

Title Page and Cover
The cover is not mandatory, but if used shall contain the information shown in Fig. 9.1, in approximately the same positions on the page. Cutouts may be used to allow the same information to show through from the title page shown in Fig. 9.2. Data interchange submittal copies shall not bear "Company Confidential" or similar stampings restricting circulation by the procuring activity.

Tabular Summary Sheet
A tabular summary sheet shall be included as the first page of all component or parts test reports containing all of the information called for in Fig. 9.3. Test reports on systems, subsystems, equipments and others of a broad scope or general nature may require the use of the general report summary sheet, shown in Fig. 9.4 or the test summary sheet shown in Fig. 9.5 in lieu of that shown in Fig. 9.3. This alternative shall be taken in reporting tests where the detail summary sheet (Fig. 9.3) is definitely not applicable.

Notice Page
The notice shown at the top of page 9.35 shall be included as a full-size page of all data interchange submittal copies of reports. Only the first paragraph shall be required as part of all other copies.

Universal
Report No.* _____

Originator's
Report No. _____

Revision _____

REPORT OF TEST ON* _____

(Add necessary additional detail of type, size, rating, Mfg., brief purpose
or type of test.)

TEST PERFORMED BY:
TEST AUTHORIZED BY:**
Contract No. _____

*   As defined by the Procuring Activity

**   Include only if other than the organization performing test.

COVER PAGE

NOTE: The cover shall contain information shown, either reproduced on
the cover itself, or visible through openings cut in the cover.

Figure 9.1—Cover Page

Universal
Report No. _____

Originator's
Report No. _____

Revision _____

REPORT OF TEST ON _____

(Add necessary additional detail of type, size, rating, Mfg., brief purpose
or type of test.)

TEST PERFORMED BY:

TEST AUTHORIZED BY:**

Contract No. _____

	Date	Signature	
Test Initiated			
Test Completed			
Report Written by			
Technician			
Test Engineer			
Supervisor			
Supervisor			
Government Repr. (if applicable)			
Final Release			

Figure 9.2—Title Page

REPORT SUMMARY SHEET

1. Component/Part Name Per Generic Code		2. Program or Weapon System					
				3.	Day	Mo.	Yr.
		3. Originator's Report No.		Test Compl			
2. Originator's Report Title				Rept Compl			
		6. Test Type, Etc.					

7. This Test (Supersedes) (Supplements) Report No:

8. Item	8A Part Type, Size, Rating, Lot, Etc.	9. Vendor	10. Vendor Part No.	11. Ind/Gov.Std No.	12. Total Tested
1					
2					
3					
4					

13	INTERNAL SPECS ETC REQ'D TO UTILIZE REPT	ENCL	SENT WITH REPORT NO.	14	MIL SPECS/STDS REFERENCED IN 15C
A				D	
B				E	
C				F	

15A Test or Environment B ITEM	C Per Spec	D Spec Paragraph Method/Condition	E Test Levels, Duration and Other Details	F No. Tested	G No. Failed
					(over)

16 Summary of Report, Nature of Failures and Corrective Actions Taken:

(over)

17 Tested Beyond Vendor Catalog Specifications	YES	18 Vendor Informed of Test Result By Letter Copy of Rept Oral	19 Signed	20 Contractor	Subcontractor

REPRODUCTION OR DISPLAY OF THIS MATERIAL FOR SALES OR PUBLICITY PURPOSES IS PROHIBITED.

Figure 9.3—Report Summary Sheet

GENERAL REPORT SUMMARY SHEET

1. Component/Part Name Per Generic Code	2. Program or Weapon System				
		3.	Day	Mo.	Yr.
	3. Originator's Report No.	Test Compl			
2. Originator's Report Title		Rept Compl			
	6. Test Type, Etc.				

7. This Test (Supersedes) (Supplements) Report No:
8. Outline, Table of Contents, Summary, or Equivalent Description:

9 Signed	10 Contractor	Subcontractor

REPRODUCTION OR DISPLAY OF THIS MATERIAL FOR SALES OR PUBLICITY PURPOSES IS PROHIBITED.

Figure 9.4—General Report Summary Sheet

TEST SUMMARY SHEET

Item: _____ Contr: _____ Contr's Type: _____ Date Test Completed: _____ Sample Nos. _____

Spec _____ Mfr. _____ MFR's Type _____ Date Test Begun: _____ FR ___ TO ___

Line	Test Group	Data Ref. Page	Spec Ref Para	Test Condition	Spec. Limits	Measured Values		No. Samples		Remarks
						Min.	Max.	Tested	Passed	

Figure 9.5—Test Summary Sheet

9.34

NOTICES PAGE

Copies of specifications, standards, drawings, and publications required by contractors in connection with specific procurement functions should be obtained from the procuring activity or as directed by the contracting officer.

Copies of this standard for Military Use may be obtained as indicated in general provisions to the Index of Military Specifications and Standards.

The title and identifying symbol number should be stipulated when requesting copies of Military Standards.

Where security regulations are involved, the requirements herein shall be adapted as necessary to comply, but whenever possible, classified or proprietary components or parts test reports shall be downgraded by deleting classified or proprietary portions relating to usages and assemblies, without impairing the usefulness of documented contents pertaining to component or part performance. In addition to the notice provided above, the following information shall be typewritten on the notice page of classified test reports:

WARNING:

This material contains information affecting the national defense of the United States within the meaning of the espionage laws, title 18, the U.S.C., secs. 793 and 794, the transmission or revelation of which in any manner to an unauthorized person is prohibited by law.

Table of Contents

A table of contents shall include paragraph numbers, the subject of each paragraph and the beginning page number for each.

Reason for Test

The report shall contain a statement describing the specific reason for conducting the test, together with pertinent background information as applicable.

Description of Test Samples

Whenever possible, each test report shall describe tests on only one type of component, part, equipment or subsystem. The number of vendors whose products are represented in a single report shall be kept to a minimum. Where space does not allow sufficient detail on the summary sheet, additional description shall include the part manufacturer's address and when available all of the following: size, type, rating, serial number(s), batch, lot and date of manufacture. Vendor, trade association, federal stock and military part number designations shall be given when such numbers exist, but none of these shall be substituted for a complete description. Further description shall include method of sample selection and whether tested item(s) are prototypes, pilot samples from a model shop or production items. When specimen(s) are components of a system, a brief description of the function within the system shall be given. Arbitrarily assigned numbers, if used to identify specimens during test, shall be tabulated against serial numbers or other means of positive identification.

Disposition of Test Specimens

Disposition of test samples shall be given.

Narrative Abstract, Conclusions and Recommendations

This combined paragraph shall contain an expansion of the remarks on the tabular summary sheet or of any other portions of the test report. The test engineer shall include in this section any corrective measures taken, his recommendations as to better test methods, procedures and sampling quantities. In connection with preproduction or qualification testing, this section shall contain a statement of the contractor's intention regarding each instance wherein the test items do not fulfill the specified requirements, i.e., corrections to be made on production items or a statement that it is intended to request a waiver.

References

If not already completely listed on the tabular summary sheet, all specifications and other applicable documents referred to in the report shall be listed here. Specifications and other documents necessary for proper report interpretation, which are not normally available to persons outside the report originating location, shall be included with the report either as an appendix or an exhibit, and shall be listed as "attached."

Main Body of Report

Factual Data

The following section shall be included under a main heading entitled "Factual Data:"

Description of Test Apparatus

A description of test apparatus shall include a tabulation of all instruments and equipment used, the manufacturers' names, serial numbers, ranges, accuracy and dates of latest calibration.

Test Procedure

This section shall contain a detailed explanation of what tests or measurements were made, how they were made and any other pertinent criteria which may affect the interpretation of the test data in sufficient detail for separate formulation of conclusions by interested parties not witnessing the test. When sketches, diagrams and drawings are used, they shall be presented on separate sheets following the test data. Curves and graphs showing the spread of the results shall be provided, with performance tolerance brackets superimposed on graphic data. Sample calculations shall be included in this section. Criteria used to define a success or a failure shall be clearly stated after each test. If a military specification or standard specifies precisely the limits used as pass-fail criteria for the test, it may be referred to by specific paragraph for each test in lieu of writing out detailed descriptions. Also, when internal (company) specifications, drawings or other corporate documents are included with a report as appendixes or exhibits, and these include test procedures and limits in detail, such documents may be referred to in the same manner. However, where the limits for a particular test cannot be precisely identified by such reference, they must be stated in detail. Where feasible, each test procedure shall reference the data page(s) containing the detail of the corresponding measurements obtained.

Results of Tests; Summations and Analyses

In tests that are very long, data shall be summarized for study and analysis using either graphical or tabular techniques indicating the spread and distribution density of results, means and deviations, mean time to failure or any applicable expressions or techniques summarizing the facts shown by the test data. Instructional detail may be added to a statistical and graphical presentation. More detailed test results shall be added when a test is of such complexity that such detail is not covered by summations and test data tabulations. All results shall be keyed to the test procedure, test data tabulations and to specifications requirements to ensure ease of identification and relations between requirements, procedures and results.

Test Data

Test data compiled in the performance of tests or measurements shall be included as data sheets or as an appendix. All tabulated data shall show the exact measurement value regardless of whether or not a failure is the result of deliberate test to destruction. Data interchange submittal copies of reports may include only summarizations of significant occurrences from a number of data pages in a single tabulation or one representative page of each type included with a statement that the balance of "n" pages is available on request from the test file.

Revisions, Additions, Reissues

Title Page

The title page shall bear the notation "Revision" directly under the originators report number. The latest revision letter shall be used to identify this issue of the entire report. A revision letter shall not be used on the initial issue.

Revision Page

A revision page listing the revised pages and a brief description of the changes shall be inserted between the cover and the title page or between the title page and the tabular summary sheet if no cover is used. This insertion shall be numbered 1a, 1b, etc.

Corrected Pages

All corrected pages in a revised report shall bear the notation "Revision A," "Revision B," etc., directly under each page number.

Appendixes

When only small parts of a long related document are applicable to a report, those portions may be excerpted and included as an appendix and shall be properly identified on each page and in the table of contents.

9.3.1.2 Additional Requirements for MIL-STD-461C EMC Test Reports

The EMI Test Report prepared to demonstrate that equipments comply with MIL-STD-461C shall conform to MIL-STD-831 and shall also conform to the additional requirements of Data Item Description DI-EMCS-80200. The additional requirements imposed by the data item description are specified below.

9.3.1.2.1 Administrative Data

The EMI Test report shall contain an administrative section covering the following:

1. Contract number
2. Authentication and certification of performance of the tests by a qualified representative of a procuring activity
3. Disposition of the test specimen
4. Description of the test sample, including function and intended use or installation, if known
5. List of tests performed and changes in limits or test frequencies previously authorized

9.3.1.2.2 Appendixes

A separate appendix shall be prepared for each test. Each appendix shall cover the applicable test procedure or reference to the approved EMI Test Plan, data sheets, graphs, illustrations and photographs. The log sheets shall be contained in a separate appendix which will be shown last. Definitions of specialized terms or word usage shall be covered in another appendix. Each appendix shall contain the following factual data:

1. Nomenclature of interference measuring equipment
2. Serial numbers of interference measuring equipment
3. Date of last calibration of interference measuring equipment, procedures used and their traceability
4. Photographs or diagrams of the test set up and the test sample with identification
5. Transfer impedance of current probes
6. Antenna factors of specified antennas, impedance of LISN and insertion loss and impedance curve of 10 μF capacitors, as applicable
7. Measured levels of emission at each frequency before and after the application of suppression devices, including data specified in Fig. 9.6
8. Graphs or X-Y recordings of applicable limits and measured data in units as specified in MIL-STD-461C for that requirement
9. Data to show compliance with susceptibility requirements and thresholds of susceptibility or limitations of test equipment, including data specified in Fig. 9.7
10. If suppression devices are employed to meet the contractual requirements they shall be identified, using schematics, performance data and drawings
11. Sample calculations, if any

Technician: Date:

Equipment nomenclature: Serial:

(check as applicable)

Test method: Type of measurement:

Radiated: ☐ NB   ☐ BB

Conducted: ☐ NB   ☐ BB

Frequency range of test:

Measurement technique:

Mode of operation:

Calibrated volt.	☐

Test equipment used:

Slideback	☐
Substitution	☐

Detector Function:

Peak	☐
Average	☐
Other	☐
Specify_____	

Test Frequency	Meter Indication	Attenuator	Correction factors A B C D	Corrected	Limit	Remarks

A   Current probe
B   Bandwidth
C   Cable losses
D   Antenna factor

Figure 9.6—Sample Data Sheet for Emission Tests

Technician:		Date:				
Equipment nomenclature:		Serial:				
Test method:		Type of measurement: (Check) Radiated: ☐ Conducted: ☐				
Measurement point:		Mode of operation:				
Frequency range of test:		Description of test signal:				
Test Equipment Used:						
Test frequency	Meets Limits Yes? | No?		Susceptibility threshold level	Description of degradation	Maximum Text signal applied if not susceptible	N O T E

Figure 9.7—Sample Data Sheet for Susceptibility Tests

9.3.1.2.3 Recommendations and Conclusions

Recommendations and conclusions, including results of the tests in brief narrative form, a discussion of remedial actions already initiated and proposed corrective measures which will be implemented to assure compliance of the equipment or subsystem, with the contractual EMI requirements, shall be covered. In addition, any test sample characteristics which may influence the equipments ability to meet the contractual EMI requirements shall be discussed. These characteristics may include: power consumption, shock hazard, weight, water-tightness and utilization of nonferrous materials.

9.3.2 Reports and Certifications: FCC Parts 15 and 18

The Federal Communications Commission requires the submission of reports and certifications under provisions of its Rules and Regulations, Parts 15 and 18. The FCC sets forth the specifications which all nongovernment communications-electronics equipment; industrial, scientific and medical (ISM) equipment; and other incidental radiation equipment must meet.

9.3.2.1 Reports and Certifications Required

The nature of the reports and certification required and the forms or formats to be used will vary depending upon the equipment or devices requiring certification. This is explained in the applicable parts of the FCC Rules and Regulations. However, certain generalizations regarding the reports and certification may be made as follows:

1. No equipment manufactured shall be operated without a station license unless it has been certificated to demonstrate compliance with the radiations interference limits.
2. The owner or operator need not certificate his own equipment as meeting the radiation interference limits if it has been certificated by the manufacturer or the distributor.
3. Certification made by the manufacturer or the distributor shall be based on tests made on equipment actually produced for sale. Tests shall be performed on a sufficient number of production units to assure that all production units comply with the requirements.
4. The certificate must be executed by an engineer skilled in making and interpreting such measurements as are required.

5. The certificate shall contain the following information:
   a. Name of the manufacturer or distributor of the equipment
   b. Model number
   c. Brief description of equipment
   d. Brief statement of the measurement procedure used (Note: If a standard procedure is used, it is sufficient to identify the standard. Other measurement procedures must be described in detail.)
   e. Date the measurements were made
   f. A summary of the data obtained
   g. A statement certifying that on the basis of measurements made, the equipment is capable of complying with the requirements of this part under normal operation with the usual maintenance
   h. The name and address of the certifying engineer and name and address of his employer, if any
   i. Date of the certificate
6. The certificate shall be retained by the owner, the manufacturer or the distributor (as may be appropriate) for a period of five years and shall be made available, upon reasonable request, to an authorized FCC representative or photostat furnished by mail.

9.3.2.2 Information To Be Filed With Commission

1. Each manufacturer, distributor or other certifying agency that issues certifications shall file with the Commission a description of its measurement facilities used for certification.
2. A copy of each certificate prepared by a manufacturer, distributor or certifying agency shall be filed with the Commission at the time the certificate is performed.

9.4 Bibliography

Apollo Program NHB 5320.3, *Electromagnetic Compatibility Principles and Practices* (NASA, October 1965).

MIL-D-8706B (AS), "Data and Tests, Engineering: Contract Requirements for Aircraft Weapon Systems (U.S. Dept. of Defense, August 1968).

MIL-D-8708 (AS), "Demonstration Requirements for Airplanes" (U.S. Dept. of Defense, January 1969).

MIL-D-18300D (WP), "Design Data Requirements for Avionic Equipment (U.S. Dept. of Defense, December 1961).

MIL-E-6051D, "Military Specification, Electromagnetic Compatibility Requirements, Systems (U.S. Dept. of Defense, September 1967).

MIL-STD-831, "Test Reports, Preparation of."

USAF Design Handbook, AFSC DH 1-4, *Electromagnetic Compatibility* (U.S. Air Force, WPAFB, Ohio).

Chapter 10

EMC Measurement Procedures

There are various rules, regulations, specifications and standards that establish limits on emissions and susceptibility of equipments and systems. To ensure that equipments comply with the applicable limits, it is necessary to measure the emissions and susceptibilities associated with the equipments. This chapter summarizes the measurement procedures that are used to ensure compliance with the FCC and VDE limits for computing devices and MIL-STD-461C emission and susceptibility limits. For a more detailed examination of EMC test methodology and procedures, see Volume 6 of this handbook series.

10.1 FCC Test Procedures for Computing Devices

The FCC rules are concerned with both conducted and radiated emissions from computing devices. This section summarizes some of the important elements associated with testing computing devices to demonstrate compliance with FCC Part 15 Subpart J.

In general, the conducted emission tests are straightforward and reliable, and repeatable measurements can be achieved. The FCC conducted limits for Class A and B equipment are based on a 50 Ω/50 μH line impedance stabilization network (LISN). The levels are measured with a CISPR quasipeak (QP) function. If the emissions exceed the limit, they may be redone with an average function. If the signal level in average mode is significantly less than in the QP mode, the emission is considered broadband and the QP value may be reduced by 13 dB for comparison to the limit.

The FCC radiated limits are based on an open area test site (OATS) criteria. The appropriate antenna distance is 30 m for Class A (commercial) equipment and 3 m for Class B (residential) equipment. The physical arrangement of the test site is shown in Fig. 10.1. This drawing is from FCC document OST-55 which describes the set up of a radiated emissions test range. (More information on setting up a facility can also be found in FCC document MP-4.) The radiated test site consists of a ground plane (if required) sufficient in size to obtain proper site attenuation data. An antenna is mounted on a mast which is capable of raising and lowering the antenna as described in the figure. The equipment under test is placed on a nonconductive structure at one end of the test site. That device is rotated and cables attached to it are moved in order to find the configuration resulting in maximum emissions. The antenna height is raised and lowered and its polarization changed to do the same. Readings are then taken on a measuring device such as a spectrum analyzer or receiver. The set up seems, from the FCC documents, to be simple and very straightforward. The areas of major concern are the selection of antennas (dipole versus broadband), the selection of measurement gear (receiver versus spectrum analyzer), the selection of a site (anechoic chamber versus an open field) and the methodology of the test itself (now defined in the FCC's MP-4).

The antenna types that are typically used when performing FCC tests on computing devices are either dipoles or broadband types such as biconicals or log periodics. The dipole has the advantage of better accuracy, but it can be somewhat inconvenient to use because it must be tuned at each measurement frequency. Furthermore, the dipole cannot be easily vertically polarized at the lower frequencies because of its large physical length.

Alternatively, broadband antennas avoid the necessity of retuning. However, because these antennas are somewhat complex, accuracy in translating from field strength to voltage output cannot be ensured by calculation alone. Rather, these types of antennas have to be correlated against a simpler, more precise type such as a dipole or an isotropic standard. Therefore, dipoles have the advantage of accuracy, and biconicals and log periodics have the advantage of convenience in changing polarity as required by the FCC.

10.2

FCC measurements on computing devices may be performed with either a receiver or a spectrum analyzer. Receivers have the advantage of sensitivity and the ability to use the CISPR quasipeak detector. Spectrum analyzers, on the other hand, allow a panoramic display of a wide range of frequencies, simplifying the measurement procedure. Although the FCC rules specify the use of a quasipeak detector, the use of a spectrum analyzer is allowed, provided that appropriate accessories are used to provide overload protection, additional sensitivity and repeatable measurements. The measurement procedures require cables to be attached to equipment under test and for those cables to be moved experimentally in every configuration likely to be found by the end user. It takes approximately five minutes to find the configuration resulting in maximum emissions at any particular frequency. While a spectrum analyzer allows the test engineer to find the configuration resulting in maximum emissions in a whole band of frequencies at one time, a receiver does not.

FCC measurements may be performed on an open field test site as illustrated in Fig. 10.1 or in an anechoic chamber. The open field test method is simple and accurate. The major problem with the open field test site is that the ambient environment may contain a number of high-level signals from local radio broadcast and television stations and other radio services in the test area. Although it is usually possible to identify and measure radiated emissions from computing devices in the presence of severe ambients, this can be a meticulous process. Shielded anechoic chambers, on the other hand, provide a low ambient environment in which to conduct the tests. However, the anechoic chamber is much more costly than the open field test site and, to be acceptable for FCC measurements, it is necessary to correlate the chamber results with those obtained from an open field test site.

Regarding the test procedures, the FCC's MP-4 specifies that the interface cables must be oriented in a configuration that tends to maximize the emission profile, and the selection of a specific configuration must be justified and defined precisely in the test report. With regard to what cables must be attached to the equipment, the procedure states:

> It is imperative that interface cables be connected to the available interface ports on the EUT. The effect of varying the position of the cables must be investigated to find the configuration that produces maximum emissions. The configuration must be precisely noted in the test report.

10.3

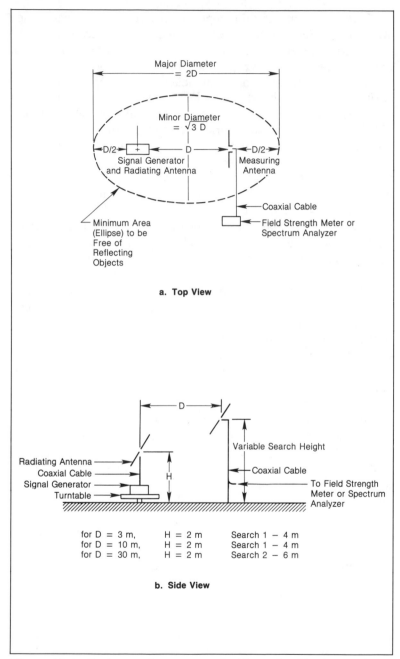

Figure 10.1—Equipment Arrangement for Measuring Site Attenuation of a Radiation Test Site

10.4

Where there are multiple interface ports all the same type, connecting a cable to just one of that type of port is sufficient, provided it can be shown that additional cables would not significantly affect the results.

The Commission has adopted a different procedure for unique interface ports. While most of the ports on computing equipment are standard types (IEEE 488, RS-232, etc.), some are unique to the manufacturer, and peripherals may not yet exist for these ports. In that case, the Commission states:

> Products that provide a unique interface port for peripherals that are not yet available may be tested by attaching a cable extended one meter vertically above the device and left unterminated.

It should be kept in mind that the purpose of promulgating MP-4 was to describe in more detail how to perform FCC tests. The procedures outlined in MP-4 are not arbitrary; they evolved over a number of years. In performing FCC tests, it is essential to follow the FCC's procedures carefully.

10.2 VDE Test Procedures for Computing Devices

The VDE also has two classes of equipment, A and B. Class A is generally for large products that are less widely distributed. Class B products are those that are smaller and more widely distributed, such as personal computers.

The VDE conducted limits for Classes A and B use a 50 Ω/50 μH LISN and a QP detector. They allow several dB of relaxation for broadband emissions, depending on frequency. For the VDE, the cables associated with the system under test must be laid in a specific fashion. Also, each cable port must have a cable on it for the VDE. The VDE radiated limits are based on an OATS criteria, but the horizontal antenna distances are more complicated. Class A equipment uses a 30 m distance for the 30 to 470 MHz range, a 10 m distance from 470 to 1,000 MHz and a 100 m antenna distance for magnetic fields from 10 kHz to 30 MHz. For Class B equipment, a 3 or 30 m distance is used in the magnetic field range of 10 kHz to 30 MHz while a 10 m distance is used from 30 to 1,000 MHz.

The VDE also allows the manufacturer to measure the EMI power instead of the radiated EMI field strength in either of two cases:

1. The individual equipment tested has a maximum dimension (along any edge) of 1 m.
2. Interconnected systems tested have a dimension no greater than 1 m whereby the interconnected cables must be stretched to their maximum length between the individual equipments of the systems. The interconnecting cables must not be extendable.

The EMI power must be measured on all input and output cables that are or can be connected. The measured EMI power shall not exceed a specific EMI limit: 33 dBpW at 30 MHz and increasing linearly with the logarithms of frequency to 43 dBpW at 300 MHz.

10.3 MIL-STD-462 Test Procedures

This section summarizes the test procedures specified by MIL-STD-462 for conducted and radiated emissions and susceptibilities. MIL-STD-462 specifies procedures for measuring conducted emissions on power leads, control and signal leads and antenna leads. Conducted susceptibility tests are performed on power leads and antenna leads. Radiated emission tests include magnetic field and electromagnetic field measurements. Radiated susceptibility tests include both magnetic field and electromagnetic field measurements.

10.3.1 Conducted Emission Test Procedure

This section summarizes conducted emission test procedures for power leads, control and signal leads and antenna leads.

10.3.1.1 AC and DC Power Lead Conducted Emission Tests

The purpose of power line conducted emission tests is to confirm that levels existing on power leads of test samples do not exceed acceptable specification limits. More specifically, emissions on ac or dc power leads (or both) originating from a test sample may conductively couple to other potentially susceptible equipments which would be connected to the same power mains in actual installations. Thus, the objective of these tests is to assure that these emission levels will not likely result in a conducted EMI problem via the power line coupling mode.

Test methods of MIL-STD-462 are used for measuring conducted emissions on ac and dc power input and output leads of test samples which connect externally or interface with other equipment not part of the test sample. This includes ground or neutral lines which are connected externally to the test sample. Bonding straps, if used, and test samples with self-contained power are excluded from measurement. The conducted emission measurements apply to both narrowband and broadband emission types.

Figure 10.2 illustrates the typical test setup used in MIL-STD-462 for power lead conducted emission measurements. The EMI receiver is tuned over the applicable frequency range to confirm that the emissions are not above the applicable limits as specified in MIL-STD-461.

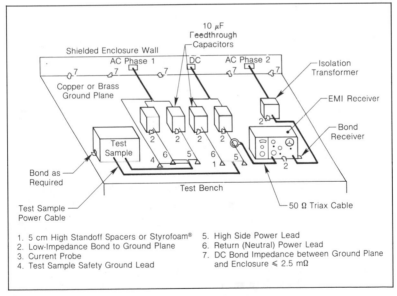

1. 5 cm High Standoff Spacers or Styrofoam®
2. Low-Impedance Bond to Ground Plane
3. Current Probe
4. Test Sample Safety Ground Lead
5. High Side Power Lead
6. Return (Neutral) Power Lead
7. DC Bond Impedance between Ground Plane and Enclosure ⩽ 2.5 mΩ

Figure 10.2—Test Setup for Power Lead Measurements

10.3.1.2 Conducted Power Lead Test: Time Domain Spikes

This test is performed on power leads and is applicable to equipment that can generate transients. It is used to measure the amplitude of transients or spikes in the time domain. Thus, there exists no frequency scanning. Figures 10.3 and 10.4 illustrate a typical test setup for measuring the amplitude of transients on a power lead.

Figure 10.3 shows a current probe positioned close to the 10 μF capacitor on the power lead to be tested. The transfer impedance of the probe is presumed to be flat from 10 kHz to 50 MHz. The output from the current probe is connected to either a memory oscilloscope or peak-storage voltmeter of similar bandwidth.

Figure 10.4 shows a voltage probe positioned close to an inductor feeding the 10 μF capacitor on the power line to be tested. The inductor must provide a corner or notch frequency with the capacitor below 10 kHz and be resonant above 50 MHz. Thus, its value must be at least 25 μH and be capable of carrying the current from the test sample. The output from the voltage probe is connected to either a memory oscilloscope or peak reading storage voltmeter.

In the test setup of Fig. 10.3 or 10.4, the 10 μF capacitor (and inductor) may be replaced with a line impedance stabilization network (LISN) provided one is selected which offers from 30 to 50 Ω from 10 kHz to 50 MHz when terminated in a 50 Ω pad. For current measurements, the current probe is positioned on the test sample lead close to the LISN. For voltage measurements, the output of the LISN pad is connected to the oscilloscope or storage voltmeter.

The test sample is exercised through its modes of operation a minimum of five times or as specified in the EMI test plan. This includes on-off switches. One recording is made of the greatest upper bounds corresponding to the five (or more) times that each test sample mode or function is exercised. When synchronization is possible, test sample switching should be timed to occur at both the peak and zero crossing of the ac power line.

Since the bandwidth of the oscilloscope or peak storage voltmeter is presumed to be wide with respect to the reciprocal of the 50 percent width of the current amplitude of the transient, the voltage recordings are all narrowband.

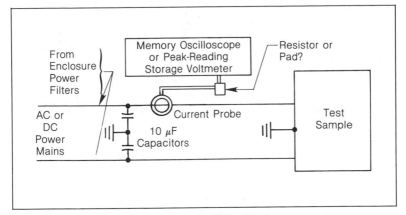

Figure 10.3—Short-Circuit, Current-Spike Test

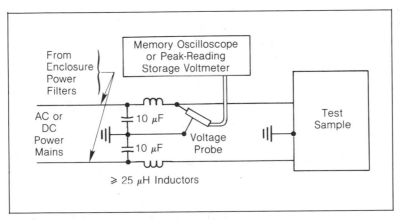

Figure 10.4—Open·Circuit, Voltage-Spike Test

10.3.1.3 Control and Signal Lead Conducted Emission Test

The purpose of these tests is to confirm that conducted emission levels existing on control and signal leads of test samples are equal to or below acceptable specification limits. More specifically, emissions on control and signal leads, originating from a test sample, may conductively couple to other susceptible equipments which would be connected to the other end(s) of these leads in actual installations. Thus, the objective of these tests is to assure that emission levels will not likely result in a conducted EMI problem via the control and signal lead coupling mode. These tests apply to both narrowband and broadband emission types.

Figure 10.5 illustrates a typical test setup for control and signal leads conducted emission measurements. The EMI receiver is tuned over the applicable frequency range to confirm that emissions are not above the applicable limits.

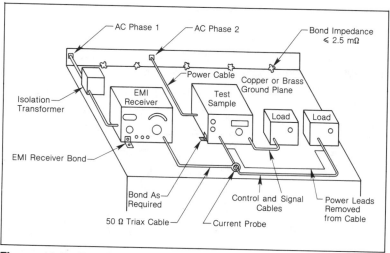

Figure 10.5—Test Setup for Control and Signal Lead Measurements

10.3.1.4 Antenna Conducted Emission Tests

The antenna conducted emission test applies to emission levels existing on antenna leads of transmitters, receivers, RF amplifiers and other equipments and subsystems designed to be connected to antennas. The purpose of the test is to confirm that these emission levels are equal to or below acceptable specification limits.

Antenna radiation, originating as conducted emissions on the output of RF devices, is one of the most significant culprit sources of intersystem EMI among communication-electronic equipments. For example, unnecessary modulation sideband emissions, harmonics and other spurious outputs from transmitters can be very damaging, as can be a local oscillator, base crystal oscillator and its harmonics and synthesized frequency output from receivers. It is not uncommon to observe broadband EMI emissions on antenna terminals which originated from internal relay action, blower motors and the like. Thus, the objective of these EMI tests is to assure that these unwanted emission levels will not likely result in radiated interference via the antenna conducted emission mode.

The antenna conducted emission test involves measuring both the narrowband and broadband antenna conducted emissions from receivers and from transmitters in the key-up mode. Antenna conducted emissions are also measured for transmitters in the key-down mode. Figures 10.6 through 10.9 illustrate the typical test setups used in MIL-STD-462 antenna conducted emission measurements.

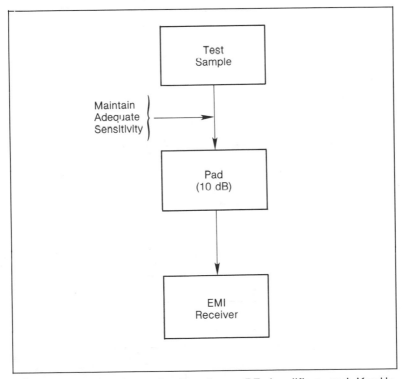

Figure 10.6—Test Setup for Receivers, RF Amplifiers and Key-Up Transmitters

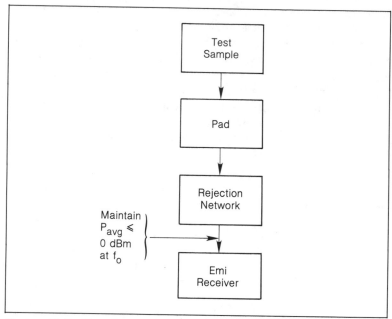

Figure 10.7—Test Setup, Transmitter Key Down: $P_{avg} \leqslant 43$ dBm and $f_{high} \leqslant 1.25$ GHz

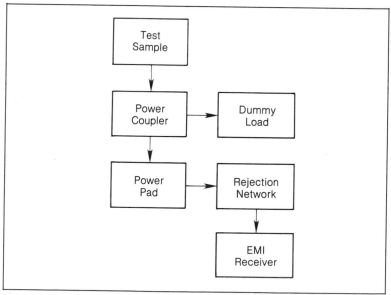

Figure 10.8—Test Setup, Transmitter Key Down: 43 dBm > P_{avg} < 67 dBm; 10 kHz $\leqslant f_o \leqslant$ 300 MHz; No Antenna

10.12

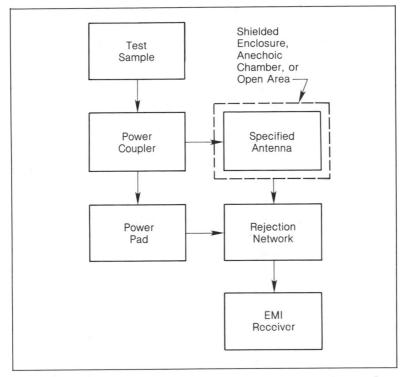

Figure 10.9—Test Setup, Transmitter Key Down: 43 dBm $> P_{avg}$
< 67 dBm; 10 kHz $\leqslant f_o \leqslant$ 1,240 MHz; Specified Antenna

10.3.2 Conducted Susceptibility Test Procedures

This section summarizes conducted susceptibility test procedures for power leads and receiver antenna leads.

10.3.2.1 Power Lead Conducted Susceptibility Test

The purpose of these conducted susceptibility tests is to confirm that EMI emission of specified levels injected on power leads of test samples will not cause performance degradation or malfunction. More specifically, either susceptible equipments are coupled to power lines which are connected to emitting equipments, or the power mains are themselves contaminated. Thus, the objective of these EMI tests is to assure that these susceptibility levels will not likely result in a conducted EMI problem via power line coupling media.

Power lead conducted susceptibility (CS) test methods of MIL-STD-462 are used for measuring conducted susceptibility on ac or dc power leads of test samples which are connected to the outside world or interface with the equipment or subsystem being measured. Where the test sample does not contain any amplifiers, or is not connected to the outside world or interfaced with the equipment or subsystem being measured, conducted susceptibility tests are generally not required. Examples of subsystems or equipments which need not be tested are electromechanical relays, solenoid motors and generators, power tools and machinery and automobiles. Note that, in satisfying the above conditions for avoidance of CS testing, it generally results that the test sample is itself an EMI emitter.

Figure 10.10 illustrates a typical test setup used in performing power lead conducted susceptibility tests from 30 Hz to 50 kHz under MIL-STD-462. The isolation transformer shown in Fig. 10.10 permits series injection of the susceptibility test signal in the input power leads. Because of the finite output impedance of the injection transformer, under a heavy test sample load condition, the voltage drop across the transformer may become very significant. For this situation the supply voltage will have to be raised to compensate for this loss.

Figure 10.11 illustrates a typical test setup used for MIL-STD-462 conducted power line susceptibility measurements from 50 kHz to 400 MHz. The series coupling capacitor is used to block the power line frequencies so that the signal generator or amplitude monitor of Fig. 10.11 will not burn out when exposed to 115 Vac. The capacitor is to be transparent at 50 kHz and above. Thus, its value is chosen to be not more than 5 Ω at the lowest frequency of a test range (e.g., 1 μF for 50 kHz). The capacitor will have to be changed during the test because of self-resonance effects at higher frequencies.

A series inductor of about 25 μH may help achieve the conducted susceptibility specification limit at the lower frequencies. In the Army's Notice 3 to MIL-STD-462, a LISN is used instead of the series inductor (see Fig. 10.12).

10.14

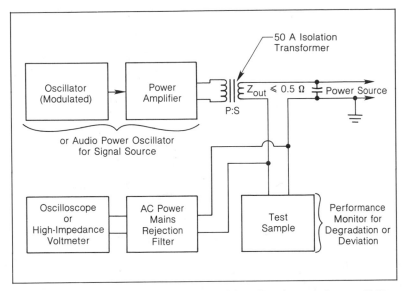

Figure 10.10—Test Setup for Power Line Conducted Susceptibility Measurements, 30 Hz to 50 kHz

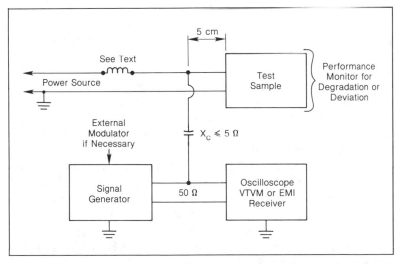

Figure 10.11—Test Setup for Power Line Conducted Susceptibility Measurements, 50 kHz - 400 MHz

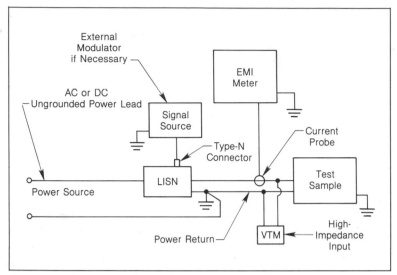

Figure 10.12—Army Test Setup for Power Line Conducted Susceptibility Measurements

   The signal generator is connected to the type-N terminal of the LISN which is ordinarily used for conducted emission tests. The power leads between the LISN and test sample are monitored with both a current and voltage probe. Power in the signal generator is set at the applicable Notice 4, MIL-STD-461 limits. The power is obtained by multiplying the monitored RF power lead voltage and current. The specification limit is based on developing 1 V from a 50 Ω signal source applied to the test sample power input terminals (excluding power cable). When a signal source of 1 W (+30 dBm) or greater of 50 Ω impedance (7 V indicated for +30 dBm under matched conditions) cannot develop 1 V at the test sample power input terminals (excluding power cable), and the test sample is not susceptible to the output of this signal source, then the equipment is considered to be nonsusceptible. This may result from the test sample power input terminals appearing to be much less than 50 Ω at some frequencies, e.g., input EMI filters having a shunt capacitor as the first stage.

10.3.2.2 Power Lead Conducted Susceptibility Tests for Spikes

The purpose of the power lead conducted susceptibility tests for spikes is to measure equipment or subsystem susceptibility to transients or spikes on power lines feeding all ungrounded ac and dc power leads connected externally to the test sample. Figures 10.13 and 10.14 illustrates typical test setups used in conducting susceptibility measurements for time-domain injected spikes. A spike generator is used to simulate transients on ac and dc power lines and to determine the test sample susceptibility for these transients. The spike tests are especially directed to determining the susceptibility of test samples employing pulse and digital circuits.

Figure 10.13 and 10.14 show series and parallel spike injection methods, respectively, into the test sample power leads via the isolation transformer. The choice between the two methods is predicated upon a number of things, including the RF impedances of both the power lines and the test sample. The role of the shunt 10 μF capacitor and the series 25 μH inductor is to isolate the power lines from the test sample input so that the spike will appear primarily across the test sample without voltage-dividing to the power mains (series injection) or being loaded by the power mains (parallel injection).

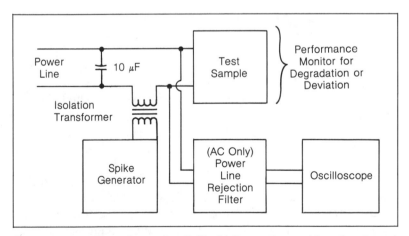

Figure 10.13—Test Setup for Spike Voltage, Power Line Conducted Susceptibility Measurements, Series Injection

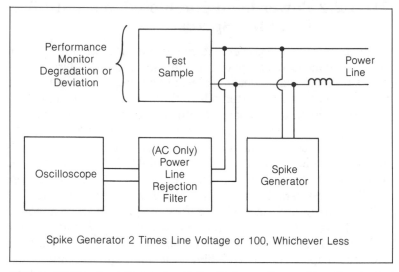

Figure 10.14—Test Setup for Spike Voltage, Power Line Conducted Susceptibility Measurements, Parallel Injection

10.3.2.3 Receiver Intermodulation

The purpose of the receiver intermodulation test is to confirm that the receiver is not susceptible to two signals, at the specified levels, injected simultaneously into the receiver antenna input terminals. Figure 10.15 illustrates the typical test setup for intermodulation conducted susceptibility measurements.

The signal generators shown in Fig. 10.15 typically provide a calibrated output from about -120 to approximately 0 dBm. The low-pass filters are intended to remove harmonics which may be present from the signal generators which would otherwise confuse test results. However, since the cutoff frequency of low-pass filter (LPF) no. 2 is limited to about one-half octave above f_0 during scanning of signal generator no. 2, it would have to be replaced many times. This significantly slows down testing. Thus, it is not uncommon to omit the filters entirely and use them only if there appears to be a test failure (i.e., test sample appears not to meet specification requirements).

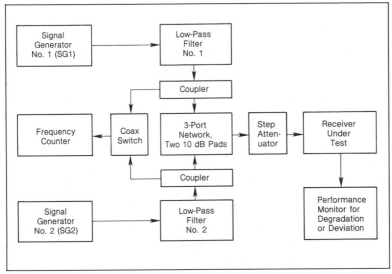

Figure 10.15—Test Setup for Receiver Intermodulation Measurements

The outputs from the filters (or signal generators, if the filters are not used) are combined in a three-port network. Typically this is a 6 dB power divider with two 10 dB pads located between the two signal generators to avoid frequency pulling or intermodulation. The combined output of the common arm of the 6 dB power divider then contains both signals.

In performing the tests, signal generator no. 1 is modulated and set to the frequency and level as specified in MIL-STD-461C. Signal generator no. 2 is unmodulated and is also set to the frequency and level specified in MIL-STD-461C. Signal generator no. 2 is then scanned over the applicable frequency range (maintaining the frequency relationship so that intermodulation products will occur at the receiver tuned frequency) to confirm that the receiver is not susceptible to intermodulation as a result of being exposed to the two interfering signals.

10.3.2.4 Receiver Rejection of Out-of-Band Emissions

Receiver rejection of undesired signals refers to spurious responses other than intermodulation or cross modulation. The spurious responses may result from the mixing process in a superheterodyne receiver. In this situation, the interfering signal (or one of its harmonics) mixes with the local oscillator signal (or one of its harmonics) to produce a mixing product that falls within the IF amplifier passband. Once this occurs, the spurious response will be processed along with the signal of interest.

On the other hand, the responses may be more subtle in that receiver desensitization may take place due to automatic gain control (AGC) action, when AGC is present. For desensitization, rather than an undesired signal appearing at the output, the signal of interest is reduced to compromise performance. In other words, the signal-to-interference plus noise ratio is reduced because of a reduction in the signal level resulting from the interference.

Figure 10.16 illustrates a typical setup for measuring receiver rejection to spurious responses. Signal generator no. 1 is tuned to the receiver frequency, modulated as required by the receiver equipment specifications and adjusted to the level that produces a standard response in the receiver. Signal generator no. 2 is unmodulated, set to the levels indicated in MIL-STD-461C and tuned over the applicable frequency range to confirm that no undesired responses or other effects occur in the receiver under test.

The signal generators shown in Fig. 10.16 typically provide a calibrated output from about − 120 to 0 dBm. The low-pass filters are intended to remove harmonics from the signal generators which

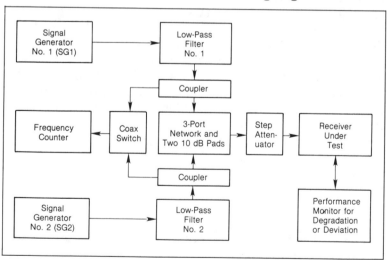

Figure 10.16—Test Setup for Spurious Response Measurements

can otherwise confuse test results. However, since LPF no. 2 set frequency is limited to about one-half octave above f_0 during scanning of signal generator no. 2, it would have to be replaced many times. This significantly slows down testing. Thus, it is not uncommon to omit the filters entirely and use them if there appears to be a test failure (i.e., test sample appears not to meet specification limits).

The outputs from the filters (or signal generators if the filters are not used) are combined in a three-port network. This is typically a 6 dB power divider with two 10 dB pads located at each arm of the divider. Thus, at least 20 dB of isolation exists between the two signal generators to avoid frequency pulling or intermodulation. The combined output of the common arm of the 6 dB power divider then contains both signals.

10.3.2.5 Receiver Cross Modulation

Cross modulation differs from intermodulation and spurious responses in that cross modulation does not involve a carrier transposition process from front-end mixing. Rather, cross modulation is generally an adjacent-channel situation in which the signal penetrating the receiver front end (e.g., through the preselector) modulates, by non-linear action, the gain of the RF amplifier. Since these gain variations are also seen by the signal of interest, the baseband information of the culprit signal becomes modulated upon the intended signal.

Under certain conditions, undesired signals can simultaneously produce both cross modulation and spurious responses. Cross modulation involves no carrier mixing with the receiver local oscillator and the baseband information is directly transferred to the signal of interest. If there is no desired signal being received, then there is no cross modulation.

Figure 10.16 illustrates a typical test setup for cross modulation conducted susceptibility measurements. Signal generator no. 1 is tuned to the receiver frequency, modulated as required by the receiver equipment specifications and adjusted to a level that produces a standard response in the receiver. Once the standard response level is obtained with signal generator no. 1, its level is increased by 10 dB. Signal generator no. 2 is modulated as required and set at a level that is 66 dB above that required to produce a standard response. Signal generator no. 2 is tuned away from the receiver frequency (f_0) until a standard response results (f_1).

Continue to tune signal generator no. 2 away from the receiver tuned frequency and monitor the output of the test sample for any responses resulting from signal generator no. 2. If a response occurs, remove the modulation from signal generator no. 2 to determine whether the response resulted from cross modulation (if the response disappears, it was due to cross modulation).

10.3.2.6 Squelch Susceptibility Tests

The purpose of the squelch susceptibility test is to determine if a receiver which has squelch circuits has adequate protection against impulse noise applied to the input terminals.

Figures 10.17 and 10.18 illustrate typical test setups to be used for squelch circuit conducted susceptibility measurements. The first test, illustrated in Fig. 10.17, involves measurements to determine squelch circuit performance in the presence of impulsive noise alone. This simulates possible squelch-circuit capture by impulsive noise before an intentional signal is received. The second test (Fig. 10.18) involves the presence of both an unmodulated signal and lower-level impulsive noise to determine compliance with specification limits. This simulates possible squelch-circuit capture by impulsive noise. The isolation network is intended to decouple both generators and serve as a means for coupling their outputs to a single port for injection into the test sample.

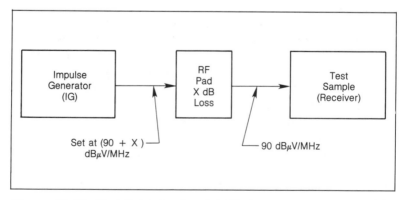

Figure 10.17—Test Setup for Squelch Circuit Measurements, Test 1

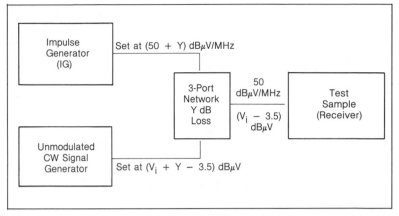

Figure 10.18—Test Setup for Squelch Circuit Measurements, Test 2

For the first test, the procedures are as follows:
1. The squelch circuit is adjusted so that it just opens at the level of an injected RF voltage, V_i at the receiver antenna input terminals stated in the equipment specification.
2. The impulse generator (IG) is set to a level of 90 dBμV/MHz in Fig. 10.17 as appearing at the test sample input terminals. Thus, the IG will be set higher by an amount to compensate for the loss of the RF pad.
3. For the condition in step 2, the squelch circuit should not open. If it does, back down the IG level until the squelch circuit closes. The amount by which the IG is backed down is the dB out-of-spec condition.

For the second test, the procedures are as follows:
1. The squelch circuit is adjusted so that it just opens at the level of an injected RF voltage, V_i at the receiver antenna input terminals stated in the equipment specification.
2. The unmodulated CW signal generator in Fig. 10.18 is set at a level equal to two-thirds of that in step 1, i.e., 3.5 dB less. It is tuned to the receiver to give maximum response. The IG is set to a level of 50 dBμV/MHz as appearing at the test sample input terminals. Thus, the IG will be set higher by an amount to compensate for the loss of the isolation network.

3. For the condition in step 2, the squelch circuit should not open. If it does, back down the IG level until the squelch circuit closes. The amount by which the IG is backed down is the dB out-of-spec condition.

10.3.3 Radiated Emission Test Procedures

This section summarizes MIL-STD-462 radiated emission test procedures.

10.3.3.1 Magnetic-Field Radiated Emission Tests

The purpose of the magnetic-field (H-field) radiated emission tests is to confirm that magnetic fields existing from test sample boxes and wires are equal to or below acceptable specification limits. More specifically, H-field emissions from the test sample may inductively couple to other nearby susceptible cables and equipments when installed in operational vehicles or housings. Thus, the objective of these EMI tests is to assure that these emission levels will not likely result in a radiated EMI problem via the H-field coupling media.

The H-field radiated emission test methods of MIL-STD-462 are used for measuring H-field emissions for equipments and subsystems including their cables and interconnecting wiring. Wiring includes control, pulse, audio, video, antenna transmission lines and power cables. The test methods cover non-antenna (i.e., backdoor exit) transmitter H-field radiations involving the fundamental and all spurious emissions (e.g., LF/ELF transmitters).

Figure 10.19 illustrates the typical MIL-STD-462 test setup used for performing H-field measurements. The test procedures for H-field measurements are as follows:

1. Select an EMI receiver bandwidth between 10 and 50 Hz. Position the center of the loop (or other magnetic sensor) 1 m from the center of the test sample as shown in Fig. 10.19. Orient the plane of the loop 45 degrees to all three orthogonal axes of the test sample.
2. Scan the EMI receiver from 20 Hz to 50 kHz to locate the frequency corresponding to maximum magnetic flux density indication.

3. At the frequency in step 2, move the loop (or sensor) horizontally, vertically, or both, as applicable, parallel to the test sample layout configuration, while monitoring for a maximum indication. Maintain the 45 degree, three-axis diagonal polarization when locating the position corresponding to maximum emission. Secure the loop at this location.

4. Scan the EMI receiver from 20 Hz to 50 MHz and record at least three maximum magnetic flux density emissions per octave and at the test sample critical frequencies, if applicable. Identify emissions as either narrowband or broadband.

5. Reduce data and plot on semi-logarithmic graph paper the flux density in units of dBpT vs. frequency, together with specification limits. In reducing data, add 6 dB to account for the 45 degree orientation to the three orthogonal axes of the test sample.

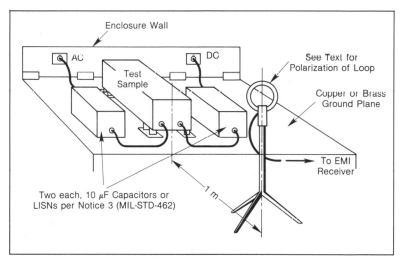

Figure 10.19—Typical Test Setup for H-Field Measurements

10.3.3.2 Electric-Field Radiated Emission Tests

The purpose of the electric-field (E-field) radiated emission tests is to confirm that electric fields existing from test samples including their wires and cables are equal to or below acceptable specification limits. More specifically, E-field emissions from the test sample may couple to other nearby susceptible cables and equipments when installed in operational vehicles or housings. Thus, the objective of these EMI tests is to assure that these emission levels will not likely result in a radiated EMI problem via the E-field coupling media.

The E-field radiated emission test methods of MIL-STD-462 are used for measuring E-field emissions from equipments and subsystems including their cables and interconnecting wiring. Wiring includes control, pulse, audio, video, IF, antenna transmission lines and power cables. This test method applies to transmitter fundamental, harmonics and spurious E-field radiations, receiver oscillator and other radiations and broadband emissions. It excludes all radiations emanating from antennas, where antennas apply, and stresses non-antenna (i.e, back-door exit) emissions. Thus, any electrical, electromechanical or electronic source within the confines of the test sample housing and cables are suspected of possible leakage in the E-field radiated emission.

Figures 10.20 and 10.21 illustrate typical test setups used in MIL-STD-462 E-field measurements. In both figures, significant effort is used in deploying the test sample and its power cable and interconnecting leads. The rationale for the apparent meticulous layout is:

1. To permit representative ground current loop area to exits, if indeed it does, by controlling the height (5 cm) of the cable leads above a ground plane and employing a specified lead length. The loop area effects both magnetic- and electric-field emissions (and susceptibility), which are proportional to the area of the loop.

2. To permit a nominal cable lead exposure to exist. This exposure is nominally defined as 2 m in MIL-STD-461. The apparent rationale for this value is that this minimum length is sufficient to establish the radiation characteristics of the cable. For cables, any common-mode emission (or susceptibility) is primarily by E-field media, disregarding contributions by ground-current loops. For a constant level signal applied to the cable, coupling increases with frequency and becomes very significant when cable length $l_c = 0.1 \lambda$.

As a consequence of the above, when $l_c = 0.1 \lambda = 2$ m (Fig. 10.20) or 1 m (Fig. 10.21), $f \approx 15$ to 30 MHz. Thus, a test item, if it either radiates or is at all susceptible to electric fields, may be expected to evidence this primarily through its power and interconnecting cables in the upper HF and above frequency range.

10.26

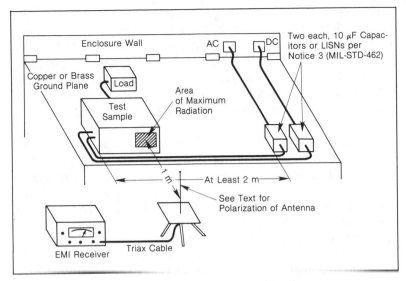

Figure 10.20—Typical Test Setup for E-Field Measurements

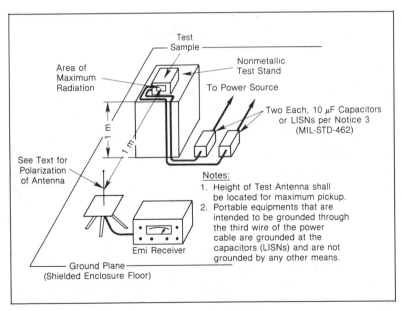

Figure 10.21—Typical Test Setup for E-Field Measurements on Portable Equipment

Irrespective of the cable length shown in Figs. 10.20 and 10.21, if the cable(s) are truly part of the test sample, the real cable(s) must be used regardless of its length and configuration. This should be covered in the Test Plan. If the contract for the test item involves only the box or equipment with no power cables, then the cables in Fig. 10.20 may be shielded with aluminum foil, a sheet metal trough or other suitable shield and the shield grounded throughout its length.

The question remains how to deploy a long cable ($l_c \gg 1$ m) if the cable is truly part of the test item. The real cable presents a different transmission line impedance and load to the internal noise source of the test box than would a 2 m reference cable. Thus, cable emission and radiation is different. Also, a coiled cable can present a worst case of radiated emission and susceptibility; a serpentine cable (one folded back and forth) presents the best case, and a straight run offers in-between results. Consequently, the criterion for deployment should be either a straight run or trial run to simulate a real-life installation. This also should be covered in the Test Plan.

10.3.3.3 Open Field Spurious and Harmonic Radiation

The purpose of these radiated emission tests is to confirm that relative spurious and/or harmonically-related signals emanating from a test sample transmitting antenna are equal to or below specification limits. More specifically, these unintentional radiations may couple into other antenna-receiver victims existing in the environment. Thus, the objective of these EMI tests is to significantly reduce the probability that these spurious and harmonic radiation levels will result in EMI to other communication-electronic (CE) receivers operating in the ambient electromagnetic environment.

Figures 10.22 and 10.23 illustrate the test setups used in open field spurious and harmonic radiation tests. If a spectrum analyzer is used, it must be protected with either preselectors or a number of bandpass filters to avoid intermodulation and spurious responses. Since the sensitivity of spectrum analyzers is poor relative to EMI receivers, it is often necessary to precede them with low-noise, wide-band amplifiers. The requirement for protecting filters is more important under these conditions. For the reasons given above, EMI receivers may be preferred over spectrum analyzers.

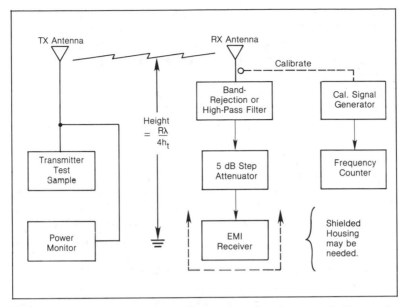

Figure 10.22—Typical Test Setup for Spurious and Harmonic Measurements Using an EMI Receiver

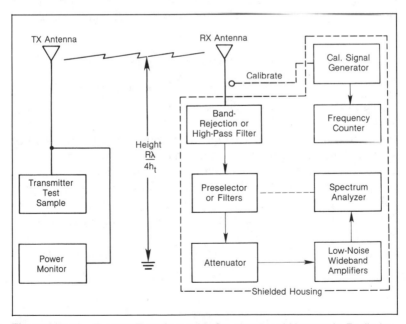

Figure 10.23—Typical Test Setup for Spurious and Harmonic Radiation Measurements Using a Spectrum Analyzer

Another consideration involves shielding the housing of the measurement receiver. If the transmitter antenna directly illuminates the measurement receiver, case penetration may result in spurious responses. EMI receivers are generally better shielded than spectrum analyzers.

The RF coaxial cable from receiver antenna to equipment input should be kept short. To preclude fundamental responses due to direct cable pickup, it should be either triaxial cable or a 30 cm (1 ft) piece of lossy tubing should be slipped over the end nearest to the band-rejection filter input. Triax should have a grounded outer shield at the receiver only.

The band-rejection filters are used to block the fundamental frequency of the transmitter. They are necessary to prevent spurious responses from developing in the test receiver when trying to make weak-signal measurements in the presence of a strong out-of-band emission (i.e., the transmitter's fundamental).

The calibration signal generators are shown in Figs. 10.22 and 10.23 for substitution injection at the receiver antenna-output coaxial cable. It is best to calibrate at or as near to this point as possible in order to compensate for the unknown insertion loss of the band-rejection filter and other uncertainties. However, precalibration procedures may be employed to define all insertion losses.

10.3.3.4 Radiated Emissions from Vehicles and Engine-Driven Equipment

The purpose of these radiated emission tests is to confirm by measurement that electric fields emanating from vehicles and engine-driven equipment are equal to or below specification limits. More specifically, broadband radiated emissions from mobile test items may couple to other nearby susceptible vehicles, systems or equipments when deployed in operational postures. Thus, the objective of these EMI tests is to reduce, to an acceptable risk, the probability that these emission levels will result in an EMI problem.

Figures 10.24 and 10.25 illustrate typical test setups used for measuring radiated emissions from vehicles and engine-driven equipment. The antennas are oriented vertically for maximum pickup at a number of positions around the test sample to obtain an effective test of maximum radiation.

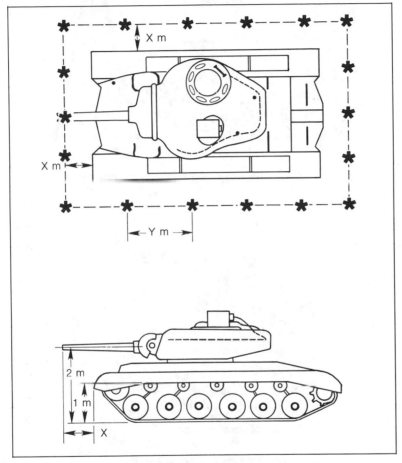

Figure 10.24—Measuring Antenna Deployment about Test Vehicle

10.31

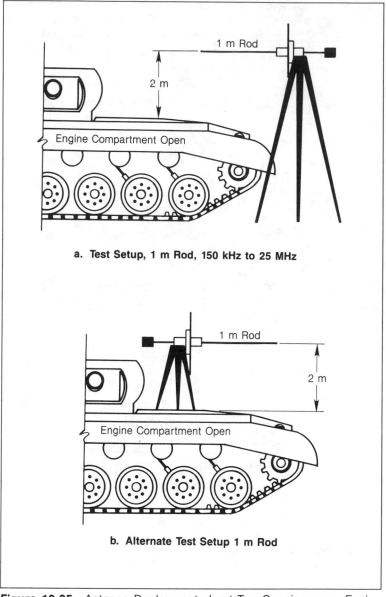

a. **Test Setup, 1 m Rod, 150 kHz to 25 MHz**

b. **Alternate Test Setup 1 m Rod**

Figure 10.25—Antenna Deployment about Top Openings over Engine Compartments (continued next page)

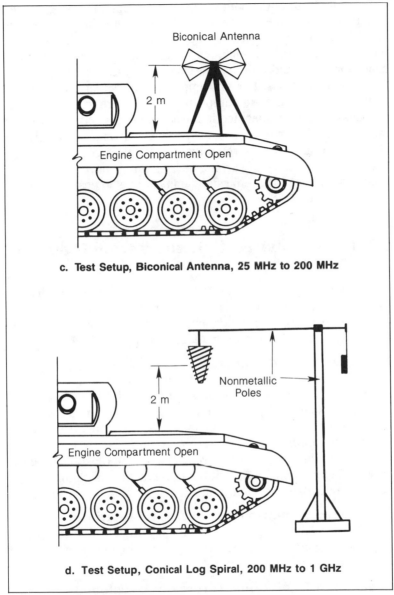

c. **Test Setup, Biconical Antenna, 25 MHz to 200 MHz**

d. **Test Setup, Conical Log Spiral, 200 MHz to 1 GHz**

Figure 10.25—(continued)

The vehicle or equipment to be tested is operated or exercised in a manner to cause maximum radiation within normal operating procedures. Thus, the tests are performed with all electrical equipment in operation. This includes mechanical and/or electrical load conditions adjusted so that the charging system is in operation throughout the tests. For example, voltage regulators, hydraulic power packs, pneumatic pumps and the like, are to be exercised.

Unless otherwise specified in the equipment specification, starting motors and switches associated with starting, short-duration starting aids and engine-protective warning devices do not require tests. However, low-air warning devices for air-brake vehicles are required to meet the emission limits while indicating low air pressure.

10.3.3.5 Radiated Emissions from Overhead Power Lines

The purpose of these radiated emission tests is to confirm by measurement that E-fields emanating from overhead power lines are equal to or below specification limits. Radiated emissions from power lines may be of one or more types:

Narrowband Radiations

Overhead power lines act as an extended pickup antenna system which can also conductively transmit CE and other narrowband irradiating sources for many miles. Narrowband inductive fields from the power lines can couple into nearby victims. Also RF impedance discontinuities (cracked or dirty insulators or change in direction) in the lines can cause radiations of the CE transmissions. In severe situations, intermodulation of CE signals might develop at some impedance discontinuities.

Broadband Radiations; External Irradiations

This includes the same coupling physics as above, but the originating sources are broadband emitting elements which exist near an overhead power line.

Broadband Radiations; Internally Developed

This is the class for which most EMI control is possible and includes the following sources of either coherent (impulsive) or incoherent (random) broadband emissions:
1. Load changes

Users and substations may either switch on or off large loads of thousands of amperes and/or inductive loads. Transients will develop on the overhead power lines having pulse durations and rise times of the order of 10 ns.

2. Gap-Type Discharge

A complete electrical discharge (i.e., a transient arc over or sparking) at twice the line frequency, with a pulse group or oscillation existing at insulators, tie wires, between hardware parts, defective electrical apparatus, etc. This type of internal noise tends to predominate for overhead power lines carrying less than 70 kV and for most lines at VHF and lower UHF.

3. Corona Discharge

A partial electrical discharge due to ionization of the air at or near the conductor surface. Conductor contamination, surface burrs, rain, snow, frost, fog, high-relative humidity, etc. tend to enhance corona up to 20 dB over dry conditions. This type of internal noise tends to predominate for overhead power lines greater than 110 kV, but the intensity of corona radiation falls off rapidly above about 15 MHz.

As a result of the above, to further complicate matters, overhead power line emissions may show either a coherent or an incoherent relation and may fall off with distance, d, from the apparent source at rates ranging from 1/d to $1/d^3$.

Figure 10.26 illustrates a typical test setup for radiated emissions from overhead power lines. Measurements are made in the clear, well removed from nearby objects, including personnel, in order to preclude proximity effects on antennas. A separate monitoring receiver is shown in Fig. 10.26, tuned to a frequency clear of any narrowband conducted emission (e.g., around 350 kHz) but corresponding to a broadband intercept from the overhead power line. Throughout the test, this monitor output should not vary by more than 6 dB or it is necessary to rerun the measurements. If the elimination of non-power-line emissions is to be made, then this 6 dB allowable variation criteria must be correspondingly reduced. Typical operation of power line voltage, (e.g., no brownout conditions in effect) should be verified at a substation during the period of test.

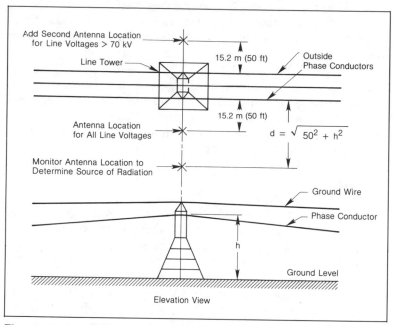

Figure 10.26—Typical Test Deployment for Radiated Measurements on Overhead Power Lines

Measurements are usually made during fair weather and during the daytime when temperature and humidity conditions do not cause condensation on the overhead lines. Since broadband emissions originate primarily from the tower hardware rather than from the power line *per se*, the MIL-STD-462 restriction regarding "the entire length of line shall be under the same conditions" seems both unnecessary and difficult to determine for some situations. Measurements under unusual conditions can be avoided such as distant electrical storms or during periods of short-term dry spells when insects, dust and other contaminants may temporarily collect on the power line and tower hardware. Under these conditions, radiated emissions may be abnormally high.

10.3.4 Radiated Susceptibility Test Procedures

Radiated susceptibility testing is performed to demonstrate, through test, that the test sample will neither malfunction nor experience degraded performance when exposed to incident fields of preselected intensities. It is, of course, possible to cause any electric equipment to fail as a result of sufficiently high incident fields. In many cases, the field intensities required to cause such failure are rarely achieved in real life or may not practically apply. From radiated susceptibility testing, however, it is possible to determine if nominal field intensities as may be experienced in typical operating environments can cause the occurrence of a susceptibility condition.

In general, radiated susceptibility testing requires a slightly different organization for test than those test methods described in previous sections. Radiated susceptibility testing requires that a field intensity of a minimum known value having a stipulated modulation be developed at a given location. The test sample is then placed at this location and exposed to the predetermined field intensity over the range of frequencies desired.

An additional consideration that is applicable to all radiated susceptibility tests is that the monitoring cable or harness can be the victim. This would either indicate erroneous susceptibility conditions or provide a direct path for susceptibility emissions to sensitive circuit areas which would cause failure of test requirements.

10.3.4.1 Magnetic-Field Susceptibility Measurements

The objective of this test is, where applicable, to confirm that the operation of equipments will not be degraded as a result of exposure to magnetic fields at the levels specified in MIL-STD-461. These tests are generally applicable to Navy equipments that would be used inside submarines or for specialized types of airborne antisubmarine warfare (ASW) equipment. These tests are not usually applied to other types of military electronic systems.

Figure 10.27 illustrates a typical test setup for H-field susceptibility measurements. The test procedures are as follows:

1. Position the field radiating loop 5 cm from the surface of the test sample face with the plane of the loop parallel to the plane of surface. This spacing is accomplished by the 5 cm spacer on the loop form being placed directly on the surface of the test sample.

2.   Supply the loop with sufficient current to produce magnetic flux densities approximately 20 dB greater than the applicable specification limit at the test frequencies. This is accomplished by adjusting the oscillator drive to the test loop until the desired level is read by the EMI receiver.

3.   Move the loop over the test sample surface and signal input and output cables and connectors to determine the location(s) at which the applied field produces maximum susceptibility, if indeed there is any response.

This particular step of the test procedure is the most time consuming. The test item must be scanned in frequency for various locations of the loop. An optimum procedure for this is not defined in MIL-STD-462. For small samples, not bigger than twice the loop diameter, the location of the test loop is on the center of the face and the frequency scan is performed. The loop is then relocated and the frequency scan again performed. For large test samples this same procedure is followed, except many repetitions are required to complete the test.

4.   With the frequency and loop at the location of maximum susceptibility, adjust the loop current until the performance of the test sample is no longer affected by the applied field. This is the susceptibility threshold level to be recorded.

4a. For test samples with an aural output, adjust the loop current until the test sample gives a reading 20 dB greater than its internal noise. If a 20 dB value cannot be obtained, a 6 dB interference-to-noise ratio will be used.

4b. For test samples with outputs other than aural, the degree of degradation is defined in the test plan.

4c. For test samples with aural and nonaural outputs, the test is performed to meet both steps 4a and b.

5. Repeat steps 1 through 4 at the test frequencies approved in the test plan or as determined in step 3.

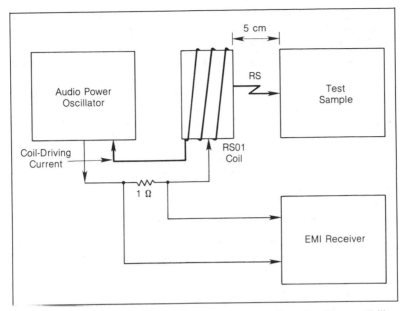

Figure 10.27—Test Setup for Magnetic Flux Density Susceptibility Measurements

10.3.4.2 Magnetic Induction-Field Susceptibility Measurements

The purpose of induction-field testing is to determine if the test sample is susceptible to low-impedance (magnetic) fields generated by the flow of current in nearby power lines. This current flow may be either at the operating power frequency or from transients which may be present due to the operation of other equipment on the same power bus. Since all non-battery powered equipment is located in proximity to a power line, the rationale for the test is that magnetic fields generated by the flow of current at fundamental power frequencies (i.e., 60 or 400 Hz or due to transients) could cause the occurrence of a susceptibility condition in the test sample.

Figure 10.28 illustrates a typical test setup for magnetic induction field susceptibility measurements. In preparing the test setup, the following considerations apply:

1. AC power input and output leads are exempt from the cable test.
2. It is not the intention of the cable test to test individual wire pairs but to test groups or bundles of wires.
3. Keep testing wires 15 cm away from cable connectors.
4. To minimize test time, test as many wire bundles at the same time as practical. The tests are conducted by applying the spike to the test sample and monitoring for indications of susceptibility.

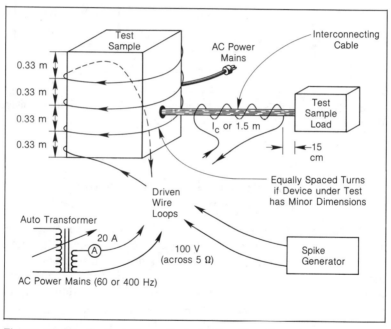

Figure 10.28—Typical Magnetic Induction Test Setup

10.3.4.3 Electric-Field Radiated Susceptibility Measurements

E-field susceptibility testing is performed to determine whether the test sample demonstrates susceptible performance in the presence of an electric field of known amplitude and polarization. Because of the test levels that may be involved and the large frequency range, this test is possibly the most difficult to perform, particularly if the test item requires stimulation and loading by another electric field. If this applies, then this loading and stimulation must be present in the enclosure in addition to the susceptibility test fields.

In general, E-field radiated susceptibility testing should be performed in a shielded enclosure. The fields generated may otherwise cause interference with other equipments or systems in the vicinity of the test site. This may require working different time shifts to avoid EMI problems. Additionally, FCC permission would be required to generate such fields in an open area.

Figures 10.29, 10.30 and 10.31 illustrate typical test setups for E-field radiated susceptibility measurements. The tests are conducted by radiating the test sample with an E-field at the level specified by the limits and monitoring the test sample for susceptibility.

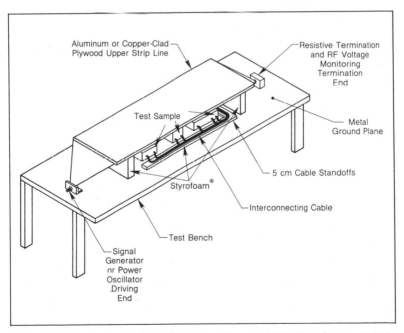

Figure 10.29—Typical E-Field Radiated Susceptibility Test Setup, 14 kHz to 30 MHz

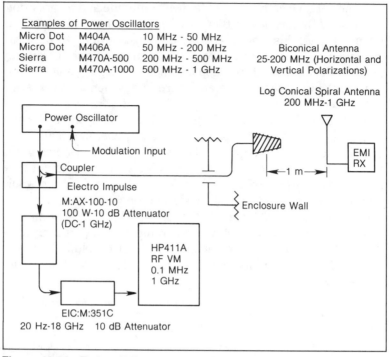

Figure 10.30—Typical E-Field Radiated Susceptibility Test Setup, 25 MHz to 1 GHz

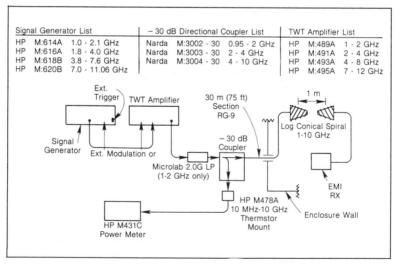

Figure 10.31—Typical E-Field Radiated Susceptibility Test Setup, 1 to 10 GHz

10.4 Bibliography

Bronaugh, E.L., "Comparison of Four Open Area Test Sites," Seventh International Zurich Symposium and Technical Exhibition on EMC, 3-5 March 1987.

Dvorak, T., "Measurement of Electromagnetic Field Immunity," *IEEE Transactions on EMC,* Vol. EMC-16, no. 3, August 1974.

FCC Bulletin OET055, "Characteristics of Open Area Test Sites," August 1982 (formerly OST-55).

FCC/OET MP-4, "FCC Methods of Measurement of Radio Noise from Computing Devices," December 1983.

Heirman, D.N., "Investigating Open Area Test Site Measurement Differences," Seventh International Zurich Symposium and Technical Exhibition on EMC, 3-5 March 1987.

Ma, M.T.; Kanda, M.; Crawford, M.L. and Larsen, E.B., "A Review of Electromagnetic Compatibility/Interference Measurement Methodologies," *Proceedings of the IEEE,* Vol. 73, no. 3, March 1985, pp. 388-411.

MIL-STD-462, "Electromagnetic Interference Characteristics, Measurements of (U.S. Dept. of Defense, July 1967).

Smith, A.A., Jr., "Standard Site Method for Determining Antenna Factors," *IEEE Transactions on EMC,* Vol. EMC-25, no. 3, August 1982, pp. 316-322.

Smith, A.A., Jr., et. al., "Calculation of Site Attenuation from Antenna Factors," *IEEE Transactions on EMC,* Vol. EMC-25, no. 3, August 1982, pp. 301-316.

Chapter 11

The EMI/EMC Community

In any science, technology or discipline, there always remains the question of what agencies or elements constitute "the community." This does not mean, "Who are the elite?" but rather, "Where does one go to get assistance, information, opinions and the like." The EMC disciplines are no different. For the purpose of the following discussion, the EMC community as defined here includes the federal government and various EMC organizations. The following sections cover the regulatory and control agencies, EMI/EMC committees, organizations and standardization bodies.

11.1 International Regulation

It is an often repeated truism that radio waves are no respecters of national boundaries. It is equally apparent that radio communications between nations, on the high seas and in international airspace would be chaotic indeed without internationally accepted regulations and standards. Such international regulations and standards not only exist but are widely observed, which is an indication of the degree to which international cooperation can be achieved when it involves a high degree of mutual self interest for cooperating nations.

11.1.1 International Telecommunications Union

International regulation is achieved under the aegis of the International Telecommunications Union (ITU), which was originally formed as the "International Telegraph Union," just at the close of the American Civil War in 1865. Its purpose then was to regulate international telegraph and cable rates. The first step toward the international regulation of radio was made at the first of many World Administrative Radio Conferences (WARCs), which met in Berlin in 1906. The result of this conference was the allocation of 500 to 1,000 kHz for ship-to-shore telegraphy. The latter frequency is still in use for calling and distress. In effect, the first radio "service" recognized was maritime mobile, and this continued to be the only concern of the World Administrative Radio Conference until the Madrid Conference in 1932.

As of 1972, the ITU had 143 member nations. It is one of several treaty organizations affiliated with the United Nations. Its present charter includes both regulation and use of the radio spectrum, and regulation of international telephone and telegraph. Its government, policies and procedures are established through a Plenipotentiary Conference of all members every five years. Because of its size and the infrequency of its meetings, the Plenipotentiary Conference has found it desirable to delegate much of its responsibility to a 29-member Administrative Council, which meets annually and acts for and on behalf of the Plenipotentiary Conference. Administrative conferences of all members are called as required on special issues as they arise. Recent examples are the 1967 World Administrative Radio Conference convened to consider much needed revisions in the radio regulations dealing with the maritime services and the 1971 **Space WARC**, which undertook a major review of the regulations to provide for the needs of the burgeoning space services.

The day-to-day work of the ITU is carried on by a General Secretariat who, with a full-time staff, is headquartered in Geneva, Switzerland. It conducts a good deal of the required planning for the various international conferences, publishes ITU material, including the all important ITU Radio Regulations and a monthly magazine, *Telecommunications*. It also coordinates the activities of the other permanent organs of the ITU.

11.1.2 Organs of the ITU

Among the permanent organs of the ITU are the International Frequency Registration Board (IFRB), the International Radio Consultative Committee (CCIR) and the International Telegraph and Telephone Consultative Committee (CCITT). The IFRB maintains a worldwide record of frequency assignments based on records supplied by ITU member countries. It also acts as an advisory body to member countries concerning problems of spectrum management and avoidance of interference. The CCIR and CCITT exist primarily to study technical and operating questions with a view toward improving radio and wire line communications. They work principally through permanently established study groups made up of experts from many countries, mostly working on a volunteer basis. The Plenary Assemblies of the CCIR and CCITT draw up **questions** for the study groups to consider. The study groups, after adequate study, may then come up with **recommendations** for submission to the next Plenary Assembly. Upon approval by the Plenary Assembly, the recommendations are published and disseminated by the ITU. The published recommendations do not have the force of radio regulations, but they have important influence with telecommunication agencies, engineers, designers and manufacturers, particularly when communication across national boundaries is involved.

Of particular interest in the area of mobile radio is CCIR Study Group 8, whose charter is "to study the technical and operating aspects of the aeronautical, mobile, maritime mobile, land mobile and radio-determination services, including the use of satellites." Its recommendations are published in Volume VIII of the CCIR XIII Plenary Assembly, Geneva, 1974, published by the International Telecommunications Union, Geneva, Switzerland. It is obvious that the international nature of maritime mobile communications has made it dominant in the considerations of the CCIR Study Group 8 in the past. However, recent activity indicates an increasing interest in satellite applications in the mobile services. Because satellites provide the means for covering oceans and large uninhabited areas, the benefits are expected to accrue primarily to the maritime and aeronautical mobile services. Although there is a need for coordination to avoid interference along national boundaries (e.g., along the U.S.-Canadian and U.S.-Mexican borders) it is to be expected that there is less need for international regulation of land mobile systems than there is for maritime and international aeronautical mobile systems.

11.1.3 International Frequency Allocation

The ITU allocates frequencies by blocks according to **services**. A service is defined by the nature of spectrum use. There are, for example, the **fixed services**, the **mobile services**, **broadcast services**, **radio location services**, **satellite services**, etc. By the end of the 1971 Space WARC, 41 individual services were recognized. The rationale of block allocations, actually established very early in the history of international radio regulation, is the separation of services which might be incompatible if they shared the same frequencies. Thus, for example, pulse (e.g., radar) and continuous wave (CW) services are kept separate, as are high-power (e.g., broadcast) and low-power services, fixed and mobile services, etc.

The ITU also allocates by region, there being three principal regions of the globe recognized by ITU. These are:

Region I - Europe and Africa

Region II - North and South America

Region III - Asia, Australia and Oceana

Frequency allocations within the United States comply with ITU allocations for Region II.

11.2 Regulation Within the United States of America

Frequency usage within the United States and its territories is regulated by the federal government. Although the United States is a member of ITU, participates in its activities and acts within its radio regulations, it is the federal government that actually assigns and regulates the use of frequencies within its own boundaries, airspace and coastal waters.

Frequency usage by agencies of the federal government, including the military services, is administered by the National Telecommunications Information Agency (NTIA) within the Executive Office of the President. Frequency usage by all others, including state and local governments as well as private organizations and individuals, is administered by the Federal Communications Commission (FCC). Both NTIA and FCC work from a national Table of Frequency Allocations which appears in Part 2 of the FCC Rules and Regulations and in the NTIA *Manual of Regulations and Procedures for Radio Frequency Management*. Frequencies are allocated as government, nongovernment and, in some cases, are shared. Allocations between the government and nongovernment entities can be changed by NTIA/FCC agreement.

11.2.1 National Telecommunications Information Agency

The NTIA has a wide range of responsibilities in support of policy-making activities of the executive branch. Very important from the standpoint of frequency management relations is its authority to assign, modify and revoke frequencies with respect to radio stations operated by the federal government. From a practical view point, it relies heavily in this particular function upon the advice of a number of advisory committees. These are:

1. Council for Government Communications Policy and Planning (CGCPP)
2. Electromagnetic Radiation Management Advisory Council (ERMAC)
3. Interdepartment Radio Advisory Committee (IRAC)
4. Frequency Management Advisory Council (FMAC)

The CGCPP is made up of one policy-level officer from each government agency department and each independent agency which has a significant operational responsibility in communications. The director of the NTIA serves as CGCPP chairman. The council advises on matters pertaining to the development, procurement and use by the federal government of communications facilities, systems and services.

The ERMAC is essentially a council of experts from within the government. It includes persons skilled in electronics, engineering, physics, the biological and medical sciences and similar related disciplines. Its job is to advise and make recommendations concerning the effects and adequacy of control of electromagnetic radiation arising from communications activities. Emphasis is on investigation and mitigation of the potentially harmful effects of strong fields. This includes biological effects on man and other living creatures and physical damage to equipment and materials.

11.5

The IRAC is the oldest of the advisory committees, having been established in 1922 to find means for making the most effective use of frequencies then being used by the government for broadcasting. In 1927, it assumed the responsibility for advising the President with respect to all frequency assignments within the federal government. It maintains essentially the same responsibility today, recommending for NTIA approval the assignment of frequencies to government radio stations, including the withdrawal or modification of such assignments. Generally, the duties of the IRAC are to recommend objectives, plans and actions to the NTIA in connection with the management and usage of the radio spectrum by the departments and agencies of the federal government. As a practical matter, the IRAC recommendations concerning frequency assignments are almost routinely approved except where a major policy issue or dispute with another government agency is involved.

The FMAC is the one advisory committee to NTIA that is composed of persons outside the government. Its purpose is to bring in the views of the private sector and to provide fresh appraisals and practical advice on government programs, policies, procedures and practices with respect to frequency management. It provides advice to both NTIA and FCC.

11.2.2 Federal Communications Commission

Established by the Communication Act of 1934, the FCC regulates commercial (common-carrier) interstate and international telegraph and telephone and all radio and television operations in the United States and its territories, excluding agencies of the federal government. The regulation of radio operations is accomplished through the licensing of radio stations and transmitter operators and through monitoring all radio operations to detect non-complying and illegal operations.

The FCC is composed of seven commissioners who are appointed by the President and confirmed by Congress a seven-year term. In its day-to-day operations, the Commission is assisted by a large staff of civil servants. The staff is organized into 11 principal units, which are:

1. Office of the Executive Director
2. Office of the Chief Engineer
3. Office of the General Counsel
4. Broadcast Bureau
5. Common Carrier Bureau
6. Safety and Special Radio Services Bureau
7. Field Engineering Bureau
8. Cable Television Bureau
9. Office of Administrative Law Judge
10. Review Board
11. Office of Opinions and Review

The duties of each of these units is set forth in Part O of the FCC Rules and Regulation. For convenience, they are summarized here:

1. The Executive Director is responsible for the direction of the entire FCC staff organization. He reports directly to the Chairman of the Commission and is responsible to the Commission for staff performance. The Office of the Executive Director is itself organized into divisions, such as the Financial Division, Data Processing Division, Management Information Division, Personnel Division and others as appropriate to support the Executive Director in his duties. Not the least important in the Office of the Executive Director is the Secretary, to whom correspondence with the FCC is normally addressed.

2. The Offices of the Chief Engineer and the General Council exist primarily to advise the Commission concerning any engineering or legal matter involved in the making and implementation of policy or in the decision of cases before the FCC. Their work often overlaps other established offices and bureaus such that the tendency is for the General Council or Chief Engineer to concentrate on matters which cut across the interests of individual bureaus, or are of a timely or overriding importance to the Commission.

3. The Broadcast Bureau, as the name implies, is responsible for the licensing and regulation of broadcast stations and related facilities. It administers the following parts of the FCC Rules and Regulations:

Part 73: Radio Broadcast Services

Part 74: Experimental, Auxiliary and Special Broadcast and Other Program Distributional Services

With the exception of "remote pickup" for broadcast operations, the Broadcast Bureau does not regulate any of the mobile radio services.

4. The Common Carrier Bureau regulates all radio usage by communications common carriers and interstate and international communications, whether by radio or wire line. Any person or firm commercially offering private radio or wire line communications services to the general public (i.e., telegraph, telephone, etc.) is generally classed as a **communications common carrier**. Within the Bureau, the Domestic Radio Division is the division principally concerned with the regulation of common-carrier mobile radio (or RCC) systems. Other divisions are concerned with rates and tariffs, telegraph and telephone facilities, international and satellite communications and other matters. The Common Carrier Bureau administers the following parts of the rules and regulations dealing specifically with radio services:

Part 21: Domestic Public Fixed Radio Services

Part 23: International Fixed Public Radio Communication Services

Part 25: Satellite Communications

5. The Safety and Special Radio Services Bureau includes within its jurisdiction virtually all radio services not classed as broadcast, common-carrier or point-to-point microwave licensed to commercial cable operators. The only significant mobile radio operations not included is common carrier. Its operating divisions are Amateur and Citizens Radio, Aviation and Marine, and Industrial and Public Safety Facilities. It has, in addition, a Legal Advisory and Enforcement Division which supports the other divisions in the complex area of interpretation and enforcement of the rules. The parts of the FCC Rules and

Regulations for which the Safety and Special Radio Services Bureau is responsible are:

Part 81: Stations in the Maritime Services
Part 87: Aviation Services
Part 89: Public Safety Radio Service
Part 95: Personal Radio Service
Part 97: Amateur Radio Service
Part 99: Disaster Communications Service

6. The Field Engineering Bureau is primarily responsible for detecting violations of regulations pertaining to the use of radio. For this purpose, it maintains field office monitoring stations throughout the United States. In addition to monitoring the spectrum, it conducts periodic inspections of radio stations and investigates complaints. An auxiliary duty is the giving of examinations to amateur operators.

7. The most recently organized bureau is Cable Television. As indicated, it regulates the cable television industry, including point-to-point microwave licensed to cable operators. The parts of the FCC Rules and Regulations for which the Cable Television Bureau is responsible are:

Part 76: Cable Television Service
Part 78: Cable Television Relay Service

Neither of these parts provides for any mobile radio services.

8. The remaining three organizational units of the FCC, the Office of Administrative Law Judges, the Review Board and the Office of Opinions are mainly concerned with hearings held before the Commission. FCC hearings are quasi-judicial proceedings somewhat resembling court hearings but lacking the strict rules of evidence normal to court cases. Hearings are presided over by Administrative Law Judges who issue initial decisions. These decisions are then subject to review by the Review Board, consisting of three or more senior Commission staff members. All decisions are subject to the review of one or more designated commissioners, and particularly important or controversial decisions are reviewed by the entire Commission sitting. The Office of Opinions and Review assists and advises the Commission, or any Commissioner, as required on cases which come before them.

11.3 United States Federal Government EMC Community

In the U.S., there are a number of organizations and agencies that have an interest or play a role in EMC. This section identifies some of the major U.S. government organizations that play an active role in the EMC community.

11.3.1 Department of Defense (DoD)

There are a number of DoD organizations and agencies that play an active role in the EMC community. At the level of the Joint Chiefs of Staff, the focal point for EMC activities is:

Organizations of the Joint Chiefs of Staff
Directorate for Command, Control and Communications
    Systems (C3SDJ)
The Pentagon
Washington, DC 20301

Another DoD organization concerned with EMC in communication systems is:

Defense Communications Agency
Washington, DC 20304

The following sections identify some of the other more active DoD organizations in the EMC community.

11.3.1.1 Electromagnetic Compatibility Analysis Center (ECAC)

The Electromagnetic Compatibility Analysis Center is a Department of Defense facility, established to provide advice and assistance on EMC matters to the Secretary of Defense, the Joint Chiefs of Staff, the military departments and other DoD components. The center serves other government agencies and civilian activities as resources permit.

ECAC provides users with analytical solutions of EMC problems based on computer simulations. It also provides computer printouts from a comprehensive EMC data base containing the environmental file, frequency allocation application file, nominal CE characteristics file, spectrum signature file and topographic file.

11.3.1.2 U.S. Army

The following U.S. Army organizations are involved in EMC activities:

Army Avionics R&D (SAVAA-PA)
Ft. Monmouth, NJ 07703

Army Test & Evaluation Command
AMSTE-CT-CE
5001 Eisenhower Ave.
Alexandria, VA 22333

Army Electronic Proving Ground
Fort Huachuca, AZ 85613

Commander, U.S. Army Communications
Electronics Command (CECOM)
Ft. Monmouth, NJ 07703

Army Intelligence and Security Command
Attn: IATEL-ES
4000 Arlington Blvd.
Arlington, VA 22212

Department of the Army
Hdqtrs., U.S. Army Communications &
  Electronics Command
AMSEL-ED-TO
Ft. Monmouth, NJ 07703

Army Missile Command Test and Evaluation
  Directorate
EM & Nuclear Effects
Attn: AMSMI-RD-TE-S
Redstone Arsenal, AL 35898

Department of the Army
Office of the Assistant Chief of Staff for Information
  Management
Attn: DAIM-SM
Washington, DC 20310-0070

Army Test and Evaluation Command
AMSTE-CT-C
Aberdeen Proving Ground, MD 21005

U.S. Army Armament Research & Development
Center (ARDC)
Electromagnetic Evaluation Section
SMCAR-REC-TM, Dover, NJ 07801

U.S. Army Aviation Research & Development
Command Attn: DAVAA-1
4300 Goodfellow Blvd.
St. Louis, MO 63120

U.S. Army Information Systems
Engineering Support Activity (USAISESA)
Fort Huachuca, AZ 85613-5300
ASBH-SET-E

U.S. Army Aviation Systems Command
Attn: AMSAV-ES
4300 Goodfellow Blvd.
St. Louis, MO 63120

11.3.1.3 U.S. Navy

The following U.S. Navy organizations are involved in EMC
activities:

Naval Air Development Center
Code NADC 2034
Warminster, PA 18974

Naval Postgraduate School
Attn: Code 62AB
Monterrey, CA 93943

Naval Air Engineering Center
Code 945
Lakehurst, NJ 08733

Naval Research Lab
Washington, DC 20375
Dr. Lothar H. Ruhnke, Code 4110

Naval Air Systems Command
NAVAIR 5161
Washington, DC 20361

Naval Sea Systems Command
National Center #2
Washington, DC 20362

Naval Air Test Center
Electronics Systems Dept. (SY80)
EMC Section (SY82)
Patuxent River, MD 20670

Naval Surface Weapons Center
Dahlgren Laboratory
Dahlgren, VA 22448

Naval Avionics Center (NAC)
Code B/441
6000 E. 21st St.
Indianapolis, IN 46218

Naval Surface Weapons Center
White Oak Laboratory
Silver Spring, MD 20910

Naval Civil Engineering Laboratory
Port Hueneme, CA 93043

Naval Training Systems Center
Code N412, Orlando, FL 32813

Naval Electronic Systems Engineering Activity
Code 2133
St. Inigoes, MD 20684

Naval Underwater Systems Center
New London Laboratory
Electromagnetic Compatibility Branch
Code 3431
New London, CT 06320

Naval Electronic Systems
Security Engineering Center
Washington, DC 20390-5270

Naval Weapons Center
Code 3525
China Lake, CA 93555

Naval Electronics Engineering Activity
Pacific Box 130
Pearl Harbor, HI 96860

Naval Weapons Support Center
Code 7074
Crane, IN 47522

Naval Ocean Systems Center
San Diego, CA 92152

Naval Electromagnetic Spectrum Center
4401 Nebraska Ave.
Washington, DC 20390

Naval Operations
Office of Chief
Code OP-941F
Washington, DC 20350

Space & Naval Warfare Systems Command
Washington, DC 20363

11.3.1.4 U.S. Air Force

The following U.S. Air Force organizations are involved in EMC activities:

Air Force Aeronautical Systems Division
Wright-Patterson AFB, OH 45433-6503
ASD/ENACE, ASD/ENAS-AVID

Air Force Logistic Command
AFLC/IGYG
Wright-Patterson AFB, OH 45433-5001

Air Force Communications Command
485 EIG/EIEUS
Griffiss AFB, NY 13441-6348

Air Force/Space Division (AFSC)
P.O. Box 92960
Worldway Postal Center
Los Angeles, CA 90009

Air Force Communications Command
1839th Engineering Installation Group/EIE
Keesler AFB, MS 39534-6348

Air Force Systems Command
Andrews Air Force Base
Washington, DC 20334

Air Force Communications Command
1842nd Electronics Engineering Group/EEITE
Scott AFB, IL 62225-6348

Air Force Wright Aeronautical Laboratories
Avionics Laboratory
Wright-Patterson AFB, OH 45433-6543

Air Force Communications Command
1843rd Engineering Installation Group/EIEM
Wheeler AFB, HI 96854

Air Force Wright Aeronautical Laboratories
Flight Dynamic Lab
(AFWAL-FIE)
Wright-Patterson AFB, OH 45433-6553

Air Force Communications Command (AFCC)
Engineering Installation Center EIE/EIEUS
Tinker AFB, OK 73145

Armament Division
3245th Test Wing/T-1
Eglin AFB, FL 32542

Air Force Electronic Systems Division
ESD/ALET
Hanscom AFB, MA 01731

Rome Air Development Center
Griffiss AFB, NY 13441

Air Force Electronics Security Command
ESC/LGMP
San Antonio, TX 78243

USAF Frequency Management Center
Washington, DC 20330

Air Force Geophysics Lab.
AFGL/OPA
Hanscom AFB, MA 01731

USAF, Headquarters
The Pentagon
Washington, DC 20330-5040

11.3.2 National Aeronautics and Space Administration (NASA)

NASA has EMI requirements and problems among its several divisions. NASA's problems have ranged from transient EMI effects in the Saturn missile at MSFC to range instrumentation interference at Kennedy Space Center and the downrange islands. NASA issued an EMI specification, MSFC-SPEC-279, in 1964 to replace MIL-I-618ID which it had been using to more meaningfully reflect transient aspects of aerospace vehicles and system performance requirements.

11.3.2.1 Marshall Space Flight Center (MSFC)

MSFC, Huntsville, Alabama, is responsible for the management of all activities leading to the design, development, production, test and delivery of large launch vehicles, (e.g., Saturn) and related systems. MFSC is also responsible for the operations of the Machoud Assembly Facility at New Orleans, Louisiana, and the Mississippi Test Facility at East Pearl River, Mississippi, as well as cognizance over various launch vehicle stages production and test facilities.

11.3.2.2 Kennedy Space Center (KSC)

KSC, Merritt Island Launch Area (MILA), Cocoa Beach, Florida, is the site for the major launch facilities for manned and unmanned launches. KSC is responsible for prelaunch assembly and final testing of vehicles and systems.

11.3.2.3 Goddard Space Flight Center (GSFC)

GSFC, Greenbelt, Maryland, has overall responsibility for coordinating spacecraft and other space vehicle tracking. This includes the spacecraft communications within the Manned Space Flight Network as part of NASA's Tracking and Data Acquisition Program. The network has several stations scattered about the world.

11.3.2.4 Manned Spacecraft Center (MSC)

MSC, Houston, Texas, is responsible for development of spacecraft for manned missions and control of spacecraft in flight including the Mission Control Center. It is also responsible for training the astronauts and operation of a processing and safeguarding laboratory of returned lunar material, spacecraft and astronauts.

11.3.2.5 Lewis Research Center (LRC)

LRC, Cleveland, Ohio, includes the Plum Brook research installation. It is engaged in flight propulsion.

11.3.2.6 Jet Propulsion Laboratory (JPL)

JPL, Pasadena, California, is responsible for management of the Deep Space Network of NASA's tracking systems.

11.3.3 National Bureau of Standards (NBS)

The NBS, under the auspices of the U.S. Department of Commerce, performs a standards service for the United States against which the accuracy of all instrumentation may be calibrated. Thus, the expression "...traceable to NBS" means that the calibration accuracy of secondary or other laboratory instruments or standards have their origin traceable to NBS.

11.3.4 Center for Devices and Radiological Health (DRH)

The Center for Devices and Radiological Health (DRH) is a division of Health and Human Services, Public Health Service. It is primarily chartered to initiate and monitor rules and regulations regarding maximum allowable radiation levels that may be permitted from industry-manufactured products to reasonably assure protection to humans. Examples of this include the radiation hazard problem attendant with microwave ovens and high-field CE equipment.

11.3.5 U.S. Department of Agriculture (USDA)

It has been noted that the Department of Agriculture ranks seventh in the number of mobile radio licenses issued by the IRAC or FCC. Two divisions of the Department of Agriculture have a direct interest in EMI and in the use of the radio frequency spectrum:

1. Rural Electrification Administration (REA)

    The REA operates 890 power systems with 1.7 million miles of electric power transmission lines within the United States and serves over 30 million customers. These power lines are under constant surveillance for the detection of EMI, and corrective actions are taken whenever interference is detected.

    Prior to the construction or routine maintenance of power lines, an effective degree of interference control is maintained by imposing rigid standards for power line and telephone line construction. Additionally, every item or component that is connected to the power conductors is subjected to rigid EMC tests before they are listed as being acceptable for REA use.

    The interests of the REA in EMC covers the spectrum from the audio frequencies of telephone circuits through radio and television frequencies to the microwave frequencies. In practice, the limits for power line interference on REA lines are considerably below the limits of interference permitted on power lines normally located in urban areas.

2. U.S. Forest Service (USFS)

    The U.S. Forest Service presently operates 22,000 pieces of radio communication equipments in conjunction with their administration and management of the national forests. These equipments range from vehicular/fixed-mobile communications to microwave transmitters and receivers. Specific frequencies in certain bands have been reserved for use by the U.S. Forest Service.

The management of this national radio communications network is vested in the Forest Service Electronics Center, located in Beltsville, Maryland. The use of radio frequencies by the USFS is so extensive that the Director of the USFS Electronics Center represents the USDA on the IRAC.

11.4 International Organizations

There are two very active international organizations that play important roles in the overall EMC community. These organizations are the Electromagnetic Compatibility Society of the Institute for Electrical and Electronic Engineers (IEEE) and the International Special Committee on Radio Interference (CISPR). The role of these organizations in the worldwide EMC community is described in the following sections.

11.4.1 IEEE EMC Society

The IEEE is the world's largest professional society. It consists of electrical and electronics engineers and is devoted to the technical advancement of individual members through educational programs and information dissemination. The parent organization has over 250,000 members, about half of whom belong to technical societies.

The EMC Society functions through a Board of Directors elected by the Society membership. The Board includes 18 members-at-large who serve staggered three-year terms. The Executive Board comprises the President, Vice President, Secretary, Treasurer and four Technical Directors.

At the local level, EMC Society activities are provided by local chapters located in major cities throughout the United States and international chapters in Ottawa, Canada; Tel Aviv, Israel; and Tokyo, Japan.

The EMC Society is also active in technical conferences and symposia through its sponsorship of the annual International Electromagnetic Compatibility Symposium and participation in the International Symposium. Participation in symposia and conferences held outside the United States is announced in the Society Newsletter. The IEEE EMC Society publishes *Transactions on EMC* and an EMC newsletter on a quarterly basis.

Some of the major professional areas of interest of the EMC Society include:

1. The generation of engineering standards
2. Measurement techniques and test procedures
3. Measuring instruments
4. Equipment and systems characteristics such as:
   a. Susceptibility
   b. Vulnerability
   c. Related propagation effects
   d. Subjective effects, frequency allocation and assignment
5. Improved techniques and components for interference reduction or control
6. Education in electromagnetic compatibility
7. Studies of the origins of interference, both man-made and natural, and their classification
8. Spectrum conservation
9. Spectrum utilization
10. Shielding techniques
11. Side effects of electromagnetic energy in other disciplines
12. Scientific, technical, industrial or other activities that contribute to this field or utilize the techniques or products of this field, subject (as the art develops) to additions, deletions, or other modifications directed or approved by the IEEE Technical Activities Committee

11.4.2 Board of Directors

The IEEE EMC Society is managed by a Board of Directors (BoD) of 18 members whose terms of office are 3 years, 6 members of which are elected annually. Each year, the BoD elects from its members a Chairman and a Vice Chairman, and from among the group membership, a Secretary and Treasurer.

11.4.3 International Special Committee on Radio Interference (CISPR)

The International Special Committee on Radio Interference is organized under the general framework of the International Electrotechnical Commission (IEC), which is affiliated with the International Organization for Standardization (ISO).

11.4.3.1 Membership

The CISPR is composed of the following Member Bodies, all having equal status as members:
1. Each National Committee of the IEC
2. European Broadcasting Union (EBU)
3. International Broadcasting Organization (OIR)
4. International Conference on Large Electric Systems (CIGRE)
5. International Union of Producers and Distributors of Electric Energy (UNIPEDE)
6. International Union of Railways (UIC)
7. International Union of Public Transport (UITP)
8. International Commission on Rules for the Approval of Electrical Equipment (CEE)

In addition, the CISPR collaborates with the International Radio Consultative Committee (CCIR) which sends observers to CISPR meetings. The Member Bodies are known, collectively, as the National Committees of the IEC and other Member Organizations of the CISPR.

Any other international organization having a recognized interest in the international aspects of the abatement of radio interference may become a member of the CISPR, subject to acceptance by a Plenary Session of the CISPR.

11.4.3.2 Terms of Reference

The terms of reference of the CISPR are:
A. To promote international agreement on the aspects of radio interference set out below, with the primary objectives of fostering satisfactory reception of sound broadcasting and television services and of facilitating international trade:
   1. Protection of sound broadcasting and television services from interference caused by:
      a. Electrical appliances of all types
      b. Ignition systems
      c. Electricity supply systems, including electric transport systems
      d. Industrial, scientific and electromedical RF equipment (excluding radiation from transmitters intended for conveying information)
      e. Sound broadcasting and television receivers

2. Equipment and methods for the measurement of interference

3. Limits for interference caused by sources listed under No. 1 above

4. Limits for the susceptibility of sound broadcasting and television installations to interference and (in liaison with the IEC) the prescriptions of methods of measurement of such susceptibility

5. Implications of proposed limits of interference to regulations regarding the safety of electrical equipment

B. To collaborate with the CCIR as follows:

1. At the request of the CCIR, to undertake studies of radio interference to those services with which that body is concerned, and which falls outside the primary interests of the CISPR

2. To consult with the CCIR where it appears that an extension of the range of measuring equipment, or of the scope of measurements beyond those related to the primary interest of the CISPR would be mutually advantageous

3. To bring to the attention of the CCIR details of any CISPR studies which appear to interest them

C. To collaborate with other international organizations interested in radio interference

11.4.3.3 Operational Procedures

To facilitate its operation, the CISPR is divided into subcommittees as follows:

Subcommittee A: Limits

Subcommittee B: Measurements

Subcommittee C: Safety

To maintain the work of the subcommittees, Working Groups have been formed, each to study one or more clearly defined study questions referred to the Working Group. Questions referred to a Working Group normally fall within a technical category or area of interest which may be covered in the terms of reference of a Working Group. Each Working Group may be composed of one representative of each country (IEC National Committee) expressing a wish to participate actively in the work. Member Bodies of the CISPR which wish to participate in a Working Group may also appoint a representative.

The present CISPR areas of interest are:
1. Measuring equipment, measuring techniques
2. Industrial, scientific and medical apparatus
3. Overhead power lines, high-voltage equipment
4. Ignition systems of internal combustion engines
5. Radio and television receivers
6. Motors, domestic appliances, lighting apparatus, etc.
7. Impact of safety regulations on interference suppression
8. Statistical methods and correlation between measured values and disturbance effects
9. Terminology

11.5 Industrial Organizations

This section identifies several of the key industrial organizations that have a major ongoing EMC activity.

11.5.1 Electronics Industries Association (EIA)

EIA, founded in 1924 in Chicago as the Radio Manufacturers' Association, is one of the nation's oldest trade associations. "Electronics Industries Association" became the official name in 1957. EIA is the national industrial trade organization representing electronics manufacturers and distributors in the United States, and it is the only national trade association representing the full spectrum of manufacturers in the electronics industry. EIA supports and advances national defense economic growth, technical progress and other interests of the electronics industry for the betterment of the user.

EIA's membership activities and industry programs begin in the product divisions, which are:
1. Government products
2. Industrial electronics
3. Parts, solid state products
4. Tubes
5. Distribution products
6. Audio and video divisions of the consumer electronics group

EIA provides its members with regular publications and special bulletins, standards, memoranda, analyses and reports. These include responses to Federal Communications Commission (FCC) dockets and proposed federal regulations; analyses of military, space and other government budgets; and marketing statistical reports.

The EMC Committee (G-46) was established to form an industry/user position on government specifications, regulations and standards. Generally, the government submits proposed specifications and standards to the EIA for review and comment prior to release. The scope has been expanded through the formation of subcommittees to foster and facilitate the EMC discipline for the benefit of EIA member companies, the nation's industrial complex and the consumer in functional, compatible and economical products. Activities include spectrum management and conservation, personnel safety and health care electronics design, usage and installation in terms of regulated and unregulated electromagnetic emissions and receptions. Inter- and intra-environmental areas, as they affect systems, subsystems equipments, subassemblies and components are also of concern. Committee tasks include:

1. Review, assess, advise and coordinate related activities of organizations/individuals in government, industry and technical societies within EIA
2. Assure that EMC legislation, regulations, specifications, standards, requirements and evaluation procedures are adequate for procurement and applications
3. Propose and recommend action; provide support to other organizations, as deemed desirable
4. Coordinate and promulgate information to facilitate advancement of the art

11.5.2 Society of Automotive Engineers (SAE)

The Society of Automotive Engineers is a professional society of engineers dedicated to a broad spectrum of engineering disciplines within the Aerospace and Automotive fields. Under the SAE Aerospace Council, technical committees address disciplines related to land, sea, air and space, from electrical power quality to multiplex signal characteristics and from fiber optic data transmission to electromagnetic compatibility. The many elements of EMC are handled by SAE Committee AE-4 on Electromagnetic Compatibility, which was organized in 1942 under the Aerospace Council. The Committee is composed of technically qualified members, liaison members and consultants who are responsible for coordinating and advising on electromagnetic compatibility.

The thrust of Committee AE-4 is to provide assistance to the technical community through standardization, improved design and testing methodology and to maintain a technical forum for the resolution of mutual problems. Engineering standards, specifications and technical reports are developed by the Committee and issued by the Society for the general information of industry and governments worldwide.

Objectives of Committee AE-4 are to advance the state of the art, stabilize existing technology, obtain a uniformity of EMC requirements among government agencies and to further the interests of the EMC technical community. The theme of "design before the fact" for EMC is a guiding concept. Special attention is given to maintenance of EMI control requirements which are consistent with the rapidly moving technology.

The Committee has sponsored international symposia on Lightning and Static Electricity effects and served as co-sponsor for international symposia, providing panel sessions for those conferences. Members of Committee AE-4 have been appointed by SAE Headquarters to ANSI C-63 and C-95 Committees to represent the Society on all technical matters.

The Committee is currently involved in a major task to assist the Air Force in the preparation of new standards related to electromagnetic compatibility. To implement this task, standing committees were formed in the areas of conducted and radiated interference and susceptibility to provide recommendations by subsystem EMI testing methodology and to recommend techniques for tailoring limits to the requirements of the system. Committee AE-4J has addressed electrical bonding techniques and recommended a new standard. Also, Committee AE-4J has been directed to prepare recommendations for the control of electromagnetic effects of lightning at the subsystem level and to review and to provide a recommended update to the FAA "Circular on Lightning Aspects of Aircraft Fuel System Design."

Committee AE-4 has pursued diversified endeavors from strictly aerospace endeavors to the broader aspects of electromagnetic effect. Subcommittee AE-4L on Lightning prepared a recommended test technique to perform simulated lightning strike tests on aerospace vehicles and component parts. Subcommittee AE-4S searches into EMC problems that are peculiar to shipboard installations. Also, AE-4 Special Task Group A conducted a Cooperative Engineering Problem with the Division of Health and Human Services, Public Health Services, where assistance was given to the Center for Devices and Radiological Health in the evaluation of cardiac pacemakers for compatibility with the real-world electromagnetic environment. Additionally, standing committees within AE-4 address almost all aspects of EMC from standardization of EMC components to development of system-oriented EMC Specifications.

11.6 Bibliography

CBEMA ESC5/75/31 (Washington, DC: Computer and Business Equipment Manufacturers Association).

ECMA Standard 47, "Limits and Measurement Methods for Radio Interference from Electronic Data Processing Equipment," (Geneva, Switzerland: European Computer Manufacturers Association).

SAE AE4 (Warrendale, Penn.: Society of Automotive Engineers, Subcommittee AE4 on Electromagnetic Compatibility).

SAE AIR-1499, "Recommendation for Commercial EMC Susceptibility Standards," (Warrendale, Pennsylvania: Society of Automotive Engineers).

Scientific Apparatus Makers Association (SAMA), Washington, DC.

Index

Other Books Published by ICT

1. Carstensen, Russell V., *EMI Control in Boats and Ships,* 1979.
2. Denny, Hugh W., *Grounding for Control of EMI,* 1983.
3. Duff, Dr. William G., *A Handbook on Mobile Communications,* 1980.
4. Duff, Dr. William G. and White, Donald R.J., Volume 5, *Electromagnetic Interference Prediction & Analysis Techniques,* 1972.
5. Feher, Dr. Kamilo, *Digital Modulation Techniques in an Interference Environment,* 1977.
6. Gabrielson, Bruce C., *The Aerospace Engineer's Handbook of Lightning Protection,* 1987.
7. Gard, Michael F., *Electromagnetic Interference Control in Medical Electronics,* 1979.
8. Georgopoulos, Dr. Chris J., *Fiber Optics and Optical Isolators,* 1982.
9. Georgopoulos, Dr. Chris J., *Interference Control in Cable and Device Interfaces,* 1987.
10. Ghose, Rabindra N., *EMP Environment and System Hardness Design,* 1983.
11. Hart, William C. and Malone, Edgar W., *Lightning and Lightning Protection,* 1979.
12. Herman, John R., *Electromagnetic Ambients and Man-Made Noise,* 1979.
13. Hill, James S. and White, Donald R.J., Volume 6, *Electromagnetic Interference Specifications, Standards & Regulations,* 1975.
14. Jansky, Donald M., *Spectrum Management Techniques,* 1977.
15. Mardiguian, Michel, *Interference Control in Computers and Microprocessor-Based Equipment,* 1984.
16. Mardiguian, Michel, *Electrostatic Discharge—Understand, Simulate and Fix ESD Problems,* 1985.
17. Mardiguian, Michel, *How to Control Electrical Noise,* 1983.
18. Smith, Albert A., *Coupling of External Electromagnetic Fields to Transmission Lines,* 1986.
19. White, Donald R.J., *A Handbook on Electromagnetic Shielding Materials and Performance,* 1980.
20. White, Donald R.J., *Electrical Filters—Synthesis, Design & Applications,* 1980.
21. White, Donald R.J., *EMI Control in the Design of Printed Circuit Boards and Backplanes,* 1982. (Also available in French.)
22. White, Donald R.J. and Mardiguian, Michel, *EMI Control Methodology & Procedures,* 1982.
23. White, Donald R.J., Volume 1, *Electrical Noise and EMI Specifications,* 1971.
24. White, Donald R.J., Volume 2, *Electromagnetic Interference Test Methods and Procedures,* 1980.
25. White, Donald, R.J., Volume 3, *Electromagnetic Interference Control Methods & Techniques,* 1973.
26. White, Donald R.J., Volume 4, *Electromagnetic Interference Test Instrumentation Systems,* 1980.
27. Duff, William G., and White, Donald R.J., Volume 5, *Prediction and Analysis Techniques,* 1970.
28. White, Donald R.J., Volume 6, *EMI Specifications, Standards and Regulations,* 1973.
29. White, Donald R.J., *Shielding Design Methodology and Procedures,* 1986.
30. *EMC Technology 1982 Anthology*
31. *EMC EXPO Records 1986, 1987, 1988*

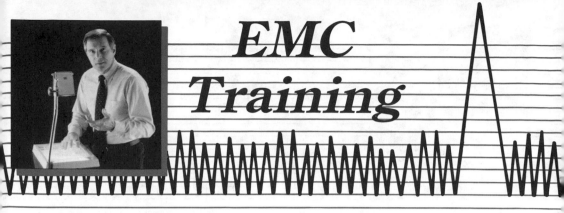

EMC Training

Interference Control Technologies, Inc. (ICT) is the premier EMI/EMC and TEMPEST training organization in the world. Founded in 1970 as Don White Consultants, Inc., ICT has educated over 45,000 degreed electronic engineers, technicians, scientists and managers from over 49 countries, representing over 1300 organizations.

All ICT seminars are designed to provide the latest pragmatic insight and methodology to *real-world* interference control and noise suppression issues. Our goal is to equip each student not only with the appropriate theory but with field-tested, proven solutions.

ICT achieves this objective in two ways. First, by providing an instructor who is both a seasoned communicator and a practicing expert in his field. Collectively our staff brings over 600 years of international work experience from diverse industrial, commercial, military and regulatory backgrounds.

Secondly, ICT updates its extensive student handout materials regularly to ensure clarity and relevancy. All students receive a notebook with a copy of every transparency presented, as well as, hardbound handbooks, computer software, an *EMC Technology* magazine subscription and other related materials.

Seminars can be taught in one of seven different languages and are regularly scheduled throughout the Unites States, Europe, the Middle and Far East, South America and Austrailia.

ICT also offers any one of its more than 25 standard seminars as is, or we can tailor any class to meet the clients specific need. These seminars can then be taught at the client's facility and at a time most conducive to the client's schedule.

Course Titles Inclide:

Grounding & Shielding
Practical EMI Fixes
EMC Design & Measurement
Intro to EMI/RFI/EMC
TEMPEST: Design & Measurement
TEMPEST: Facilities Design
Plus 15 other EMI control courses!

for more information ...

Interference Control Technologies
PO Box D
Gainesville, Va 22065
703-347-0030

ICT–

EMC Books

HANDBOOKS

ICT provides over 30 technical handbooks on EMI/EMC and related disciplines. Written by practicing experts in their field each book is designed to go beyond the tutorial by providing the reader with practical applications, illustrative examples as well as tested and proven methodologies. Each book is packed with illustrations, graphs, tables and math models, and is writen in a clear, consise format to assure the reader understanding and immediate use of the material.

GENERAL TITLES AND APPLICATIONS

Electromagnetic Shielding
Electrical Filters
ESD - Understand, Simulate and Fix
EMC Pocket Primer
EMP Environment and System
  Hardness Design
EXPO Symposium Records
How to Contol Electrical Noise
Grounding for the Control of EMI
Lightning and Lightning Protection

SPECIFIC TITLES AND APPLICATIONS

Aerospace Engineers Handbook of Lightning Protection, Coupling of External Electromagnetic Fields to Transmition Lines, EMI Control in Computers and Microprocessor-Based Equipment, EMI Control in the Design of PCBs and Backplanes, Fiber Optics and Optical Isolators.

THE MUST EMI/EMC LIBRARY

(1) EMI Control Methodology and Procedures *and* (2) Shielding Design Methodology and Procedures.

THE EMC SOURCE
(A 12-Volume EMI/EMC Series)

Vol 1 Fundamentals of EMC
Vol 2 Grounding and Bonding
Vol 3 Electromagnetic Shielding
Vol 4 Filters & Power Conditioning
Vol 5 EMC in Components & Devices
Vol 6 EMI Test Methods/Procedures
Vol 7 EMC in Telecommunications
Vol 8 EMI Control Methodology
Vol 9 USA Commercial Standards
Vol 10 Int'l Commercial Standards
Vol 11 USA MIL-STDs Part 1
Vol 12 USA MIL-STDs Part 2

for more information ...

**Interference Control
Technologies
PO Box D
Gainesville, Va 22065
703-347-0030**

ICT

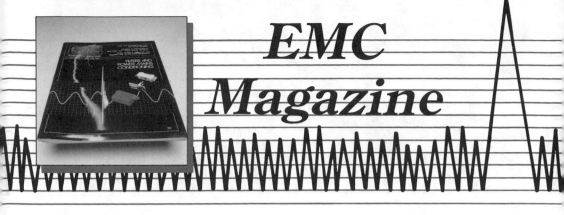

EMC Magazine

EMC TECHNOLOGY MAGAZINE

EMC Technology magazine meets the need for up-to-date information and addresses critical noise suppression issues facing the design engineer and his management. Each issue is developed around a central theme covering either new design technology or applications, product and component development, or test and measurement procedures, techniques and equipment.

Each article is written with a pragmatic slant not only to define the problem but also eliminate it. The *must* objective is that each article not only inform but instruct.

Each issue contains a number of supporting *Departments* giving the reader the latest news on *Meetings and Conferences, People, Places and Events, Products and Service, and Standards and Regulations.*

Many issues also include *Hands-on Reports* and product evaluations. Rounding out each issue are thought provoking editorials and *Letters to the Editor*, Special Products, brochure and catalog listings, and an advertising matrix and index created for easy cross referencing of product and service advertisements.

In addition to the six bi-montly issues

EMC Technology also provides two special issues each year. Its annual *Buyers Guide and Sales Directory* provides the reader with alphabetical listings of vendors complete with product description, sales contact, locations and telephone numbers, and a listing of vendors by Product or Service provided. The second special issue is set aside for unique topics requiring in-depth coverage and emphasis.

EMC EXPO

EMC EXPO is an annual international symposium designed solely for the issues of EMI/EMC, Electrical Noise suppression and other relative disciplines. Over 50 papers are presented in 20 technical workshops.

Exhibitors provide hands-on demonstrations as well as free information and literature.

---

for more information ...

**Interference Control Technologies
PO Box D
Gainesville, Va 22065
703-347-0030**

—ICT——

EMC Software

CAE SOFTWARE

These programs will predict and eliminate interference problems during product conceptualization rather than at the more costly prototype or retofit stages. Tedious calculations now take only minutes displaying with accuracy effects of design criteria supplied by the user.

PROGRAM 5220:
TWO BOX RADIATED EMI SUSCEPTABILITY CONTROL

This program will enable the user to detect and measure radiation susceptability levels from interconnected equipment, ground loops and radiation to/from cables, and common and differential mode sources.

The user is provided with comparative data predicting interference levels with both analog and logic victum sensitivities. Prompters will provide various fix options to help achieve maximim cost savings.

PROGRAM 5300:
BOX RADIATED EMISSION AND CONTROL

This program will enable you to detect and measure applicable radiated emission levels from, printed curcuits, backplanes, chips, and internal cabling.

A composite of radiation levels emanating from the input design are compared against specification limits. Prompters will provide various fix options to help achieve the most economical solution.

PROGRAM 5500:
EMC DESIGN OF BOXES, CASES, CABINETS AND ENCLOSURES

This program enables the user to design shielding housings against specified or synthesized shielding requirements. Selection criteria include type of material used (metals or composites), surface impedance and thickness. Aperature designs are defined and tested, with failures indicated and fix options provided.

All design criteria are combined and overall shielding performance is determined.

for more information ...

Interference Control Technologies
PO Box D
Gainesville, Va 22065
703-347-0030

ICT

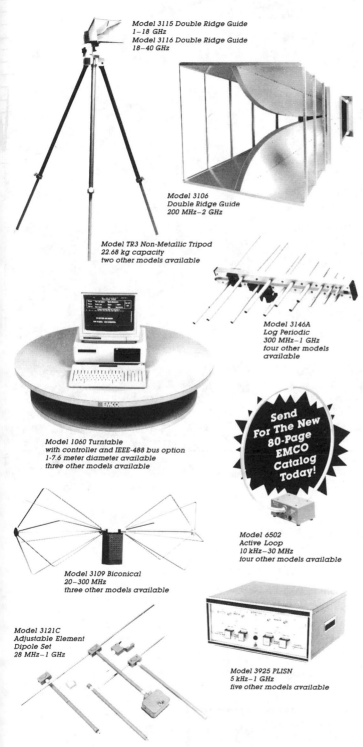

Model 3115 Double Ridge Guide
1–18 GHz
Model 3116 Double Ridge Guide
18–40 GHz

Model 3106
Double Ridge Guide
200 MHz–2 GHz

Model TR3 Non-Metallic Tripod
22.68 kg capacity
two other models available

Model 3146A
Log Periodic
300 MHz–1 GHz
four other models
available

Model 1060 Turntable
with controller and IEEE-488 bus option
1–7.6 meter diameter available
three other models available

Send
For The New
80-Page
EMCO
Catalog
Today!

Model 3109 Biconical
20–300 MHz
three other models available

Model 6502
Active Loop
10 kHz–30 MHz
four other models available

Model 3121C
Adjustable Element
Dipole Set
28 MHz–1 GHz

Model 3925 PLISN
5 kHz–1 GHz
five other models available

TEST WITH CONFIDENCE.

ENGINEERED TO PERFORM

If compliance testing is your primary responsibility, you need top-of-the-line products you can count on. Like EMCO antennas, designed for repeatable FCC/VDE testing. Manufactured for the stringent requirements of MIL-STD testing. With high sensitivity for TEMPEST testing. Most have VSWR ratios of less than 2:1. And all exhibit exceptional dynamic range and linearity.

CALIBRATED INDIVIDUALLY

Every EMCO antenna is individually calibrated using both C63.4 and ARP 958 standards, then shipped to you with a signed Certificate of Compliance—a claim no other manufacturer of test antennas can make.

MANUFACTURED WITH CARE

We choose only the best and most durable materials for EMCO products. Then we pay close attention to details—machined tolerances are often less than one one-thousandth of an inch. And while we've automated for efficiency, we still take the time to hand-assemble and inspect each one of our products.

TWO-YEAR WARRANTY, SERVICE WORLD-WIDE

Because we know how well every EMCO product is engineered and built, we can back each one with a two-year warranty—twice the industry standard. And EMCO has more than 30 representatives worldwide to help you—wherever you are. Call our 800 number for more information and the name of your EMCO representative. Ask for your free catalog of EMCO products, too!

1-800-253-3761

The Electro-Mechanics Company

Call toll-free between 7:30 AM and 4:30 PM Central Time
800-253-3761 in USA or 512-835-4684 in Texas
Telex 797627 Fax 512-835-4729
P.O. Box 1546 Austin, Texas 78767

08151/89161 Fax 08151/16610
Munchner Str. 2 D-8137 Berg 1 West Germany

NOVAMET
CONDUCTIVE PIGMENTS

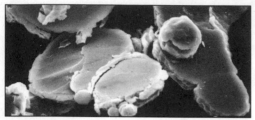

Conductive Silver Coated Nickel Flakes

Conductive Nickel Flakes

Conductive Silver Coated Nickel Spheres

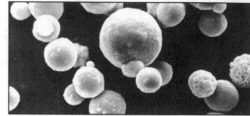

Conductive Nickel Spheres

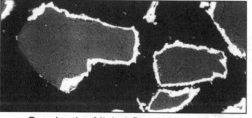

Conductive Nickel Coated Alumina

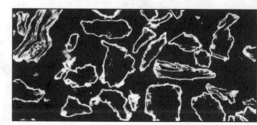

Nickel Coated Graphite

Also:
Conductive Nickel Coated Glass Frit
Conductive Nickel Coated Aluminum
Conductive Nickel Pigment 525
Conductive Silver (0.5%) Stabilized Nickel Flakes

And
Custom Nickel Coating
Custom Micron Separation of Nickel Powders
Custom Screening of all Novamet Pigments

Novamet Specialty Products Corporation, An INCO Company
10 Lawlins Park, Wyckoff, New Jersey 07481, (201) 891-7976